THE
OXY-ACETYLENE
HANDBOOK

THE OXY-ACETYLENE HANDBOOK

A Manual on Oxy-Acetylene
Welding and Cutting Procedures

UNION CARBIDE CORPORATION ● LINDE DIVISION
270 PARK AVENUE, NEW YORK, N.Y. 10017

Available throughout the United States from Linde Welding Supply Distributors or by
order sent directly to the publishers at the address given above.

First Edition — October 1943
Total Printings — 201,000
Second Edition — October 1960
Total Printings — 225,000
Third Edition — September 1976
Twenty-fourth printing — 49,000
Twenty-fifth printing — 5,000
Twenty-sixth printing — 45,000

The terms "Brazo", "Cromaloy", "Ferro", "Linde", "Oxweld", "Prest-O-Lite", "Purox" and "Unionmelt" are registered trade marks of Union Carbide Corporation.

Chapter 14 sketches executed by Dr. Walter Hood

The publishers express appreciation to Nibco, Inc., for permission to reproduce some of the illustrations used in Chapters 4 and 21

International Standard Book Number 0-914096-10-9

Printed in the United States of America

P/N 781F00

Preface to 3rd Edition

Since the Oxy-Acetylene Handbook was first published in 1943, 426,000 copies have been printed. Our records do not tell us how many copies have been used as textbooks in connection with courses offered by high schools, vocational schools, and colleges, nor how many have been used for self-instruction. We do know that demand for the book has never slackened over the entire 33-year period. We are therefore both happy and proud to make this completely-revised third edition available.

Those familiar with the earlier editions will note that the third edition has fewer pages than its predecessors. Some chapters have been dropped; some have been merged; some have been cut back. But we have largely retained the original order of presentation, and many of the original illustrations. We think that those who have used earlier editions will feel quite at home with this one.

Perhaps the most important change made in this third edition is recognition of the fact that the world of welding has expanded enormously in the past 35 years, and that oxy-acetylene welding, while still as versatile as any other welding process, is no longer pre-eminent in most fields. For example, while it is still possible to weld aluminum and stainless steel with the oxy-acetylene torch, the inert-gas-shielded welding processes, tig (GTA) welding and mig (GMA) welding, are generally preferred.

Having said that, we'd like to add this thought: That oxy-acetylene welding (*not* cutting) may have been written off too hastily by some. Experts in the pipe-welding field lament the fact that there aren't enough trained oxy-acetylene welders available to handle jobs that can be done best — in terms of both cost and quality — with the gas torch. Thousands of oxy-acetylene welding and cutting outfits, we believe, are getting less use than they should because their owners use them almost entirely for cutting, brazing, and heating, only infrequently for fusion welding of steel.

Soon after the turn of the century, oxy-acetylene welding was the only broadly successful fusion welding process. By 1930, it could be stated, without stretching the truth very much, "If it can be welded at all, it can be welded with the oxy-acetylene flame''. That statement is still pretty close to the truth. It's also true that there are *newer* ways, usually *better* ways, to weld almost every metal. But "new" isn't *always* "better", and the cost of equipment for the "new" way is invariably higher. To the reader of this book, we'd like to say this: Master the art. Keep your hand in. And don't be reluctant to say, when the occasion warrants, "I can do it *better* with the oxy-acetylene torch.''

Foreword

Units of Measurement

This edition of the Oxy-Acetylene Handbook goes to press at a time of transition. The U.S.A. is committed to change from its traditional "English" system of measurements to the metric system. During the next few years, conversion from one system to the other will probably take place at an accelerating pace. In this book, therefore, we have *generally* given measurements in both "English" and metric terms, with the metric expression stated first in most cases.

Strictly speaking, the system toward which the U.S. is moving is not the "metric" system, but the International System of Units (SI). There are several significant differences between the original metric system, as used in many countries for more than a century, and SI, as standardized during the past 15-20 years. Perhaps the most significant is the elimination of the *kilogram* as a unit to be used in expressing values for *force, stress,* or *pressure.* In SI, the kilogram is used only to express values of *mass.* The basic unit used to express force is the *newton* (N). For pressure or stress it is the *pascal* (P), which represents a force of one newton acting over an area of one square metre.

In the original metric system, pressure and stress were usually stated in terms of "kilograms per square centimeter" (kg/cm^2). To follow SI strictly, the units used to represent pressure or stress should be kilopascals (kPa) (thousands of pascals) or megapascals (MPa)(millions of pascals). For expression of stress (or strength) the megapascal is entirely satisfactory and is already being used in publications of the American Society for Testing and Materials (ASTM). In this book we have used kilopascals for expressing pressure (1 kPa is equivalent to 0.145 psi). You should soon see gas regulators in the market equipped with gauges having both psi and kPa pressure scales.

In pure SI terminology, flow should be expressed in *cubic meters per second* (m^3/s) but that unit usually produces impractical small numbers in our field of use. Therefore, we have used *cubic meters per hour* (m^3/h) to express metric equivalents of gas flows usually given in the English system as *cubic feet per hour (cfh).* A metric alternative would be *liters per minute* (L/min) quite widely used in both Europe and the U.S. for many years. Its use is being discouraged, however, since neither the liter nor the minute is a "standard" unit in SI. (While we show the conversion factors for liters per minute in the tables which follow, we do not express flows in liters per minute at any point in the text.)

With the exceptions noted above, the metric units used in this book, and the abbreviations for those units, are those found in the Metric Practice Guide (E-380-76) published by the American Society for Testing and Materials (ASTM) and accepted by the American National Standards Institute (ANSI) as American National Standard Z210.1. Virtually all temperature references are given in °C (degrees Celsius) with Fahrenheit equivalents stated only occasionally.

On the following pages, we provide two conversion tables: English-to-metric, and metric-to-English. These tables cover only units used in this book. Far more complete tables are readily available from other sources.

Conversion Table
Metric (SI) Units to Customary (English) Units

Measure	Unit	Abbrev.		Unit	Abbrev.
Length	1 millimeter	mm	=	0.0394 inches	in.
	1 meter	m	=	3.28 feet	ft.
Mass	1 kilogram	kg	=	2.205 pounds - mass	lb.
Force	1 newton	N	=	0.225 pounds-force	lbf
Pressure	1 kilopascal	bar	=	0.145 pounds per square inch	psi
Stress	1 megapascal	MPa	=	145 pounds per square inch	psi
Area	1 square millimeter	mm²	=	0.0015 square inches	sq. in.
	1 square meter	m²	=	10.76 square feet	sq. ft.
Volume	1 cubic meter	m³	=	35.3 cubic feet	cf
Flow	1 cubic meter per hour	m³/h	=	35.3 cubic feet per hour	cfh
	1 liter per minute	L/min	=	2.12 cubic feet per hour	cfh

General Note Regarding Abbreviations

The abbreviations shown for metric units are internationally recognized. Those shown for customary (English) units are the ones used in this book. For several, alternative abbreviations may be encountered in other publications. (Examples: "ft³/hr" instead of "cfh"; "lb./in²" instead of "psi".)

Conversion Table
Customary (English) Units to Metric (SI) Units

Measure	Unit	Abbrev.		Unit	Abbrev.
Length	1 foot	ft.	=	0.305 meters	m
	1 inch	in.	=	25.4 millimeters	mm
Mass	1 pound	lb.	=	0.454 kilograms	kg
Force	1 pound-force	lbf	=	4.45 newtons	N
Pressure	1 pound per square inch	psi	=	6.9 kilopascals	kPa
Stress	1 pound per square inch	psi	=	0.0069 megapascals	MPa
Area	1 square inch	sq. in.	=	645 square millimeters	mm^2
	1 square foot	sq. ft.	=	0.093 square meters	m^2
Volume	1 cubic foot ·	cf	=	0.0283 cubic meters	m^3
Flow	1 cubic foot per hour	cfh	=	0.0283 cubic meters per hour	m^3/h
	1 cubic foot per hour	cfh	=	0.47 liters per minute	L/min

General Note Regarding Abbreviations

The abbreviations shown for metric units are internationally recognized. Those shown for customary (English) units are the ones used in this book. For several, alternative abbreviations may be encountered in other publications. (Examples: "ft^3/hr" instead of "cfh"; "$lb./in^2$" instead of "psi".)

Table of Contents

WELDING PROCESSES

Depending on your point of view, the welding of metals can be considered either an ancient art or a modern skill. There is good evidence that craftsmen welded gold and brass to make jewelry at least as far back as the year 2000 B.C., and that iron was welded as early as 1000 B.C. Yet what is generally termed the Industrial Revolution, during the 19th century, was largely accomplished without the assistance of welding. From the industrial standpoint, welding is almost entirely a 20th-century advance.

The word "welding" covers a lot of ground. Normally, we think of it as a process involving heat, and the melting of metals. However, welds can be made without melting, even without heat. In theory, at least, two pieces of almost any metal might be welded together if kept in close contact, under high pressure, in a vacuum, for a period of years. If the surfaces in contact had been perfectly cleaned and highly polished before pressure was applied, there would ultimately be sufficient exchange of atoms between the two pieces so that the two pieces would essentially become one. In the modern process known as *diffusion welding* (not widely used, but invaluable for making certain critical welds in aerospace components) this theoretical process is speeded up by supplying just the right amount of heat. (The parts are not placed in a vacuum, but an inert gas atmosphere may be required). In *ultrasonic welding* the parts are held together under pressure, and then subjected to high-frequency vibration. This "jiggles" the atoms and speeds up the interchange of atoms between the two pieces.

We mention these extremely modern processes for two reasons: first, because they are closely related to the process by which the ancient artisan joined pieces of metal to make jewelry; second, to stress the fact that there are today, in actual use, a variety of welding processes which superficially bear little resemblance to the gas welding and arc welding processes with which almost everyone is at least slightly familiar. The artisan took advantage of the fact that gold is extremely malleable and is not attacked by the oxygen in the atmosphere. If he placed two pieces together, and then hammered them, the surfaces came into near-perfect contact; if he continued to hammer them long enough, they welded together. He may have used some heat to speed up the process; we are not sure. We think he could have done his work without heat if he had sufficient patience.

Forge Welding

Until very late in the 19th century, the only welding process of any significance was forge welding. This was, essentially, the art of the blacksmith. If he heated two bars of iron or steel in his forge until the ends were nearly white hot, then placed the hot sections together on his anvil and hammered them, and then reheated them, and then hammered them some more, he eventually welded them together. While such welds were seldom as strong as the parts themselves, since there was likely to be some formation of iron oxides on the hot surfaces, they were strong enough for most purposes. The uses of forge welding over a period of about 3000 years were many — far more, in fact, than most of us can imagine. There is reason to believe that a 61-foot iron column, the remains of which were uncovered in India, could only have been made by forge welding many relatively small pieces of iron; it is inconceivable that it could have been cast in one piece, or even in several large pieces. This column was made somewhere around the year 1 A.D.

Forge welding was finally developed in at least two forms well removed from the simple art of the blacksmith, which involved merely heating and hammering. One was known as die welding, in which pressure was applied by the combination of a mandrel and tube rolls. The second was roll welding, in which flat pieces were joined by passing the pieces between two plate rolls. In the late 1800's, nickel sheet was welded to steel by roll welding in an atmosphere of hydrogen.

Gas Welding

The use of an intensely hot gas flame for welding seems to date back to the middle 1800's when a torch was devised which would burn a mixture of oxygen and hydrogen. This oxy-hydrogen flame would melt and weld platinum (which has a melting point much higher than those of gold and silver) and found much use in the jewelry trade thereafter. Nonetheless, gas welding as we know it today did not get started until acetylene became available during the last years of the 19th century. Gas welding development will be covered in the next chapter.

Arc Welding

Arc welding can be considered as dating back to about 1885, (although the first patent directly relating to electric welding was granted to an Englishman in 1865). Two Russian scientists used electricity supplied from banks of storage batteries to provide current for an arc between a carbon electrode and a workpiece. The British patent issued to them in 1885 even described the use of the carbon arc for cutting, piercing, and gouging, as well as for welding. In the next few years, both Russian and American experimenters made welds successfully using bare metal electrodes. Carbon arc welding caught on rapidly; in the 1890's a British welding shop could weld wrought iron pipes up to 12 in. in diameter. Welding with bare metal electrodes developed slowly, because most welds turned out weak and brittle. In fact, until ways were found to coat electrodes with material which would produce gas and slag to shield the molten metal, welding with steel electrodes make little headway. The first coated electrodes appeared before 1910, but the major advances in coating were achieved during the 1940's. Until mig welding (GMAW) became a major factor, coated electrode welding was dominant in the arc welding of steel.

Electric Resistance Welding

Resistance welding got its start at about the same time as arc welding. In resistance welding, a high current is passed between two pieces of metal in contact. There is no arc. Electrical resistance, which generates heat, is highest at the junction between the two pieces. Pressure to maintain firm contact between the pieces is supplied through the same electrodes (originally carbon, but now copper) which feed the current. Basically, resistance welding is a spot-welding process, but can produce continuous seam welds by making a series of overlapping spotwelds. Generally speaking, resistance welding equipment is heavy, and must be designed specifically for a single application. However, resistance welding was in use for production of sheet metal assemblies before World War I, and remains a major production method today.

Submerged Arc and Electroslag Welding

Until the 1930's, the three types of welding just described briefly — gas welding, arc welding, and resistance welding — accounted for at least 90% of all industrial welding applications. In 1935, the process now called *submerged arc welding* (but originally termed submerged *melt* welding or UNIONMELT welding) was introduced. This employs a bare wire, fed from a coil by a variable speed wire drive unit, and a granular flux which is deposited in the weld zone in advance of the wire. Initiation of an arc between the wire and the work causes part of the flux to melt and form a fluid blanket which floats on top of the molten weld metal and completely protects it from the gases of the atmosphere. The flux can even be formulated so that it adds small amounts of alloying ingredients to the molten metal. Submerged arc welding uses much higher currents than most other types of arc welding, and is truly a high-speed process. However, because of the large puddle of molten metal and flux that exists during the welding operation, it is generally limited to work that can be welded in the flat position.

Electroslag welding, which originated in the 1950's, resembles submerged arc welding in some respects, but is fundamentally different. In electroslag welding, heat is generated by the electrical resistance of a molten slag (flux) to the passage of the welding current. No arc exists after the weld has been initiated.

Gas Shielded Arc Welding

During World War II, when urgent need for a method which could be used for welding magnesium metal arose, the process now known as *tig welding,* or *gas tungsten arc welding* (GTAW) was developed. In tig welding, an arc between a tungsten electrode and the work is shielded by a stream of inert gas (argon, helium, or a mixture of the two) which protects both the electrode and the weld metal from attack by atmospheric gases. Within a very few years, the tig process was being widely employed for the welding of not only magnesium, but also aluminum, titanium, stainless steel, and many exotic alloys.

From tig welding, it was a rather short step to *mig welding,* or *gas metal arc welding* (GMAW), in which the arc is struck between a consumable wire and the work, with a shielding gas again protecting both the wire and the

Fig. 1-1. Submerged arc welding. From right to left: the tube through which flux is deposited on the joint; the welding nozzle; the blanket of flux under which welding has taken place; a short section from which the loose flux has been removed, leaving only the fused portion; and the finished weld surface.

weld metal. In this process, as in tig, the shielding gases first used were inert gases — argon and helium. The tig process remains a true inert-gas-shielded process, but the GMAW process now employs a wide variety of gases and gas mixtures. Inert gases (argon, helium, or mixtures of the two) are still used exclusively for welding aluminum; however, for the welding of steel, pure carbon dioxide, mixtures of argon and carbon dioxide, and mixtures of argon with oxygen (up to 5% oxygen) are the standard shielding gases.

Flux-Cored Wire Arc Welding

A variation of GMAW, now classified as a separate process by the American Welding Society and designated FCAW (flux-cored arc welding), uses wire which has been formed around a core of flux. Although relatively new

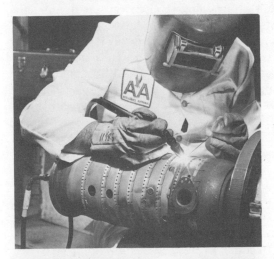

Fig. 1-2. Tig welding is widely employed for welding thin sections of high-temperature alloys, as in this aircraft maintenance operation.

Fig. 1-3. Mig welding a steel assembly, with carbon dioxide as the shielding gas. With a true inert gas, such as argon, there is less spatter.

(it originated in the 1950's) it is rapidly assuming a position of major importance in the arc welding of steel. Some flux-cored wires generate carbon dioxide, and are used without any additional shielding gas. The majority, however, are used with carbon dioxide shielding. Insofar as equipment is concerned, there is little difference between mig welding and gas-shielded FCAW.

Plasma Arc Welding

Plasma arc welding (PAW) is an inert-gas-shielding process which differs from tig-welding (GTAW) in one very significant aspect: The arc originates within the torch and then passes to the work through a stream of *plasma* generated by passing a small flow of argon through that internal arc. Plasma, or ionized gas, exists in all arc welding processes; to create an arc is to create plasma. Only in plasma arc welding (and cutting) is the plasma *constricted* by being passed through an orifice within the torch. This concentrates the arc and prevents it from spreading out rapidly, as it will under ordinary circumstances. The plasma arc welding process is not used on aluminum, but has proved extremely useful in high-speed welding of steel, stainless steel, titanium, and copper in thicknesses from as little as 0.02 mm (0.001 in.) to 6 mm (¼ in.). The plasma arc *cutting* process, which utilizes the constricted arc at higher voltages and currents than employed in the welding process, has become *the* process for cutting of aluminum and stainless steel, as well as for high-speed cutting of carbon steels.

Other Welding Processes

It would be wrong to close this chapter without mention of two relatively new welding processes which are not yet widely used but which are certain to play important roles in years to come. In electron beam welding (EBW) a stream of electrons is focused on the welding zone. This beam has great penetrating power; it can be used to weld almost any metal, in almost any thickness. (Aluminum 6 in. thick has been welded in a single pass.) However, the capital investment required for equipment is substantial (ranging from at least $75,000 to more than $1,000,000). The cost of equipment for *laser beam welding* (LBW) is somewhat less than that, but still high. In this process, a beam of light is used instead of a beam of electrons. Like the electron beam, this light beam has great penetrating power. Although so far limited to welding of metal thicknesses below 50 mm (2 in.), LBW is a high-speed process which can be controlled with remarkable precision, even to the point of making a perfect weld between two fine wires.

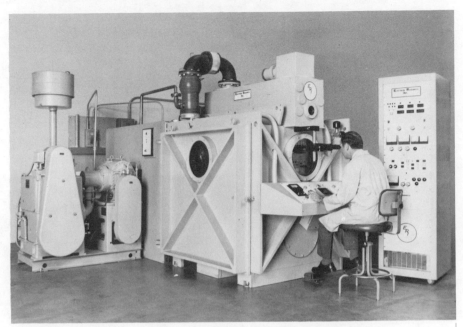

Fig. 1-4. Electron beam welding is usually performed in a vacuum chamber, as in this photograph, where the operator, seated at a control panel, is observing the welding action through a 'scope.

QUESTIONS–CHAPTER 1

1. What was the major welding process before the 20th century?
2. Of all the major welding processes used today, which is the oldest?
3. What is the oldest electric welding process?
4. What is the difference between tig and mig welding? Tig and plasma?
5. What is resistance welding?
6. What is the limitation of submerged arc welding?

OXY-ACETYLENE WELDING AND CUTTING

As mentioned in the previous chapter, gas welding, using oxygen and hydrogen, dates back to the 1850's. However, the oxy-hydrogen flame is virtually useless for welding steel. Gas welding, to be broadly useful, had to await the discovery of the remarkable properties of the oxy-acetylene flame, and of a way to make acetylene at reasonable cost. These events took place in the 1890's.

Acetylene gas is unknown in nature. Edmund Davy, a famous British chemist, is generally considered the first man to make acetylene. In 1836, attempting to produce potassium metal, he came up with a black compound (potassium carbide) which reacted with water to produce a gas which burned with great brilliancy. He thought it would make an excellent illuminating gas if it could be produced at moderate cost. That was not possible, using potassium carbide as the starting point. Calcium carbide (which, like acetylene, does not exist in nature) was not made and identified until 1862. Like potassium carbide, it reacted with water to form acetylene. Again, the process by which it was first made did not offer economic possibilities.

Although calcium carbide was undoubtedly accidentally produced in electric furnace operations before 1892, not until that year was it produced *and* identified both in France and the U.S. In both cases, the experimenters were trying to make something else. The Frenchman did not immediately recognize the potential commercial value of what he had created. The Americans did.

Major J. Turner Morehead and Thomas L. Wilson, using an electric furnace they had set up in Spray, N.C., were attempting to make calcium metal from a mixture of quicklime and coal tar. If successful, they hoped to use the calcium to reduce aluminum oxide and come up with aluminum metal. However, the product of their electric furnace run was a dark crystalline mass which reacted violently with water. They had found a way to make acetylene economically, and they were not slow to recognize the value of their discovery. Because they sent a sample of the calcium carbide to Lord Kelvin in England, together with details on the method by which they had produced it, by 1895 calcium carbide plants were operating in both England and France, as well as in the U.S. Plants in Norway and Switzerland followed close behind.

Dr. Carl Von Linde of Germany built his first plant for producing liquid air (to be used for refrigerating purposes) in 1895, the same year in which Le Chatelier discovered the remarkable properties of the oxy-acetylene flame. In 1902, Von Linde built a plant which not only liquefied air, but then fractionated it to produce pure oxygen. With acetylene already widely available, the basic resources needed for general exploitation of the oxy-acetylene processes were now available. In 1907, the first U.S. plant to use the Linde process was started in Buffalo, N.Y. Although several plants which made oxygen (and hydrogen) by electrolysis of water were started up in the 1907-1912 period, by 1914 the "liquid air" process was recognized as *the* way to produce high-purity oxygen, and it remains so to this day.

Some Early Exploits

Although oxygen cutting was actually demonstrated at the Seattle World's Fair, shortly after the century opened, commercially-useful torches were not available for several years. In 1907, Eugene Bournonville, one of the outstanding figures in the development of the oxy-acetylene processes in the U.S., showed the U.S. Navy Yard in Brooklyn that 14-inch portholes in armor plate 2-3 in. thick could be cut in 12 minutes. Before that demonstration, the portholes were being chipped out, after huge kerosene torches had preheated the steel. It had taken two torch operators and five chippers 10 days to cut one porthole. Later that year, American-made cutting torches were used on the demolition of the old Grand Central Station in N.Y. City, at one-twentieth the cost that older methods would have entailed. The next year, three men with cutting torches cut out the four 70-ton structural steel shields which had been used in construction of the H & M railroad tunnels under the Hudson River, a job which would otherwise have required 20 workmen.

Fig. 2-1. This sketch of an early oxy-acetylene welding operation was printed in a 1906 issue of the ACETYLENE JOURNAL.

In 1910, a 9000-ft. pipeline built to bring water down to hydroelectric generators from a natural reservoir in Colorado began to leak so badly, only months after it had been placed in service, that some kind of repair was essential. Pipe diameter was about four feet, with walls more than an inch thick at the lower end, where the internal pressure was 825 psi. Butt joints in the pipe had been held together by heavy steel straps riveted to the pipe on both the inside and outside. A half-million dollar investment was in jeopardy. Working through the dead of winter, welders repaired 200 joints successfully, using acetylene generated on the spot from 18 tons of calcium carbide and fed to torches through lines as long as 500 feet, and oxygen made from 23 tons of potassium perchlorate in two stationary plants and then compressed into cylinders.

During the years 1912-1917, the oxy-acetylene processes really came into their own. Five manufacturers were using cutting and welding in the building of all-steel railroad cars, and railroad shops were both using cutting and welding for manufacturing and repair purposes. (The railroads had also taken the lead in applying arc welding.) Oxygen and acetylene plants by the score were in operation. The rapid expansion in steel output required during World War I would never have been achieved if the oxygen cutting torch had not made possible cutting up of thousands of tons of scrap steel.

Fig. 2-2. This photo shows the cutting of a cast iron slag pot in 1920.

All the acetylene made from calcium carbide during the first few years was used for lighting purposes: house lighting, miners' lamps, and (a bit later automobile lamps). In 1895, however, a French chemist, Henry Le Chatelier, announced to the world that combustion of equal quantities of acetylene and oxygen produced a flame far hotter (about 6000°F or 3300°C) than any gas flame previously known. Further, he pointed out that the flame did not oxidize the metals which it melted. At once, experimenters went to work to find a way of controlling the flame for welding purposes. Credit for producing the first torch is generally given to Edmond Fouche, of France, who had already discovered a safe way to compress acetylene into cylinders. In 1903, Fouche sent one of his first torches to the U.S., where it was used with success in that same year.

While the process of making acetylene from calcium carbide which came into being in the 1890's is still used to make most of our acetylene today, the process by which virtually all oxygen used today in welding and cutting is made did not exist until the year 1902. Until then, and for some years after that date, oxygen was generally made, as it had been for many years, by heating of various compounds which were rich in oxygen.

The Oxy-Acetylene Processes Today

Welding. It is true that the electric welding processes have almost completely taken over the *production* welding field. For most welding applications, there's an electric welding process which will turn out good welds faster than the oxy-acetylene torch. If that is true, why bother with oxy-acetylene welding at all? Why are at least 50,000 oxy-acetylene welding and cutting outfits sold every year in the U.S.? Some would say that the answer lies in the two words "and cutting". There's some truth in that, but not the whole truth. A better answer is this one: That an oxy-acetylene outfit is more versatile, more readily portable, and far *less expensive* than any comparable electric welding outfit. With the oxy-acetylene torch, and an assortment of welding rods and fluxes which can be purchased almost anywhere in the country, you can weld just about everything, and do it well. You can put the outfit in the back of a truck, take it almost anywhere, and use it almost anywhere. You can weld, you can cut, you can do a variety of heating jobs. If you have such an outfit, you may use it more for cutting than for welding, but if you don't use it for a lot of welding, you probably aren't taking full advantage of its capabilities.

Cutting. While oxy-acetylene welding may have "taken a back seat" in industry (significant as it may be in repair work) the use of oxygen cutting has expanded in every decade since 1902. The cutting torch *lives* with and on steel, all the way from the primary steel mill to the scrap yard, where steel is reclaimed to be used in making more steel. Oxygen cutting is not now, and never has been, an exclusively oxy-*acetylene* process; other fuel gases are also widely used. However, more cutting torches are operated with acetylene than with all other fuel gases combined, for reasons which we'll get into a bit deeper in Chapter 23. The amount of oxygen consumed in cutting operations exceeds by many times the amount consumed in gas welding.

Steel Conditioning. It is a rather well-known fact that oxygen converters are rapidly taking the place of other types of furnaces (open-hearth, Bessemer) in the making of steel. Less well-known is the fact that long before the first oxygen converter went into service, steel mills were consuming many thousands of *tons* of oxygen for the removal of surface defects from steel blooms, billets, and slabs prior to rolling the steel to final plate or sheet form. The several types of operations covered by the term *steel conditioning* are all oxygen cutting processes; few of them today can be classified as oxy-acetylene, but all of them can be traced back to early use of oxy-acetylene cutting torches which were slightly modified so that they could *groove* steel rather than *slice* it.

Heating and Heat Treating. Probably every oxy-acetylene outfit in service today is used, at least occasionally, as a convenient source of heat for bending or forming metals, loosening "frozen" nuts, and dozens of other

Fig. 2-3. This operator is removing surface defects from a steel slab, which will then be reheated and rolled into sheet. This is one of the operations covered by the general term "steel conditioning". A length of steel rod is advanced into the preheat flames, to speed up the start of the reaction between the oxygen jet and the plate surface, each time the operator depresses the cutting oxygen valve lever.

jobs. For some of these uses, it is merely a convenient heat source, where the relatively high cost of aceylene is more than balanced by the time saved. Another widespread use for the heat of the oxy-acetylene flame is in the brazing of joints in copper tubing systems, where speed again gives it an advantage over lower-temperature flames which might be used. There are several industrial applications of the flame — for example, flame-hardening and flame-descaling, which will be covered in Chapter 22 — where the extremely high temperature of the flame is indispensable.

Fig. 2-4. The oxy-acetylene flame-hardening process can be used to produce a hardened surface on a steel shaft, while permitting retention of a tough, ductile shaft core. In this application, the shaft is revolved in front of the flames for a few seconds. Then the flames are shut off, and a water quench applied immediately.

QUESTIONS—CHAPTER 2

1. What metals can be welded by the oxy-acetylene process?
2. What metals can be cut by the oxy-acetylene process?
3. What are some of the other oxy-acetylene applications besides welding and cutting?
4. What is the underlying principle of oxy-acetylene welding?

OXYGEN AND ACETYLENE

This chapter will deal with the two gases which, burned together, produce the oxy-acetylene flame. It will cover their properties, their production, their commercial distribution, the containers in which they are stored and distributed, and the precautions which should be observed when using the gases or handling and storing the containers.

Oxygen

Oxygen, which makes up about 21 per cent of the air we normally breathe, as well as about 90 per cent by weight of all the water on earth, may be considered the most important element in the universe. Without it, there would be no life as we know it. Every living animal "burns" oxygen with carbon and hydrogen to produce the energy that it needs in order to live, grow, and move. Fortunately for the animal kingdom, all green plants produce more oxygen than they consume, so that the reservoir of oxygen in our atmosphere remains at a constant level from century to century.

Oxygen not only combines with carbon and hydrogen to produce energy (heat), but combines with most of the other elements found in the universe, including all metals. Fortunately, its reaction with most elements and compounds takes place very slowly or not at all at normal temperatures. However, almost everything made up predominantly of carbon and hydrogen (coal, wood, petroleum products) has a "kindling temperature". Once that temperature is reached, "oxidation" suddenly becomes "burning", which then proceeds to produce enough heat to maintain the reaction until the supply of oxygen or fuel runs out, or until other influences produce enough cooling effect to quench the fire.

It's perhaps fortunate we have only 21 per cent oxygen in our atmosphere, and that 78 per cent is made up of nitrogen, which won't combine with oxygen at any temperature normally reached by the burning of other materials. We don't often think of it in that way, but the nitrogen acts as a *cooling* agent. A good part of the energy produced by the burning of carbon and hydrogen in air is used up in heating the nitrogen. In an atmosphere of 100 per cent oxygen, burning takes place at a greatly accelerated rate. Given such an atmosphere, a wooden house that caught fire would probably burn flat in a matter of minutes, rather than hours. If there's one thing you must remember about oxygen, it's that things burn *much* faster in pure oxygen (or even in a mixture of half oxygen, half nitrogen) than they do in air. That's why passing a lighted cigarette to a person in an oxygen tent is almost equivalent to signing his death warrant. The other thing you must remember is this: that when surrounded by pure oxygen, some oils and greases oxidize rapidly, fast enough to reach *kindling temperature* in a short time. That's why you must always keep oxygen away from oils and grease, and keep oil and grease from getting into an oxygen regulator or hose. The only lubricants which can be used with oxy-acetylene apparatus—and then only on threads and O-rings—are special products approved for such use.

Acetylene

Acetylene is a "hydrocarbon", just as are propane, methane, and virtually all the components which make up gasoline and fuel oils. However, it differs from those hydrocarbons in this respect: in the acetylene molecule, made up of two carbon atoms and two hydrogen atoms, the carbon atoms are joined by what chemists call a "triple bond". When acetylene reaches its kindling temperature (and under some other conditions as well, which we'll cover shortly) the bond breaks and *releases* energy. In other hydrocarbons, the breaking of the bonds between the carbon atoms *absorbs* energy. The triple bond is the reason why the oxy-acetylene flame is hotter than the flame produced by burning any other hydrocarbon gas with oxygen.

Acetylene is almost unknown in the natural world. There are ways to produce acetylene from natural gas, but they are economical only on a large scale. Virtually all the acetylene distributed for welding and cutting use is created by allowing calcium carbide, an electric furnace product, to react with water. As mentioned in Chapter 2, the discovery of the electric furnace method of producing calcium carbide was accidental. It turned out to be a lucky accident. The nice thing about the calcium carbide method of producing acetylene is that it can be done on almost any scale desired. In tightly-sealed cans, calcium carbide keeps indefinitely. For years, miners' lamps produced acetylene by adding water, a drop at a time, to lumps of carbide. Before acetylene in cylinders became available in almost every community of appreciable size, as it is today, many users of acetylene produced their own gas from calcium carbide, using acetylene generators which ranged in output from as little as 20 to as much as 1000 cubic feet per hour (cfh).

The triple bond which makes the oxy-acetylene flame the hottest of all gas flames is also responsible for two rather exceptional properties of acetylene gas which you should always remember. The first is this: that free gaseous acetylene, depending on confinement conditions, is potentially unstable at pressures above 15 psig (103kPa). If subject to severe shock, or a source of ignition, some of the triple bonds may break, releasing enough energy to cause all the other molecules in the enclosed volume to decompose into carbon and hydrogen with explosive force. The force of such an explosion is not so great as that released by the explosion of most mixtures of acetylene and oxygen, or acetylene and air, but it is substantial, and can be withstood only by extra-heavy-wall steel tubing. The maximum free acetylene pressure permitted by safety codes is 15 psig. All oxy-acetylene equipment is designed and manufactured to permit the use of acetylene at less than 15 psig. How it is possible to ship acetylene in cylinders at a pressure of 250 psi (1725 kPa) or more is something we'll get to a bit later in this chapter.

The other property of acetylene which you must remember is this: that the *flammability range* of mixtures of air and acetylene is broader than that of any other fuel gas/air mixture. Let's explain that more fully: Acetylene/ air mixtures can be ignited when they contain anywhere from 2.5 per cent acetylene to 80 per cent acetylene. Mixtures of methane (the principal component of natural gas) and air are flammable when they contain as little as 5 per cent methane and not more than 15 per cent methane. The hazards resulting from acetylene leaks are therefore somewhat greater than the hazards involved in leaks of other fuel gases. Any leak in a fuel gas system is a hazard; acetylene is noticeably more hazardous than other gases only at the *upper* end of the flamability range. Except in an acetylene generator, the chances of creating a mixture which contains more acetylene than air are relatively small. Treat ALL fuel gases with respect and you'll have no trouble. (In passing, we should note that *flammability* range is sometimes called *explosive* range. There's really no difference.)

Oxygen Production

Virtually all the oxygen used commercially today is obtained from the atmosphere by air separation, or what is frequently termed the "liquid air" process. (It is also possible, but more expensive, to obtain oxygen by electrolysis—that is, by passing an electric current through water.)

If you compress air, remove the heat created by the act of compression, and then cool it some more, you can liquefy it. (This is true of any gas, just as any liquid can be turned into a gas by heating it sufficiently.) The principal components of the resulting liquid air—liquid oxygen, liquid nitrogen, and liquid argon—all have different boiling points. That means that if you reduce the pressure, or put heat back into the mixture, the nitrogen will return to the gas state at a faster rate than the oxygen. Although the temperatures involved are much lower, the problem is basically the same as that involved in obtaining pure alcohol from a fermented mixture that contains no more than 9-10 per cent alcohol. In each case, a rectification column is used. In the case of an alcohol-water mixture, the primary aim of the process is to recover, in as pure a state as possible, the lower-boiling-point component, alcohol, at the top of the column. During the first part of this century, the designers of liquid air columns were interested only in re-

Fig. 3-1. A major oxygen plant, from which both liquid oxygen and liquid nitrogen are shipped by tank trailers to use points and cylinder filling stations which may be hundreds of miles away.

Fig. 3-2. A rather small on-site plant, showing rectification column and (right) back-up liquid storage tank.

Fig. 3-3. This is one of the smallest columns designed for on-site production of oxygen or nitrogen.

covering the high-boiling-point component, oxygen, from the bottom of the column. Today, there are so many uses for pure nitrogen, either in gas or liquid form, that almost all modern "liquid-air" plants are designed to produce both high-purity oxygen and high-purity nitrogen. This normally requires a two-stage process: The liquid air is first partially rectified in one column. A nitrogen-rich liquid mixture form the top of this column, and an oxygen-rich liquid mixture from the bottom, are then passed on to a second column, operating at a lower pressure, where the final rectification takes place.

A few words about the nature of a rectification column may be in order. Such a column houses a series of trays with slots or other perforations, each of which retains some liquid at all times, and is designed so that gas entering the tray from below must pass through that liquid. In an oxygen-plant column, the gas rising from each tray is slightly richer in nitrogen than the gas which entered the tray from below; the liquid which overflows from each tray is slightly richer in oxygen than the liquid which descended to that tray from the one above it.

The problems that must be solved in designing a truly efficient oxygen plant are extremely complex. Air is "free", but it takes a great deal of energy to compress that air and liquefy it. The prime aim of the designers is to reduce to a minimum the amount of energy which must be expended per ton of product. Plants being built today are much more efficient than the plants built in the first quarter of this century.

Oxygen-nitrogen plants are made in a wide range of sizes; from small units designed to produce about 10 tons (9070 kg) of product each day to enormous ones which can produce 1,000 tons (907,000 kg) or more each day—enough to fill 100,000 standard steel cylinders of oxygen or nitrogen. Very little of the output of a large plant—often none—is put into cylinders, however. Even though cylinder oxygen is used for cutting and welding at perhaps 100,000 points in the U.S., the use of oxygen for those purposes represents only a relatively small part of total oxygen use. To the steel industry, oxygen is as vital a material as coke or iron ore. Huge quantities of oxygen are used by some chemical plants, and increasing thousands of tons are being used to increase the efficiency of sewage treatment plants. (Much of the oxygen being used in sewage treatment plants is produced by an air separation process which does not require that the air be liquefied. Instead, the oxygen and nitrogen are separated by *selective adsorption*, using adsorbents known as *molecular sieves*. The oxygen produced by this process does not have the high purity—99.5%—which is essential for oxygen cutting.)

Fig. 3-4. One unit — capacity 220 tons a day — at a major plant which delivers most of its product by pipelines serving a variety of users.

Fig. 3-5. A pressure-swing-adsorption (PSA) oxygen plant which produces oxygen (95% pure) for uses other than welding and cutting.

Oxygen Distribution

In the early days of the industry, oxygen was withdrawn from the rectification column as a cold gas, and then compressed directly into steel cylinders. The cylinders of compressed oxygen were then distributed by cart, truck, or railroad car to the places where oxygen was used. Then plants were designed from which the oxygen could be withdrawn in liquid form, and what can only be described as a "revolution" in oxygen distribution began. Today, all long-distance movement of oxygen is in liquid form, using extremely well-insulated railroad tank cars or truck trailers. However, since most of the oxygen produced today is piped directly from oxygen plants as gas, for use in steel mills, chemical synthesis, or sewage treatment, there has been another turn of the wheel. Almost all plants being built today are designed primarily for gas production, with the capability of producing some liquid. When more liquid oxygen or nitrogen is required for overland distribution, a liquefier unit is added which takes in cold gas and reliquefies it by refrigeration, not by compression.

There are essentially four ways you can get oxygen today, depending on demand and location:

1. From a plant located on your own property.
2. From a pipeline which serves several customers from one plant.
3. From a railroad tank car or trailer which delivers liquid oxygen into a storage tank on your property.
4. From gas or liquid cylinders delivered by truck to your property.

All liquid oxygen tanks, whether mobile or stationary, have three things in common: they are extremely well-insulated, they operate at very moderate pressures, and they have relief valves which will release oxygen into the atmosphere, or into a pipeline, if the pressure within the tank rises above a certain point. The insulation of these tanks is extremely efficient. Although the temperature of the liquid oxygen is -178°C (-290°F) or less, little heat passes through the insulation. Waste of oxygen, due to opening of the relief valves to relieve excess pressure resulting from heat leak, is extremely small, either in distribution or storage.

At the majority of the points where oxygen is used in welding and cutting, it reaches the use point as compressed gas in a steel cylinder, or as liquid in a somewhat larger cylinder, so let's take a look at cylinders.

Oxygen Cylinders

While compressed oxygen cylinders are made in several sizes, ranging in capacity from less than 20 cf ($0.56m^3$) to more than 300 cf ($8.5 m^3$), the cylinder most frequently used is nearly 5 feet (1.5m) tall (including cap) and 9 inches (229 mm) in diameter. Full, it contains 244 cf ($6.9 m^3$) of oxygen at a pressure of 2200 psi (15200 kPa) as measured at 20°C (70°F). The oxygen contained in a full cylinder weighs about 20 lb. (9.1 kg); the cylinder itself weighs about 130 lb. (59 kg). The cylinder is drawn from a piece of high-strength steel plate, or forged from a billet of steel, and heat-treated after drawing or forging. It is capable of retaining a pressure of almost twice the 3360 psi (23200 kPa) at which it must be tested before going into service, and at least once every ten years thereafter. Regulations covering its construction, testing, marking, filling, and maintenance are issued by the U.S. Department of Transportation (DOT), which took over this responsibility from the Interstate Commerce Commission (ICC). Stamped into the shoulder of the "standard" cylinder (where the steel is much thicker than in the cylinder wall) you will find "ICC3A2015" or "DOT3A2015". You'll also find the date when the cylinder was placed in service ("1-63", for example) and below that the dates when it was retested.

In the stamping DOT (or ICC) 3A2015, "3A" stands for the *specification* of cylinder and "2015" for the *service* filling pressure (psi) (at 70 deg. F). During World War II, the Interstate Commerce Commission permitted a 10 per cent increase in filling pressure as a temporary wartime measure. the result was so satisfactory (there was no decrease in safety) that the temporary increase in rating was made permanent for cylinders which continued to meet certain conditions laid down when the 10 per cent increase was first allowed. However, in order to avoid confusion, the original rating figures were retained, even for new cylinders.

In service today are many oxygen cylinders stamped "DOT3AA2015", or "DOT3A2400" or "DOT3AA2400". The "3AA" denotes a cylinder made of higher strength steel than the "standard" cylinder we just described. A "3AA2015" cylinder has the same dimensions and capacity as a "3A2015" cylinder but weighs about 19 lb. less. A typical "3AA2400" cylinder, only four inches taller than a "3A2015" cylinder and weighing only about 12 per cent more, can be filled with 330 cu. ft. (9.5m^3) of oxygen at 2640 psi (18200 kPa). That's a 35 per cent increase in useful capacity.

Oxygen Cylinder Valves. The oxygen cylinder valve is made largely of brass. Its outlet is threaded and machined to comply with standards set years ago by the Compressed Gas Association (CGA), and today accepted as national standards by the American National Standards Institute (ANSI). All oxygen regulators sold in the U.S. and Canada for use on industrial oxygen cylinders carry a mating inlet nut and nipple. The connection is designated "CGA 540" and today is recognized only for use with oxygen (although in years past it was also used with nitrogen and argon). Every oxygen cylinder valve is also equipped with a bursting disk which will rupture and release the contents of the cylinder if cylinder pressure should approach cylinder test pressure (as it might in case of a fire).

A typical oxygen cylinder valve is illustrated in Fig 3-6. The valve stem packing is compressed by a packing nut. When the valve is opened fully— and it should always be fully opened—a shoulder on the valve stem provides further compression. Oxygen cylinder valves are always provided with handwheels. If you ever find one that can't be opened by hand, or that lacks a handwheel, do not attempt to open the valve with a wrench. Return that cylinder to the supplier, and use a different cylinder.

Liquid Oxygen Cylinders. A typical liquid oxygen cylinder meeting DOT specification 4L is about the same height as a standard compressed oxygen cylinder, but has twice the diameter. Full, it weighs about three times as much as a standard gas cylinder. However, it holds 12 times as much oxygen; in fact, the contents, when the cylinder is full, weigh more than the empty cylinder. There are also slightly taller DOT 4L cylinders which carry oxygen equivalent to the contents of 18 standard high-pressure cylinders.

The liquid cylinder is much more complex than the gas cylinder. It has an inner container of stainless steel, and an outer shell of carbon steel. Between the two is super-insulation under extremely high vacuum. Just inside the surface of the outer shell, and attached to it, is a vaporizing coil. In operation, gas pressure above the liquid in the inner container drives liquid out into the vaporizing coil, where it picks up heat from the atmosphere by conduction through the outer shell and changes to gas.

The liquid cylinder has a liquid-level gauge to show how much liquid remains in the cylinder, a relief valve which will vent oxygen to the atmosphere if internal pressure rises above 235 psi (16200 kPa), and a by-pass "economizer" valve which allows gas to pass from the cylinder

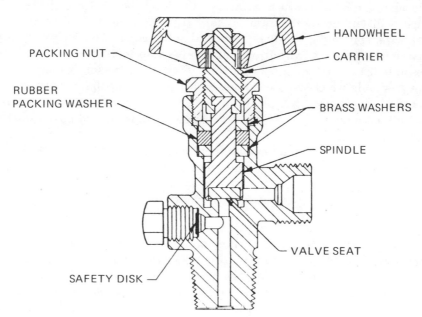

Fig. 3-6. Cross-section of a typical oxygen cylinder valve. Note the shoulder on the stem which compresses the packing when the valve is fully opened.

headspace into the vaporizer coil when heat leakage into the cylinder has caused pressure to rise above the normal operating level. It has rupture disks in both the inner container and the outer shell. The rupture disk in the outer shell will let go should an accident, or a leak in the vaporizer coil, cause pressure to build up in the normally high-vacuum insulation space between the inner container and outer shell.

We just mentioned "heat leakage into the cylinder". There is no such thing as "perfect" insulation, and some heat leaks into the inner container by conduction through its metal connections. Because there is some heat leakage, liquid cylinders are seldom employed in situations where they may be idle for several days in succession. While the loss rate is rather low (generally less than 100 cu. ft. per day even for the largest liquid cylinder) it must not be overlooked. Some liquid cylinders rely on the slight heat leakage through the insulation to maintain cylinder pressure; others are equipped with pressure-building circuits which automatically maintain desired cylinder head pressure by passing liquid through a supplementary vaporizing coil. The pressure-building circuit is provided with a shutoff valve, which should be open only when the cylinder is in use.

While the liquid cylinder holds far more oyxgen than a compressed gas cylinder, its delivery rate is limited by the rate at which heat can pass through the cylinder's outer steel shell into its vaporizer coil. If an attempt is made to withdraw oxygen at a steady rate of more than about 250 cfh ($7m^3$/hr) (the exact figure will vary with the temperature and humidity of the surrounding air) frost may form on the outer shell of the cylinder. That frost will cut down the rate of heat transfer through the shell to the vaporizer coil, and actually reduce the delivery capability. However, under most circumstances, withdrawal at a rate of up to 1000 cfh (28 m^3/hr) is possible for several minutes at a time. Further, accessory vaporizer units are available which can be connected between the cylinder outlet and the point of oxygen use. A typical unit will raise the minimum output rate to 500 cfh ($14m^3$/hr) when used with a liquid cylinder which has a pressure-building circuit.

A liquid oxygen cylinder carries the same outlet connection (CGA 540) as a gas cylinder, so standard oxygen regulators can be connected directly.

Acetylene Production

The acetylene used for welding and cutting is usually the product of a reaction between calcium carbide and water in an acetylene generator. There was a time when many users generated their own acetylene, but today onsite generation of acetylene is rather uncommon, even in plants which have acetylene piping systems. Acetylene reaches most use points in cylinders of dissolved acetylene (we'll explain that term shortly) which may be used individually, or manifolded (coupled together) for connection to a plant piping system.

Fig. 3-7. Dissolved acetylene is supplied in cylinders ranging in capacity from about 390 cf (left) to 10 cf (right). Type designations are those used by Linde Division.

Fig. 3-8. Gaseous oxygen cylinders range in capacity from 330 cf (left) to 20 cf (right).

Fig. 3-9. A liquid oxygen cylinder.

OXYGEN AND ACETYLENE 25

In an acetylene producing plant, calcium carbide (an electric furnace product) is allowed to react with water to form acetylene gas and calcium hydroxide (slaked lime). The reaction is rapid, and produces a lot of heat. Because of the heat produced, a typical generator uses one gallon of water for every pound of calcium carbide. The acetylene is dried, passed through a purification unit, and then compressed into cylinders. The water leaves the generator as a white sludge or slurry in which the calcium hydroxide is partly dissolved, partly in suspension. This sludge is then pumped or drained to a settling basin or pit.

Acetylene Cylinders

We mentioned earlier that free acetylene is somewhat unstable, and that safety codes therefore forbid its use at pressures over 15 psig (103 kPa). How then are we able to transport it in cylinders under a pressure of 250 psi (1725 kPa) or more? You might say that we do it by applying the principle "divide and conquer". First, we dissolve the acetylene in acetone, a solvent which will retain a lot of acetylene at normal atmosphere pressure, and a great deal more at elevated pressures. We don't just put that solution in an ordinary cylinder, however, because acetone expands a lot as it dissolves more and more acetylene, and shrinks as pressure is lowered and gas withdrawn from the solution. Instead, we fill a cylinder with a rigid but porous material. The pores are very fine. Should free acetylene in one pore happen to decompose through shock of some kind, or exposure of the cylinder to fire, the energy released will be soaked up by the filler, rather than transferred to the acetylene in the next pore.

This is how an acetylene cylinder is made. First, the cylinder shell is constructed from pieces of deep-drawn steel plate, welded together. A foot ring, and a head ring (where used) are attached, and a forged steel valve "spud" is welded in place at the top of the cylinder. The cylinder is then packed with moist filler and placed in an oven for several days, until a weight check shows that all the moisture has been baked out of the filler. Finally, the cylinder valve and safety devices are installed, and a metered amount of acetone is pumped into the cylinder. The exact amount of acetone which may be added depends on the internal volume of the cylinder shell and the porosity of the filler. There can be a substantial difference between the acetone and acetylene capacities of old and new cylinders of the same apparent size, since the latest calcium silicate fillers have greater porosity than fillers made up principally from other ingredients, as used until the 1940's.

Dissolved acetylene cylinders are filled to a maximum pressure of 250 psi (1725kPa) at 20°C (68°F). They are not equipped with rupture-disk safety devices, as are oxygen and nitrogen gas cylinders, but with fusible metal safety plugs or with valves having channels filled with fusible metal. The fusible metal will melt at approximately the temperature of boiling water (100°C or 212°F). Small cylinders (the 10 cu. ft. and 40 cu. ft. sizes) have one fusible metal channel located in the cylinder valve. The large cylinders normally used in welding and cutting, with capacities ranging up to nearly 400 cf of acetylene, have from two to four plugs, located in both top and bottom of the cylinders. If a cylinder is exposed to a fire, one or more safety devices will melt and allow the acetylene and acetone to escape and burn gradually. If it did not have such a safety device, a full acetylene cylinder exposed to a fire would rupture and release its contents all at once, perhaps explosively. Because of the low melting point of the fusible metal, you should never use boiling water to melt out any ice that has formed in the top of a recessed head cylinder. *Warm* water is okay; *boiling* water can cause trouble.

Here are two very important things to remember about dissolved acetylene cylinders: First, do not withdraw acetylene from a cylinder when it is not in an upright position. If you do, some of the acetone may be forced out, as liquid droplets, through the cylinder valve. This is not really a safety problem, but may cause erratic operation of the torch. Always store acetylene cylinders in the upright position, too. If by mistake, a cylinder has been stored horizontally, let it stand upright for a while before withdrawing any acetylene. Second, do not draw acetylene from the cylinder at a rate in excess of one-seventh the normal full capacity of that cylinder. From a large cylinder with a capacity of 350-390 cf (10-11 m³), the withdrawal rate should not exceed 55-60 cfh (less than 2m³/hr) except for very short periods. If acetylene is withdrawn too rapidly, quite a lot of acetone may come with it, in vapor or droplet form, and the cylinder may cool down so much that it cannot sustain the high rate. This will affect your torch flame, and will mean that your supplier must replenish the acetone in the cylinder more frequently.

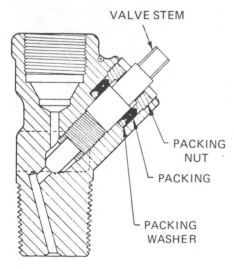

VALVE STEM

Fig. 3-10. Cross-section of a LINDE acetylene cylinder valve with CGA 510 connection.

PACKING NUT

PACKING

PACKING WASHER

Many acetylene cylinder valves are not equipped with handwheels, and must be operated by a wrench. The wrench should always be left in place while the cylinder valve is open. Further, acetylene cylinders valves need not and should not be opened wide; one and one-half turns should be the limit.

Two different outlet connections are used in the U.S. on large acetylene cylinders: the CGA 510 connection, with left-hand internal threads in the cylinder valve outlet, and the CGA 300 connection, with right-hand external threads on the valve outlet. The CGA 300 connection, and the CGA 520 and CGA 200 connections used on small cylinders (40 and 10 cu. ft. capacity) are exceptions to the general rule that all fuel gas connections used in connection with welding and cutting equipment carry left-hand threads.

In an oxygen cylinder there is a precise relationship between cylinder pressure and cylinder contents. A standard oxygen cylinder that contains 244 cf at 2200 psi and 70° (6.5 m³ at 15200 kPa at 20°C) will contain 122 cf (3.25 m³) when the pressure has dropped to 1100 psi at 70°F (7600kPa at 20°C). In the dissolved acetylene cylinder, the relationship between pressure and remaining acetylene content is less precise. An acetylene cylinder is not precisely half-full when its pressure has dropped to 125 psi (half the pressure of a full cylinder). If the cylinder temperature is 70°F (20°C), the amount of acetylene remaining in the cylinder is slightly less than half the "full" content. However, change in temperature affects the pressure in an acetylene cylinder at a much faster rate than it affects the pressure in an oxygen cylinder. Pressure in an oxygen cylinder will go up or down only about 4 percent for each 20-degree change in temperature (F) from 70 deg. A full acetylene cylinder which has a pressure of 250 psi at 70°F (1725 kPa at 20°C) will have a pressure of 315 psi at 90°F (2175 kPa at 31°C) and a pressure of 190 psi at 50°F (1300 kPa at 9°C). You must always take temperature into account when estimating how much acetylene the cylinder contains.

Manifolds and Piping Systems

While a great deal of oxy-acetylene welding and cutting is done using gases supplied by a single pair of cylinders, there are many situations which require something more. We have noted that a large acetylene cylinder should not be called upon to supply acetylene at a steady rate of more than about 60 cfh (less than 2 m³/hr). Yet there are heating heads, designed for use with standard torches, which will burn up to 250 cfh (9 m³/hr). While the withdrawal rate from oxygen cylinders is not limited, 45 minutes of cutting 3-in. steel will exhaust the contents of a standard oxygen cylinder. In such situations, portable cylinder manifolds, which link from two to five cylinders together to supply a single torch, are frequently used.

Many shops have oxygen and acetylene piping systems. Most oxygen piping systems are now supplied from liquid oxygen storage tanks, although

Fig. 3-11. A liquid oxygen cylinder manifold. The three cylinders on the right have a combined capacity of 13,500 cf; when they are empty, the reserve cylinder (left) takes over automatically.

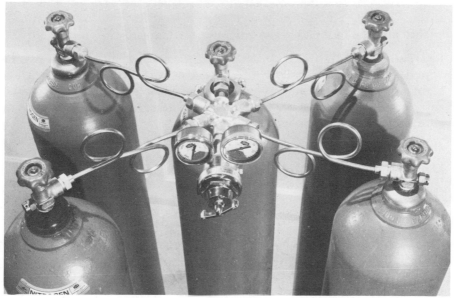

Fig. 3-12. An approved portable high-pressure cylinder manifold, which delivers gas from five cylinders through a single regulator.

permanently-mounted oxygen cylinder manifolds, to which any number of cylinders can be attached, are still used occasionally. Acetylene piping systems may be supplied by an acetylene generator, by a stationary cylinder manifold, or by an acetylene trailer. An acetylene trailer is essentially nothing more than a group of large acetylene cylinders, coupled together on a trailer, which can be hooked up directly to the user's piping system.

Precautions to be Observed in the Storage, Handling and Use of Oxygen and Acetylene

Always refer to oxygen and acetylene by their proper names. Say "oxygen", never "air". Say "acetylene", not "gas". It is very important that oxygen not be confused with compressed air, or used as a substitute for compressed air. To use "gas" instead of "acetylene" can also be trouble-making, since several other fuel gases are also used with oxygen. The other gases—natural gas, methane, or the liquefied petroleum (LP) gases, propane and butane—differ from acetylene, and from each other, in heat content, flammability limits, and safe handling requirements. Therefore, be specific when you refer to any gas.

Never release acetylene, or any other fuel gas, where it might cause a fire or explosion. Fuel gases should never be released into the air near other welding or cutting work, near sparks or flames caused by other means, nor in confined spaces. If it is necessary to release fuel gas without lighting it, release it outdoors in a place where there is least likely to be a significant hazard and the flammable gas will soon dissipate.

CAUTION! IMPORTANT! USE NO OIL! Oil, grease, coal dust, and similar organic materials are easily ignited and burn violently in the presence of high oxygen concentrations. Never allow such materials to come in contact with oxygen or oxy-acetylene equipment, including hose. Oxy-acetylene apparatus does not require lubrication.

Never use oxygen or fuel gas from a cylinder except through an approved pressure-reducing regulator. A single approved regulator may, however, be used to control flow from a group of cylinders which have been correctly manifolded. Never attempt to use a regulator except for the gas and service for which it is designed. Generally speaking, the inlet connections installed by the regulator manufacturer make mismatching impossible. However, that cannot always be the case, since there just are not enough mechanically distinct connections to permit each gas to have individual treatment. Therefore, some gases—for example, the inert gases and certain fuel gases—are treated in groups. A propane regulator will fit many acetylene cylinders, but should not be so used. Similarly, a regulator intended for service at a station on a plant oxygen piping system will fit an oxygen cylinder, but should never be used on a cylinder.

Do not use pipe-fitting compounds or thread lubricants for making connections. Connections for oxy-acetylene and oxygen-fuel gas equipment are designed so that they can be made up tight without the need for lubricants or sealants. Of special importance is the need to keep all materials containing oil and grease away from equipment that uses oxygen.

Never use a cylinder that is leaking. If leakage around the cylinder valve stem is detected after the valve has been opened (one and one-half turns for an acetylene cylinder, as far as possible for an oxygen cylinder) close the valve tight and return it to your supplier after tagging the cylinder to tell him that the valve is unservicable. Exception: In the case of an acetylene valve which has a hex packing gland nut, you may try tightening that nut gently after you have closed the valve. Then re-test for leakage.

If fuel gas leaks from any cylinder—from the outlet when the valve is closed, from around the valve stem when the valve is open, from a fusible metal plug, or from a safety relief valve—move the cylinder to an open place outdoors, well away from any possible source of ignition, and plainly tag it as having an unserviceable valve, fusible plug, or relief valve. Promptly notify your supplier and follow his instructions as to further handling of the cylinder and its return.

Never tamper with fusible plugs or other safety devices on cylinders. All oxygen cylinders are provided with bursting disks, installed in the cylinder valves. All fuel gas cylinders are provided with fusible plugs or pressure-relief devices (spring-loaded or frangible disk) or combinations of these designed to release cylinder contents in the event of exposure to excessive temperatures. The fusible plugs in acetylene cylinders melt at 100°C (212°F); in liquefied petroleum gas cylinders at 74°C (165°F).

Never use boiling water to thaw ice from the outlet of a fuel gas cylinder. Because the fusible plugs melt at or below the temperature of boiling water, never use extremely hot water, steam or a flame to melt out ice which may have formed in the valve outlet. Use **warm** water only.

Do not open an acetylene cylinder valve more than one and one-half turns. This permits adequate flow of acetylene from the cylinder and allows for quick closing of the valve in an emergency situation.

To open and close acetylene cylinder valves not provided with handwheels, always use the special wrench or key provided by the supplier. Leave the wrench or key in position, ready for immediate use should it be necessary to close the valve promptly. (When several cylinders are manifolded together, a wrench on every cylinder is not required.)

Never use the recessed top of any fuel gas cylinder as a place for tools.

It is best to keep acetylene cylinders upright at all times. Do not store them in the horizontal position; do not draw acetylene from a cylinder except when it is upright. If an acetylene cylinder is used in the horizontal position, solvent may be lost and flame quality may be affected.

Keep liquid oxygen cylinders vertical. If oxygen is provided in low-pressure liquid oxygen cylinders designed to supply gas for welding or cutting, always keep such cylinders vertical; never lay one of them on its side. The broad base and substantial weight of a liquid cylinder make accidental tipping or knocking over very unlikely.

Never use any cylinder, full or empty, as a roller or support.

Never, never use oxygen as though it were compressed air. A serious accident may easily result if oxygen is used as a substitute for compressed air. Oxygen must never be used in pneumatic tools, in oil preheating burners, to start internal combustion engines, to blow out pipelines, to "dust" clothing or work, for pressure tests of any kind, or for ventilation. Oxygen or air rich in oxygen should never be allowed to saturate any part of the clothing since a spark might easily start a serious "flash" fire.

Do not handle oxygen cylinders on the same platform with oil, or place them in any position where oil or grease from overhead cranes or belts may fall on them.

Unless they are secured on a suitable cylinder truck, do not move cylinders without first removing regulators and replacing protective caps.

Never use slings or electromagnets for lifting cylinders. Do not lift cylinders by the protective cap alone. When moving cylinders, use suitable hand truck or racks whenever possible.

Cylinders stored inside buildings must be kept at least 20 feet from combustible materials.

Store oxygen cylinders separately from fuel gas cylinders. Unless a fire-resistant noncombustible partition, at least 5 feet high, is used to separate the two types of cylinders, a minimum 20-foot separation should be maintained.

Always keep empty cylinders separate from full cylinders.

For complete information on storage and manifolding of cylinders, refer to National Fire Protection Association (NFPA) Standard No. 51.

QUESTIONS–CHAPTER 3

1. What effect does a change in temperature have on the contents of the oxygen cylinder?
2. What are some of the general precautions to follow with respect to cylinders?
3. Why is "Use No Oil" so strongly stressed?

THE OXY-ACETYLENE FLAME

In oxy-acetylene welding, the "tool" used is not really the torch; it's the *flame*. The torch should never touch the material being welded. The only purpose of the torch is to provide a gas mixture which will produce the flame best suited to the work to be done.

There are three distinct types of oxy-acetylene flames, usually termed:
    Neutral
    Excess Acetylene (or "carburizing")
    Oxidizing (or "excess oxygen")
The type of flame produced depends upon the ratio of oxygen to acetylene in the gas mixture which leaves the torch tip.

The *neutral* flame (Fig. 4-1) is produced when the ratio of oxygen to acetylene, in the mixture leaving the torch, is almost exactly one-to-one. It's termed "neutral" because it will usually have no chemical effect on the metal being welded. It will not oxidize the weld metal; it will not cause an increase in the carbon content of the weld metal.

The *excess acetylene* flame (Fig. 4-2), as its name implies, is created when the proportion of acetylene in the mixture is higher than that required to produce the neutral flame. Used on steel, it will cause an increase in the carbon content of the weld metal.

The *oxidizing* flame (Fig. 4-3) results from burning a mixture which contains more oxygen than required for a neutral flame. It will oxidize or "burn" some of the metal being welded.

Chemistry of the Flame

When acetylene is burned in air, the end products are carbon dioxide (carbon plus oxygen) and water vapor (hydrogen plus oxygen). A chemical equation covering complete combustion reads like this:

$$2\ C_2H_2 + 5\ O_2 = 4\ CO_2 + 2\ H_2O$$

In everyday terms, this means that to burn two cubic feet of acetylene you must use five cubic feet of oxygen, or 2-1/2 times as much oxygen as acetylene. Yet we have just said that the *neutral* flame is produced by burning a one-to-one mixture of oxygen and acetylene, and that the neutral flame does not contain an excess of either gas. This might seem to be a bit of a contradiction, but it is not, since the equation given above represents an over-simplification of the combustion process. Actually, combustion in the oxy-acetylene flame takes place in two distinct stages; for the first, the oxygen is supplied by the mixture leaving the torch; for the second, the oxygen is supplied by the air around the flame.

In the first stage of combustion, the acetylene breaks down into carbon and hydrogen, and the carbon reacts with the oxygen to form carbon monoxide. In chemical terms:

$$C_2H_2 + O_2 = 2\ CO + H_2$$

In words, this means that you need one molecule of oxygen for each molecule of acetylene. A cubic foot of acetylene contains the same number of molecules as a cubic foot of oxygen.

In the second stage of combustion, the carbon monoxide (CO) reacts with oxygen from the air to form carbon dioxide (CO_2). The hydrogen reacts with oxygen from the air to form water (H_2O). The chemical equations are these:

$$2\ CO + O_2 = 2\ CO_2$$

$$2\ H_2 + O_2 = 2\ H_2O\ (or,\ H_2 + O = H_2O)$$

It is this two-stage combustion process which produces the well-defined inner cone in the oxy-acetylene flame. The first stage of reaction takes place at the boundary between the inner cone and the pale blue outer flame. The second stage takes place in the outer flame. If the proportion of acetylene supplied to the tip is increased, a white "feather" appears around the inner cone. This feather contains white-hot particles of carbon which, for lack of sufficient oxygen in the original mixture, cannot be oxidized to carbon monoxide at the inner cone boundary. On the other hand, if the proportion of oxygen fed to the tip is increased, the inner cone will shorten noticeably and the noise of the flame will increase.

Flame Adjustment

For most welding, a neutral flame is desired. Not even a skilled welder can distinguish visually between a true neutral flame and a *slightly* oxidizing flame. But anyone who knows what to look for can tell the difference between a neutral flame and a flame with a slight excess acetylene feather. Therefore, we always adjust the flame to neutral from the excess-acetylene side. We start with an excess of acetylene when we light the torch, and then

Fig. 4-1. The neutral flame, which results from burning a mixture containing approximately equal volumes of oxygen and acetylene. The well-defined core of the flame (extremely bright pale blue) is known as the "inner cone".

Fig. 4-2. The excess acetylene flame, which has a whitish feather around and beyond the inner cone.

Fig. 4-3. The oxidizing flame, which results from an excess of oxygen in the gas mixture, has a shorter, more sharply-pointed inner cone than the neutral flame.

increase the flow of oxygen until the excess-acetylene feather just disappears. If the flame is then too large for our purposes, we reduce the oxygen flow first, to produce a feather, then cut back on the acetylene flow until the feather just disappears.

Occasionally, you will read instructions which call for a *slight* excess of oxygen, or a *slight* excess of acetylene. Generally speaking, such instructions imply that a slight excess of one gas cannot cause trouble, but that a slight excess of the other gas may. Unless otherwise defined, a *slight excess* of acetylene means that you can just see a short "feather". A *slight excess* of oxygen means that you've reduced the acetylene flow until the "feather" has disappeared, then reduced it a bit more to cause a slight shortening of the inner cone.

For some operations, a substantial excess of acetylene is desired. The amount of excess is then expressed numerically, as "2X", "3X", or perhaps "1-1/2X". As shown in Fig. 4-4, in a "2X" excess acetylene flame the feather (measured from the end of the torch tip, not the end of the inner cone) is twice as long as the inner cone.

When a precise statement of amount of excess oxygen is required, it is always expressed in terms of the shortening of the inner cone from the neutral flame length. Again, this is shown in Fig. 4-4.

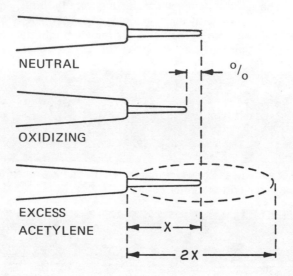

Fig 4-4. The degree of excess oxygen in the oxidizing flame is expressed in terms of the per cent shortening of the inner cone length, when adjustment is made by increasing the oxygen flow beyond that required to produce the neutral flame. The degree of excess acetylene in a flame is expressed by comparing the lengths of the inner cone and of the excess acetylene feather, measuring both from the face of the tip.

QUESTIONS–CHAPTER 4

1. What is the tool of the oxy-acetylene process?
2. What are the results of the reaction when acetylene is burned with oxygen?
3. How much oxygen is required to burn one volume of acetylene completely?
4. What are the three types of oxy-acetylene flames? Describe the distinguishing features of each.
5. Describe the two stages of combustion.
6. What is the most commonly used flame for welding? How do you obtain this flame?
7. How is the amount of excess oxygen in a flame specified? Excess acetylene?

EQUIPMENT FOR THE
OXY-ACETYLENE PROCESS

As we said in the preceeding chapter, the real "tool" of the oxy-acetylene welding process is the *flame,* not the *torch.* When we come to oxygen cutting, we must consider the pure oxygen jet as a second "tool", working hand-in-hand with the flame. To produce only the *flame,* we use a welding torch, fitted with the appropriate size *welding head* or *tip.** To produce both flames and the oxygen jet, we use a *cutting torch* or *cutting attachment,* equipped with the appropriate *cutting nozzle* or *tip.**

The equipment needed for oxy-acetylene welding and oxygen cutting is relatively simple and inexpensive. If the gases are to be supplied in cylinders, these are the *minimum* requirements:

A cylinder of oxygen
A cylinder of acetylene
A cylinder pressure regulator for oxygen
A cylinder pressure regulator for acetylene
A welding torch, with one or more welding heads
A cutting attachment, with one or more cutting nozzles
A length of oxygen hose, with fittings
A length of acetylene hose, with fittings
Goggles and gloves for the operator
A friction lighter for igniting the flame

Mount the cylinders on a suitable truck, as shown in Fig. 5-1, and you have an outfit that will go almost anywhere and need no further power of any kind except a bit of muscle power.

The Welding Torch

The gas welding torch is made up of a torch *handle* and a welding *head.* For marketing convenience, the handle is often packed separately, and

---

*Industry terminology is not fully standardized. Generally, the term welding *head* applies to a unit which includes a device for mixing the oxygen and acetylene, as well as a copper *tip.* Sometimes the tip, or even the complete head, is called a *nozzle.* In this book, the term *welding head* will always refer to a replaceable assembly which includes a mixer, and the term *welding tip* will refer to the one-piece replaceable flame-producing section of the *head.* We shall always refer to the replaceable front end part of the cutting torch or cutting attachment as a *nozzle.*

labelled "torch", but it can't be used for welding until you put the welding head on it.

The key parts of a complete welding torch, as shown in the simplified sketch (Fig. 5-2), are valves to control the flow of oxygen and acetylene, a mixer through which the gases pass, a mixing chamber into which the gases are allowed to expand and mix after leaving the mixer, and a welding tip. Of these four sections, only the valves are normally in the handle. The mixer, mixing chamber, and tip are in the welding head.

The valves (often called *throttle* valves) must be big enough to pass the volumes of gas required for the flame without too much pressure drop. In an "all-purpose" handle, where the flow rate for each gas may range from 4 to 200 cfh (0.1 to 5.6 m³/hr), they must be more generously proportioned than in a small handle designed for flows up to about 55 cfh (1.5 m³/hr). Valves must be equipped with leakproof packing, and are normally fitted with packing nuts which allow the pressure on the packing to be adjusted for the desired "stiffness" of the valve operation.

Fig. 5-1. A portable welding outfit, with oxygen and acetylene cylinders chained to an easy-rolling cylinder truck. Cutting attachment, normally a part of such an outfit, is not shown.

The *mixer* is perhaps misnamed, since it doesn't actually mix the gases, but merely meters them into the mixing chamber. Two types of "mixers" are widely used: the medium-pressure type, to which the gases are usually supplied at approximately equal pressures, and the injector type, to which the oxygen is supplied at relatively high pressure (up to 55 psi or more) and the acetylene is supplied at rather low pressure (down to less than 1 psi). In the injector type, the oxygen passes through a very small orifice in the injector, and the expansion of the oxygen as it leaves that orifice pulls the acetylene into the mixing chamber. An advantage of the injector is that minor fluctuations in oxygen pressure and flow cause changes in the amount of acetylene drawn into the mixing chamber and maintain the normal ratio of the gas mixture. This is especially helpful when oxygen is supplied to the torch from a plant piping system, where changes in demand placed on the system may cause pressure fluctuations.

As already stated, the mixer, whether medium-pressure or injector type, is normally a part of the welding head. The reason is this: There must be a relationship between the sizes of the orifices in the mixer and the size of the orifice in the welding tip. A single mixer cannot serve a wide range of tip sizes. Further, all the passages in the welding head must be designed so that if the flame is forced back into the head, as by momentary contact of the torch tip against the work, it will not continue to burn just ahead of the mixer, but will be extinguished without damage to head or torch.

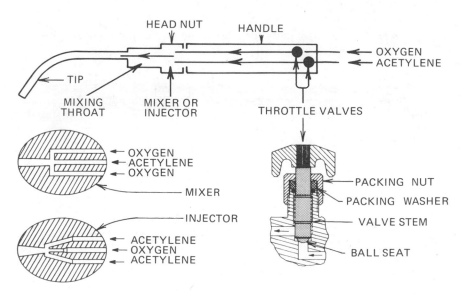

Fig. 5-2 Simplified sketch of a typical welding torch, with details showing the construction of a throttle valve and the flow of gases through a "mixer" and an "injector".

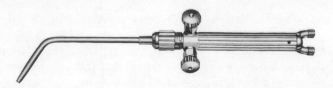

Fig. 5-3. A small welding torch, with throttle valves located at the front end of the handle. Ideally suited to sheet metal welding. Can be fitted with cutting attachment in place of the welding head shown.

Fig. 5-4. Welding torches of this general design are by far the most widely used. They will handle any oxy-acetylene welding job, can be fitted with multiflame heads for heating applications, and accomodate cutting attachments that will cut steel 6 in. thick.

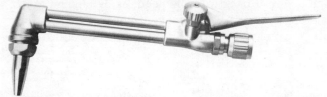

Fig 5-5. Cutting attachment for use on the welding torch shown immediately above.

Fig. 5-6. A full-size oxygen cutting torch which has all valves located in its rear body.

Fig. 5-7. Another style of cutting torch, with oxygen valves located at the front end of its handle.

The Cutting Torch

The cutting torch must not only meter and mix oxygen and fuel gas to feed the flames required for oxygen cutting, but must also control the stream of oxygen required for the cutting jet. In almost all torches designed for hand cutting, all the oxygen is fed to the torch through one oxygen hose. Just inside the torch body, the stream of oxygen is split, with one part passing through the valve which provides "on-off" control of the cutting oxygen jet, the other part passing through the throttle valve which controls oxygen flow to the mixer. Cutting torches for use in cutting machines usually are fitted with two oxygen inlet connections, with oxygen supplied through separate regulators.

As in the case of welding torches, cutting torches are offered with two types of mixers: the injector type, and the medium-pressure type. The medium-pressure type is by far the more common. An injector is generally used in torches designed to operate with natural gas as the fuel, since natural gas piping systems are often operated at pressures of 5 psi or less. A few acetylene piping systems are still operated at low pressure (less than 1 psi) and require use of injector-type torches.

In most cutting torches, a single mixer is used to cover the full range of nozzle sizes. This is feasible because the mixed-gas requirements for cutting steel 8 in. thick are only about four times the mixed-gas requirements for

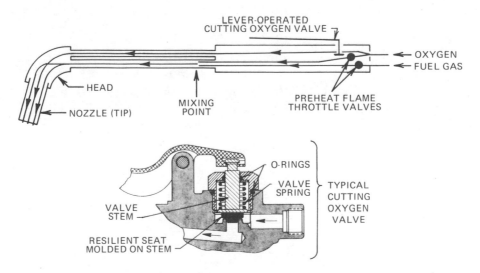

Fig. 5-8. Simplified sketch of a typical cutting torch, in which the preheat oxygen and acetylene are mixed at a point between torch head and handle. Detail shows construction of a cutting oxygen valve.

cutting ½-in. steel, while even a light-duty welding torch uses a range of tips whose requirements vary much more widely, as noted under "Welding Torches".

Every hand cutting torch has some kind of a lever for opening and closing the cutting oxygen valve. Designers try to locate the lever so that it can be squeezed or pressed slowly to start the cut, and then easily held wide open while the cut is in progress. Latches for locking the lever in "wide open" position are provided on some torches.

Cutting Attachments

A cutting attachment is a scaled-down version of a cutting torch, for direct connection to a welding torch handle in place of a welding head. It's a real convenience to the operator who wants to be able to switch back and forth from welding or heating to cutting, or vice versa. It takes only seconds to remove a welding head and install the cutting attachment, whereas it may take a couple of minutes to disconnect hoses from the welding torch handle and reconnect them to a full-sized cutting torch. Most cutting attachments are capable of cutting 2-in. steel, or thicker, with ease.

A cutting attachment does not need its own throttle valve for controlling acetylene flow, since the valve on the welding torch handle serves that purpose. It always has two valves for oxygen, however: a throttle valve to control flow of oxygen to the mixer, and a lever-operated valve to control the flow of cutting oxygen.

Regulators

The pressure in a full cylinder of oxygen is about 2200 psi at 70°F (15200 kPa at 20°C); in a full cylinder of acetylene, pressure is about 250 psi at 70°F (1725 kPa at 20°C). Oxygen must be supplied to welding and cutting torches at pressures ranging downward from about 100 psi to 5 psi (69 to 35 kPa) and acetylene at pressure of 15 psi (103 kPa) or less.

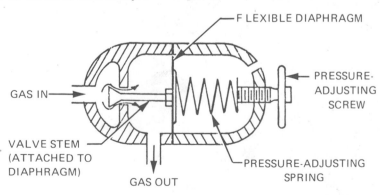

Fig. 5-9. Simplified sketch of a one-stage gas pressure regulator.

To reduce cylinder pressures to desired working pressures, we use adjustable pressure-reducing regulators. They are designed so that they will maintain a steady working pressure as cylinder pressure drops.

Fig. 5-9 presents the basic elements of a typical regulator. The high-pressure gas passes through a valve which is actuated by a flexible diaphragm. On one side of the diaphragm there is gas at the pressure to which it has been reduced by passing through the valve. On the other side, there is a spring. The loading on the spring can be varied by means of the pressure-adjusting screw. When demand for gas reduces the force applied by the gas against the diaphragm until it is less than the force applied by the spring, the diaphragm moves left and the valve opens wider. When gas pressure against the diaphragm increases, due to a decrease in demand, or the closing of a torch valve, the diaphragm moves to the right, and the valve opening is reduced, or the valve closes completely.

Fig. 5-10. Three regulators for use on oxygen cylinders: one-stage with gauges (upper left), gaugeless (upper right) and two-stage (lower).

To make a regulator that works well, and is truly useful for welding or cutting, we must add a few refinements to the basic design. Fig. 5-11 is a literal cross-sectional view of a type of regulator that has proved itself in service for nearly 50 years. All the parts are named. A valve spring on the high-pressure side of the diaphragm, and a valve stem guide which slides in the valve seat clamping screw, smooth out the movement of the valve stem so that the regulator won't "chatter" (due to rapid opening and closing of the valve). There's a pressure gauge which shows how much pressure there is in the cylinder, and another (not shown) which registers the pressure of the gas on the delivery side of the regulator. The inlet nipple which makes up to the cylinder valve contains a porous-metal filter to remove particles or dirt which might otherwise enter the regulator and be harmful. Every regulator contains such a filter, and it is most important that the filter always be in place. Should it become clogged, do not merely remove it. Lack of a filter can lead to trouble. Always REPLACE it with a clean filter.

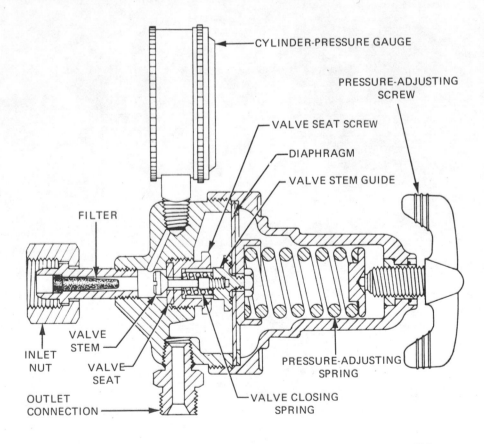

Fig. 5-11. Cross-section of a single-stage stem-type regulator. This basic design has been serving industry for a half-century.

Two-Stage Regulators

It is impossible to build a one-stage regulator which will, without any readjustment of the pressure-adjusting screw, maintain *absolutely* constant delivery pressure as the gas in a cylinder is used up and the cylinder pressure falls. Why? Because the inlet pressure itself, acting against the valve parts, is a variable force. Depending upon the valve design, the delivery pressure may *rise*, or may *fall*, as the cylinder pressure decreases. In many types of operations, that rise or fall is not enough to be troublesome. It can be eliminated entirely by using a two-stage regulator. In such a regulator, the first stage reduces cylinder pressure to a fixed intermediate pressure (usually about 350 psi in an oxygen regulator) and the adjustable second stage reduces that intermediate pressure to the final working pressure. While the intermediate pressure may change as much as 20 psi as the cylinder pressure drops, that change in pressure supplied to the second stage is not enough to cause a measurable change in delivery pressure. After cylinder pressure has dropped below the level of the first-stage pressure setting, the first-stage valve remains open and the regulator acts like a single-stage regulator.

The big advantage of the two-stage regulator is this: the materials used in each stage can be selected for their serviceability over a much narrower range of working conditions. For example, the second-stage valve seat can be a resilient material which seals much more readily than the harder materials which must be used to hold full oxygen cylinder pressure. (Full cylinder pressure will force its way right past any rubber seat.) The net result is this: Two-stage regulators will generally stand up better in heavy-duty, constant service, and require less maintenance than single-stage regulators.

Regulator Pressure Gauges

The pressure gauges used on regulators are almost always of the "Bourdon-tube" type. Gas is admitted to a closed-end, bent tube made of phosphor bronze alloy. Internal pressure tends to straighten that tube. The end of the tube is connected to a curved rack which rotates a shaft upon which the gauge pin is mounted.

Treated right, Bourdon tubes are tough, and will maintain their original properties for years. What do we mean by "treated right"? The big thing is this: Avoid subjecting them to a rush of gas pressure which will make the tube jump from its static position to its fully-stretched position in "nothing flat". Always open cylinder valves slowly. Before opening a cylinder valve, always be sure that the pressure-adjusting screw on the regulator has been backed off so that there is no spring pressure against the regulator diaphragm and the regulator valve is therefore closed. By opening the cylinder valve slowly, you protect the cylinder pressure gauge. By making sure that the regulator valve is closed, you protect the delivery-pressure gauge against the sudden rush of pressure through an open valve.

There's another very good reason for opening cylinder valves, especially on full oxygen cylinders, as slowly as possible. The gas which is "dead-ended" in the Bourdon tube is recompressed and heats up significantly if there is a *sudden* jump in pressure. This doesn't do the tube any good, although it will not, in itself, cause the tube to rupture. However, if there has been any accumulation of combustible particles in the tube—and it is chiefly to prevent such particles from getting into the tube that it's so essential to keep a filter in the regulator inlet—the heat may start a reaction between oxygen and those particles. And then you have a regulator "burn-out", which will at least ruin the regulator, and perhaps do even more damage or cause personal injury.

Don't think that oxygen regulator "burnouts" are an everyday occurrence. They are not. There are hundreds of thousands of oxygen regulators in use on cylinders in the U.S., and only a few burn out every year. But evidence accumulated over the years shows that most of the burnouts have occurred in regulators from which the inlet filter was missing. While filters are necessary in all uses and all environments, clean filters are especially important in auto body shops, garages, foundries, coal mines and other environments where metal and hydrocarbon particles may be present. If you always check to make sure that the regulator has a filter (it is often mounted in the inlet nipple so that you can see it), and "take it easy" when you open the oxygen cylinder valve, you should never experience a burnout.

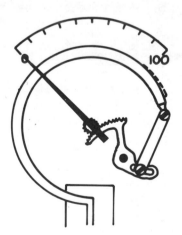

Fig. 5-12. A Bourdon tube gauge movement. Pressure in the semi-circular closed-end tube causes the free end of the tube to move (dashed line). This movement is transmitted through a fixed pivot point (black dot) to a curved rack which engages a pinion gear on the pointer shaft.

Gaugeless Regulators

In some locations, regulator gauges may be subject to frequent mechanical damage from external forces. Therefore, some people prefer "gaugeless" regulators. In such regulators, cylinder pressure is roughly measured by a spring-loaded "pop-up" indicator. When the cylinder is full, this indicator is fully extended; when pressure drops to the point where it's about time to change cylinders, the pop-up indicator has retracted to the point where the color on its shaft (usually red) is no longer visible. A sliding indicator in the regulator front cap shows the setting of the regulator pressure-adjusting screw. Since delivery pressure is a function of that setting, the approximate pressure can be read on a scale mounted alongside the pointer.

Regulator Safety Devices

All regulators fitted for use with non-combustible gases (oxygen, nitrogen, carbon dioxide, argon, etc) are equipped with safety relief devices which will "let go" if excessive pressure builds up in the delivery pressure chamber of the regulator. The most frequently used device is a metal rupture disk which will burst if, because of regulator malfunction, the pressure rises well above the maximum delivery pressure for which the regulator is designed. The bursting of a rupture disk is usually an indication that there's something wrong with the regulator valve and that the regulator is in need of repair. Such repair should only be made by trained personnel in a properly-equipped repair station.

Regulators fitted for use with combustible gases (acetylene, hydrogen, propane, etc.) are not equipped with rupture disks, or other safety release devices. There's always a slight chance that a disk may burst prematurely, as the result of metal fatigue, or that a spring-loaded relief valve may open due to spring failure. However, regulators approved for welding or cutting use must be made so that the diaphragm will let go, and release pressure through a vent opening in the regulator cap, before the regulator cap can blow off. (The vent opening may be covered by a thin label on some regulators, but it's always there.)

Cylinder-to-Regulator Connections

Standards for the connections used in the U.S. on compressed gas cylinders and regulators are established by the Compressed Gas Association (CGA) and recognized as American National Standards. Each standard covers the size and form of thread to be used on the cylinder connection, the size and form of thread to be used on the mating regulator nut, and the configuration of the regulator inlet nipple and the mating seat in the cylinder outlet. For oxygen, the standard connection is designated as CGA 540. For nitrogen, argon, helium and other oil-free inert gases, the standard connection is CGA 580; for hydrogen, CGA 350; for carbon dioxide, CGA 320. Only for acetylene are there two or more "standards" in general use. One is CGA 510, which is used on all large LINDE acetylene cylinders, and on other brands as well. The other is CGA 300 which is used on AIRCO acetylene cylinders and a number of other brands. In addition, there are two more CGA standard connections (520 and 200) for use on small acetylene cylinders (or tanks) which usually hold 40 cu. ft. or less of gas. To complicate matters a little more, CGA 510 is also the standard connection for propane, another flammable gas.

Why are there multiple standards for acetylene? Chiefly because standardization on an industry-wide basis was not undertaken until nearly 50 years after the manufacture of the first large acetylene cylinders for welding and cutting service. By that time, the number of cylinders in use was so great, and the connections used so evenly divided between two types, that standardization on either of the two connections in general use would have been economically impractical.

The important thing to remember about cylinder connections is that you should not buy, nor should you ever attempt to make, an adaptor which will permit the use of an oxygen regulator on a fuel gas cylinder, or a fuel gas regulator on an oxygen cylinder. However, you can buy adaptors which permit the use of acetylene regulators with CGA 510 connections on cylinders with CGA 300 connections, and vice versa, as well as adaptors which permit use of acetylene regulators with either 510 or 300 connections on small acetylene cylinders.

One final point: All CGA standard connections for oxygen and for oil-free inert gases carry right-hand threads; all CGA standard connections for acetylene, other fuel gases, and for gases which may have been compressed through oil-lubricated compressors carry left-hand threads *except* for the CGA 300 acetylene cylinder/regulator connection, and the two cylinder/regulator connections used with small acetylene cylinders. Left-hand threads are always indicated by a groove cut in the middle of the connection nut or in the hex section adjacent to the connection thread.

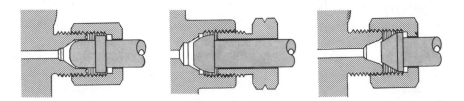

Fig. 5-13. Cross-sections of three cylinder-to-regulator connections, each represented as only partially tightened. Connections are CGA 540 for oxygen (left) CGA 510 for acetylene (center) and CGA 300 for acetylene (right).

Piping System Station Equipment

When oxygen and acetylene (or another fuel gas) are supplied to torches through plant piping systems, three types of equipment not mentioned previously in this chapter are used. At each station on a piping system, there must be a *shutoff valve,* and a *check valve* which will prevent backflow of gas into the system. On the fuel gas system, there must also be another device which will prevent a flashback from reaching the fuel gas supply. A *hydraulic back-pressure valve* is usually employed for that purpose. One such valve may serve the complete system, if branch lines are smaller than 2-in. diameter. In some systems, hydraulic back-pressure valves are installed at each station. When so used, they eliminate the requirement for a separate check valve at each station. Each hydraulic back-pressure valve (or any other device which will fulfill the anti-flashback requirement) must be equipped with a relief valve set to open at a pressure not greater than 150% of the normal line pressure. The relief valve must be fitted with a vent line which will discharge any vented gas to a safe location outside the building.

Any pressure regulator in good condition will act as a check valve in the event of a jump in pressure downstream from the regulator. Until 1974, codes generally permitted a regulator to fulfill the station check valve requirement. This is no longer the case; neither a regulator nor a small reverse flow check valve of the type widely sold for installation in hose lines (either at the torch end or regulator end) is considered an acceptable substitute for a permanently-installed check valve.

Regulators designed for use at piping system stations should never be used on cylinders and are always marked to warn the user against such use. Therefore, never attempt to use a station oxygen regulator (which, like a cylinder regulator, can be equipped with a CGA 540 inlet connection) on an oxygen cylinder. Many station oxygen regulators are equipped with frangible-disk safety release devices which will rupture if the regulator is subjected to an *inlet* pressure of more than a few hundred psi. A complete statement of regulations governing the installation and operation of oxygen and fuel gas piping systems for welding and cutting processes is given in National Fire Protection Association (NFPA) Pamphlet No. 51.

Hose and Hose Fittings

Only hose made to standards established jointly by the Compressed Gas Association and the Rubber Manufacturers Association (RMA) should be used for welding and cutting purposes. Such hose is always labelled (at least once every 25 feet) with "grade" and "type" letter designations. The grade will be shown as "M" (oil-resistant cover and liner), "RM" (oil-resistant cover) or "R" (neither cover nor liner oil-resistant). The type will usually be shown as "VD" (on double hose) or "S" (on single hose). Hose should not be used at pressures in excess of 200 psi, although the minimum bursting pressure for brand-new hose is much greater. Oxygen hose has a green cover, smooth or corrugated; acetylene hose has a red cover, smooth or corrugated. Double hose—an oxygen line with green cover joined by a rubber web to an acetylene line with a red cover—is extremely popular.

Hose Size: The I.D. (internal diameter) of hose used for most welding and cutting purposes ranges from $\frac{3}{16}$-in. to $\frac{3}{8}$-in (4.8 to 9.6 mm). When the length of hose required between regulator and torch is not more than 25 ft., $\frac{3}{16}$-in. hose is adequate for all welding, and for most cutting and heating. It is, of course, lighter and more flexible than $\frac{1}{4}$-in. hose. However, when you need hose lines longer than 25-ft., or expect to do some fairly heavy cutting or heating, $\frac{1}{4}$-in. hose is better, since at high flows there's much less pressure drop in the larger hose. One way of retaining the advantage of $\frac{3}{16}$-in. hose flexibility without creating a pressure-drop problem is to attach 12-$\frac{1}{2}$-ft. lengths of $\frac{3}{16}$-in. hose to your torch, then couple those to $\frac{1}{4}$-in. or $\frac{3}{8}$-in. lines leading back to the regulators.

Hose Connections: A complete connection at either end of an oxygen or acetylene hose consists of three parts: a nipple with a seating surface to match up with the internal seat on the torch or regulator connections, a swivel nut, and a hose ferrule or clamp which locks the hose gas-tight onto the hose end of the nipple. We'll discuss the nipple-to-hose joint in a minute; right now, let's look at the nut and the seating end of the nipple. These are standardized, again by the Compressed Gas Association. In general use, there are three *sizes* of connection (A, B, and C) and four *types:* for oxygen, for fuel gas, for oil-free inert gas, and for oil-pumped air or inert gases or water. To completely describe a connection, you must specify *connection size* (A, B, C); *type* (oxygen, fuel gas, etc.); and *hose size* ($\frac{3}{16}$-in., $\frac{1}{4}$-in., etc.)

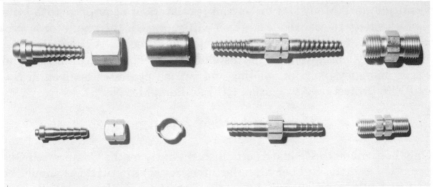

Fig. 5-14. Standard hose connections. Top line shows "B" size nipple ("screw-type"), oxygen nut, brass ferrule, hose splice, and hose connection coupling. Lower line shows "A" size nipple ("push-type"), fuel gas nut, circle clamp, hose splice, and hose connection coupling.

"B"-size connections are used on most torches and regulators for oxygen and fuel gas. The thread sizes are the same, but oxygen threads are right-hand, fuel gas threads are left-hand. The nipples are identical. "B"-size nipples are available to accept 3/16-in., 1/4-in., 5/16-in., and 3/8-in. oxygen and acetylene hose.

Some small torches and regulators are fitted with "A"-size connections, smaller than "B" size. Only one size of nipple, to accept 3/16-in. hose, is generally available for "A" connections.

The "B" size connection for inert gases and water is quite different from the "B" size connection used for oxygen and acetylene. Most noticeable is the fact that the connection *nut* has the male thread, while the fixed connection in the regulator has the female thread. The thread size is slightly larger (5/8-in. instead of 9/16-in.) and the nipples have longer shanks, to accomodate the longer nuts. The hex size on "B" inert gas/water connections, however, is the same as that used on the oxygen and fuel gas connections. There are both left-hand-thread and right-hand-thread versions.

As already stated, "B" size hose nipples are available to fit four hose sizes (3/16, 1/4, 5/16, and 3/8-in.) and for use interchangeably in either oxygen or fuel gas service. The "hose end" of the nipple can be formed in two ways: with two or more "barbs", or with a spiral "thread". The latter is usually called "screw-type", the former, "push-type". The "screw-type" is literally screwed into the end of the hose after a snug-fitting brass ferrule has been placed on the hose. The "push-type" is pushed into the end of the hose, after slipping a ferrule or a hose clamp onto the hose. Fig. 5-15 shows four ways used to make strong, leak-tight nipple-to-hose connections. The crimped-ferrule connection is universally used on pre-fitted hose assemblies (and most hose for welding and cutting is sold pre-fitted). The circle-clamp connection is normally preferred when you must make up your own connections. Never try to use "screw-type" nipples with circle-type hose clamps. If you must use a clamp, use the "Sherman" type.

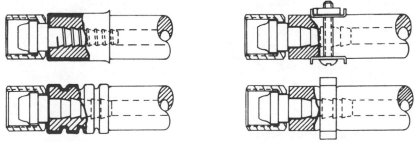

Fig. 5-15. Cross-section views of four methods used to fit hose with leak-tight connections. (Upper left) Screw-type nipple with heavy brass ferrule. (Upper right) Push-type nipple with screw-tightened "Sherman" clamp. (Lower left) Push-type nipple with machine-crimped ferrule. (Lower right) Push-type nipple with circle clamp, which is tightened with special pliers.

To link two pieces of hose already equipped with fittings, couplings are available. With these, you can connect $\frac{3}{16}$-in. hose with "A" size fittings to larger hose with "B" size fittings. To repair a hose from which you have had to cut out a damaged section, use a hose splice. Couplings and splices are shown in Fig. 5-14.

Goggles

When welding or cutting, safety goggles with approved filter lenses must always be used to protect the eyes from the glare of the flames, from heat, and from flying particles of metal or slag. Goggles should fit snugly and be equipped with ventilating ports. They must have cover lenses (glass or plastic) and hardened glass filter lenses, which are supplied in several shades. Shade 4 is adequate for light cutting or sheet metal welding. Darker shades 5 or 6 should be used when welding plate or castings, or during heavy cutting. "Coverall" goggles which can be worn over prescription eyeglasses are readily available.

Gloves

It's a serious mistake not to wear gloves when welding or cutting. For light work, flame-resistant cotton gloves are often satisfactory. For most purposes, however, all-leather gloves, or gloves with leather palm and fingers, will prove more serviceable. Gloves should always have gauntlets long enough to cover the ends of your sleeves.

Clothing

The chief point to make about clothing is this: Protect yourself. Wear long sleeves, so that your wrists will be covered. Wear high-top work shoes if

Fig. 5-16. Oxy-acetylene welding goggles (above) and gauntlet-style leather welding gloves (right).

possible, especially when cutting, to keep sparks from your ankles. Wear cuffless trousers. Stay away from flammable synthetic materials if you can; cotton and wool are less susceptible to damage by sparks.

Friction Lighters

ALWAYS use some type of friction lighter to light your torch. NEVER use matches. Don't even have them on your person when welding or cutting. Friction lighters are cheap and easy to use. A three flint lighter, which carries two reserve flints all mounted and ready for use, makes a lot of sense.

Mechanical Accessories

Good workmanship is difficult without a suitable place to work. For welding, you need some kind of a sensibly-designed, 100% fireproof work table. A table with a slotted cast iron top, as illustrated in Fig. 5-17, is ideal for many purposes. The slots allow you to position C-clamps at almost any work-holding position desired. You can make up a somewhat similar table from steel angles and strips with the top framed and fitted with supports for holding loosely-set fire bricks.

For lining up parts, you'll normally need a couple of heavy steel straight-edges, and some V-blocks, which can be supplied by any dealer in machinist supplies, or machined from steel 1-1/2-in. or 2-in. thick.

For bevelling the edges of parts to be welded, anything from a course file to a power grinder may be needed. When steel 1/4-in. or more in thickness is to be welded, you can often bevel it with the cutting torch or attachment. Wire brushes are always needed.

Fig. 5-17. Friction lighter (above) and welding table with slotted cast iron top (right).

1. What items are needed for the simplest oxy-acetylene welding and cutting outfit?
2. What two components are needed to make up a welding torch?
3. What are the two types of mixers used in welding and cutting torches? What is the purpose of a mixer? Which mixer is intended for operating from low-pressure acetylene source? Why?
4. Compared to a welding torch, what additional function does a cutting torch have?
5. What is a cutting attachment? Why is it convenient to have one in a welding and cutting outfit?
6. What is the purpose of a regulator?
7. How do regulators accomplish pressure reduction?
8. What is the advantage of a two-stage regulator?
9. Why must all regulators be equipped with a filter in its inlet nipple?
10. What is meant by the working-pressure side of a regulator?
11. What is meant by gaugeless regulators?
12. What is the main difference between an oxygen and acetylene regulator?
13. What are the general requirements for the oxygen and acetylene hoses?
14. How is oxygen hose distinguished from acetylene hose? What are the differences in the connections?
15. What are some of the personnel protection items that should be worn for welding and cutting operations?
16. What should be used for lighting torches? Why?
17. What mechanical accessories should be available for welding and cutting accessories?

SETUP AND OPERATION OF EQUIPMENT

This chapter will describe how to set up a typical oxy-acetylene welding or cutting outfit, and how to light the torch and adjust the flame. Precautions which must be observed during setup and lighting will be covered. The next chapter (7) will cover precautions which should be observed in the course of actual welding and cutting operations. Please do not attempt to set up and operate an outfit until you feel thoroughly familiar with the content of both chapters.

The make-up of a complete outfit was given in the opening paragraphs of Chapter 5. Please make sure that you have on hand everything needed before you start to set up.

Attaching Pressure-Reducing Regulators

Fasten the cylinders to be used in an upright position so that they cannot be knocked or pulled over. If cylinders are not on a suitable cylinder cart, they should be securely fastened, with chain or equivalent, to a workbench, wall, or post. As explained earlier in Chapter 3, acetylene cylinders should never be stored or used other than in a vertical position.

Remove the protective cap from the oxygen cylinder, and from the acetylene cylinder, if so equipped.

"Crack" the cylinder valves. Stand so that the gas leaving the cylinder outlet will not be directed onto your face or clothing. Open the valve quickly about one-quarter of a turn, then close it immediately. This will clear the valve outlet opening of accumulated dust or dirt which might, if not blown out, mar the seat of the regulator nipple or be carried into the regulator.

PRECAUTION: Never "crack" a fuel gas cylinder valve near other welding or cutting work in progress, or near sparks, flame, or other possible source of ignition.

Connect the oxygen regulator to the oxygen cylinder and the acetylene regulator to the acetylene cylinder. If the acetylene regulator and the acetylene cylinder have different threads, it will be necessary to use an adaptor between the regulator and the cylinder. As stated in Chapter 5, two quite different acetylene cylinder connections are widely used in the U. S.

Fig. 6-1. Always crack cylinder valves, to blow out dust and dirt from the outlets.

Fig. 6-2. Always tighten regulator connection nuts with a wrench.

The CGA 510 connection has left-hand threads, internal on the cylinder outlet; the CGA 300 connection has right-hand threads, external on the cylinder outlet.

Tighten both regulator connection nuts firmly with a wrench. (Avoid use of adjustable wrenches. Wrenches with two or more fixed openings, designed specifically for use with gas welding and cutting apparatus, are available from all apparatus suppliers.)

    PRECAUTION: Should it ever be necessary to retighten the regulator union nut after the outfit has been set up and the cylinder valves opened, be sure to close the cylinder valve before tightening the nut.

Rotate the pressure-adjusting screw of each regulator to the left (counter-clockwise) until it turns freely. It is essential that the valve in the regulator be closed before cylinder pressure is admitted to the regulator. To achieve this, the pressure-adjusting screw must be backed off until it no longer is pushing against the pressure-adjusting spring in the regulator.

Open each cylinder valve SLOWLY. Stand in such a position that you can see the cylinder-pressure gauge hand on the regulator, but never stand directly in front of the regulator gauge faces. It is especially important that you open the oxygen cylinder valve only very slightly at first, and that you wait until the cylinder-pressure gauge hand has stopped moving before

Fig. 6-3. Always release regulator pressure-adjusting screw fully before opening the cylinder valve.

Fig. 6-4. Always open the oxygen cylinder valve as SLOWLY as possible.

opening the valve *fully*. Remember that acetylene cylinder valves should not be opened more than one and one-half turns.

Always leave the wrench in place on the acetylene cylinder valve while the valve is open. However, when two or more cylinders have been manifolded together, it is sufficient to leave a wrench on one of the cylinders. The point is this: you should not be forced to waste time looking around for a suitable wrench should an emergency make it necessary to close the cylinder valve or valves without delay.

Note: The cylinder-pressure gauge on each regulator shows you the *pressure* in each cylinder. In the case of both oxygen and acetylene, *pressure* is a rough measure of *contents*. If you are using a large cylinder of oxygen which when full contained 244 cf at 2200 psi and 70°F (6.5 m³ at 15200 kPa and 20°C), the cylinder is half-full when the cylinder-pressure gauge reads 1100 psi (517 kPa), so that you have 122 cf (3.2 m³) available. When the pressure in an acetylene cylinder is approximately 125 psi at 70°F (862 kPa at 20°C) it is also true that the cylinder is about one-half full. However, if you are using a liquefied fuel gas, such as propane, cylinder pressure remains constant until virtually all the liquid has been vaporized. For that reason, regulators designed for propane service are seldom supplied with cylinder-pressure gauges. Liquid oxygen cylinders are equipped with liquid-level gauges which will indicate the amount of liquid oxygen remaining in the cylinder.

Connecting Gas Supplies to the Torch

Always use hose and hose connections made specifically for gas welding and cutting purposes. Oxygen hose has a green cover; acetylene hose has a red cover. Never interchange oxygen and acetylene hose. Do not use acetylene hose with propane unless you know that is acceptable for use with propane. (Hose with natural rubber liner is satisfactory for acetylene service, but not for propane service.)

Make up all connections dry; do not use pipe-fitting compounds, thread lubricants, oil, or grease. All connections are designed with metal-to-metal seals. They do not require lubricants or sealants. However, they must always be made up wrench-tight, not merely hand-tight.

Never force connections which do not fit. If you cannot run the threads together by hand with ease, either the threads are damaged, or you are trying to put together parts that were not made to go together.

If the hose does not have connections on both ends, put these on next. Connection nuts for oxygen hose have right-hand threads, connection nuts for acetylene have left-hand threads. Instructions for installing hose connections are given in the Appendix.

Fig. 6-5. Always use wrench to open acetylene cylinder valve; leave wrench in place after opening valve.

Fig. 6-6. Always tighten all connection nuts firmly with a wrench.

Attach the oxygen hose to the oxygen regulator and to the oxygen connection on the torch. The torch connection is usually identified by a marking in the torch body or in the torch handle, opposite the oxygen valve. Cutting machine torches usually have two oxygen connections, one for the oxygen supplied to the cutting jet, one for the oxygen used on the preheat flames. Unless an adaptor is used on the torch to unite these connections, such a torch requires two oxygen hoses, two regulators, and two oxygen sources.

Attach the acetylene hose to the acetylene regulator, and to the acetylene connection on the torch. On some torches, the acetylene connection may not be specifically identified, even though the oxygen connection is labelled.

Tighten all hose connection nuts with a wrench.

Test all connections for leaks. First, close both torch valves. Then turn in the pressure-adjusting screw on the oxygen regulator until its delivery-pressure gauge reads about 25 psi (172 kPa). Turn in the pressure-adjusting screw on the acetylene regulator until its delivery-pressure gauge reads about 10 psi (69kPa). Using a suitable leak-test solution and a brush (you can buy such a solution ready-made, or make up your own by dissolving Ivory soap in water), check for leakage (which will be indicated by bubbling) at the cylinder valves, the cylinder-to-regulator connections, and at all hose connections, as indicated in Fig. 6-7. If leakage is detected at either cylinder valve stem, close the valve, release the pressure-adjusting screw on the regulator, remover the regulator from the cylinder, and return the cylinder to your supplier, as directed in Chapter 3. If a leak is detected at either cylinder-to-regulator connection, close the cylinder valve, tighten the regulator connection nut with a wrench once more, re-open the cylinder valve, and test again. If a leak is detected at any hose connection, retighten the connection nut with a wrench and retest. If any connection fails to pass the second test, release all pressure from that side of the system (oxygen or acetylene). To do this, close the cylinder valve, release the regulator pressure-adjusting screw, open the torch valve, and finally turn in the regulator pressure-adjusting screw until no pressure is indicated on either regulator gauge. Then break the leaky connection, inspect the mating seats carefully for nicks or foreign particles which may be the source of trouble. If none can be seen, wipe both seats carefully with a clean cloth, remake the connection, and retest after restoring pressure.

To check for leakage through the torch valves you should, after making sure that all other connections are leaktight, dip the torch tip or nozzle in water, or place leak-test solution across the tip or nozzle orifices. If bubbling occurs, open and close each torch valve rapidly to see if that will stop the leakage. If it does not, replacement of one or both torch valve stem assemblies, or reseating of the torch body, may be necessary. After lighting the torch (as directed hereafter) you should use leak-test solution to check for leakage around the torch valve stems, and tighten the valve packing nut or nuts as needed to stop the leaks.

Adjusting Operating Pressures

After making sure that the system is leak-tight, release the pressure-adjusting screws on both regulators, and open the torch valves. Then proceed as follows:

With torch oxygen valve open, turn in the pressure-adjusting screw on the oxygen regulator until the desired working pressure is indicated on the regulator delivery-pressure gauge. Then close the torch oxygen valve. If you are adjusting pressure for a cutting torch, open only the torch cutting oxygen valve. If you are adjusting pressure for a cutting attachment, open the oxygen valve on the torch handle and the cutting oxygen valve (but not the preheat oxygen valve) on the cutting attachment. Avoid setting pressures higher than those recommended by the equipment manufacturer for the welding head or cutting nozzle installed in your torch.

With the torch acetylene valve open not more than one full turn, turn in the pressure-adjusting screw on the acetylene regulator until the desired working pressure—NOT OVER 15 PSI (103 kPa)—is indicated on the regulator delivery-pressure gauge. Close the acetylene valve immediately.

> PRECAUTION: Never release acetylene, or any other fuel gas, near any possible source of ignition or into any space which is not adequately ventilated. If such conditions cannot be met, adjust pressure with the torch fuel gas valve closed. Readjust pressure, as necessary, after the torch has been lighted in accordance with the instructions which follow.

If acetylene or other fuel gas is being supplied to the torch from a piping system which is not equipped with regulators at each station outlet, merely open the service valve at the station outlet. Do not open the torch fuel gas valve until you are ready to light the flame.

Lighting the Flame

In lighting the torch and adjusting the flame, always follow the manufacturer's instruction for the specific torch being used. In general, the procedure to be followed in lighting an oxy-acetylene welding or heating torch is this:
1. Open the torch acetylene valve about one-half turn.
2. Immediately light the flame with a friction lighter. NEVER USE A MATCH.

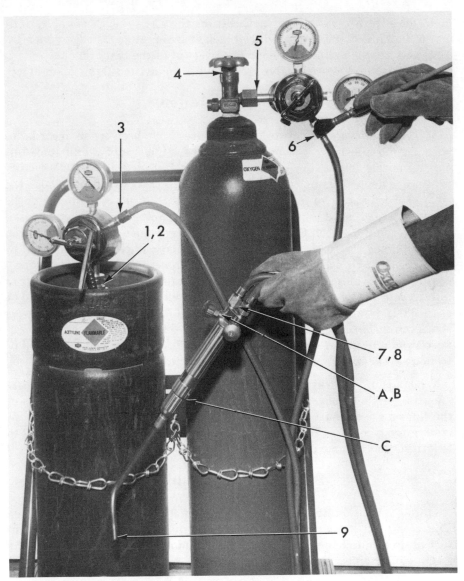

Fig. 6-7. After pressurizing both hose lines (with torch valves tightly closed) test for leakage at the following points, using an approved leak-test solution or a thick solution of Ivory soap and water: (1,2) Acetylene cylinder connection and acetylene cylinder valve spindle (3) Acetylene regulator-to-hose connection (4) Oxygen valve spindle (5) Oxygen cylinder connection (6) Oxygen regulator-to-hose connection (7,8) Hose connections at the torch (9) Torch tip (for leakage past the torch valves). Later, after lighting the torch, check for leakage at the throttle valve stems (A,B) and at the welding head-to-torch handle connection (C).

3. Reduce the acetylene flow, by throttling the torch acetylene valve, until the flame just starts to produce black smoke around its edges; then increase acetylene flow just enough to get rid of the black smoke.
4. Open the torch oxygen valve slowly until the desired flame is obtained.

Flame Adjustment

If oxygen and acetylene working pressures have been set in accordance with the manufacturer's recommendations for the size of welding head or cutting nozzle in use, the lighting procedure outlined above will usually produce a neutral flame (as described in Chapter 4) which has about the right characteristics for most welding and cutting purposes. However, if the flame, when adjusted to neutral, burns away from the tip (in other words, if there is a gap between the tip and the flame) reduce the flow of oxygen slightly, using the torch oxygen valve, and then reduce the acetylene flow until the flame is again neutral. If you find that you must repeat this procedure two or more times to eliminate the gap between flame and tip or nozzle, your acetylene working pressure is probably too high, and should be reduced. If, however, you find that the neutral flame produced by following the recommended lighting procedure seems to be too "soft" for your purposes, you may open the acetylene valve a little, and then readjust the flame to neutral by opening the oxygen valve some more.

When using natural gas for cutting, do not attempt to secure truly "neutral" flames. Instead, adjust the oxygen flow until the inner cones of the flames are as short as possible. This is not hard to do, because any increase in oxygen flow beyond a certain level will cause the inner cones to lengthen, and become paler and more pointed.

Backfire and Flashback

During operation, the torch flame may go out with a loud pop or snap. This is called a "backfire", and is most frequently caused by accidental contact of tip or nozzle against the work, or by momentary interruption of the flame by a droplet of hot metal of slag.

A torch that has backfired can be relighted at once. It may even relight itself, if the flow of gas is directed against molten or hot metal. If a torch backfires repeatedly, however, without evident contact with the work, the cause should be investigated. Backfiring may be due to use of improper operating pressures, or to a loose tip or nozzle in the torch, or to dirt on the cutting nozzle seats.

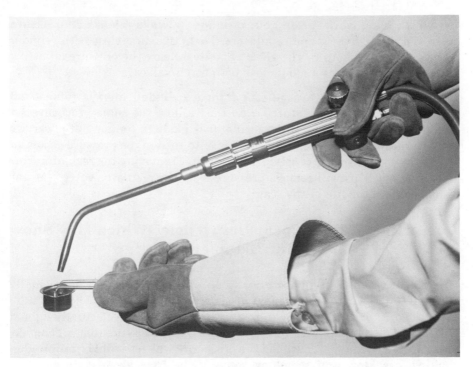

Fig 6-8. Always use a friction lighter when lighting a torch. Be ready to adjust the torch acetylene valve immediately after flame is lit.

If the flame goes out and burns back within the torch, which usually produces a pronounced hissing or squealing noise, immediately shut off the torch. This is termed a "flashback" and is always a sign that there is something wrong with the torch or with your operation of it. After a flashback, *always* allow the torch to cool before attempting to relight it. *Always* check your operating pressures before attempting to relight it. Further, before relighting, allow oxygen (NOT acetylene) to flow through the torch for several seconds to help clear out soot which may have accumulated within the torch. Then relight, following the usual procedure. If what appears to be normal flame, or flames, is produced, proceed with your work, but be prepared to shut the torch off instantly if the flame goes out and that characteristic flashback sound is heard again. If there is a second flashback, remove the torch from service and return it to an approved repair station for check and necessary repair.

Stopping Work

To extinguish the flames, first close the torch fuel gas valve, then the oxygen valve. Closing the fuel gas (acetylene) valve first reduces the chance of allowing unburned fuel gas to escape and be ignited accidently.

When stopping work for an hour or longer, always release all pressure from the torch, hoses, and regulators. To do this, first close both cylinder valves, then open both torch valves. Finally, release the pressure-adjusting screws of both regulators and close both torch valves.

Before disconnecting a regulator from a cylinder, always release all pressure from the regulator. To do this, follow the same procedure set forth immediately above. If the regulator is likely to remain out of service for several weeks or more, it is a good idea to turn in the pressure-adjusting screw until some spring resistance is felt (after removing the regulator from the cylinder). This will remove pressure from the regulator valve seat and thus lengthen the life of the seat.

Correction of Equipment Deficiencies Which May Show Up During Setup and Testing

Never use torches, regulators, or hose in need of repair. It is usually difficult to tell whether equipment needs repair until you have hooked it up and tested it. Some flaws may not show up until you have actually lighted the torch. We have stressed the importance of making sure that all connections are leak-tight, and outlined the procedure which should be followed in making, breaking, and remaking connections. Now we wish to go a bit farther, and provide some general instructions covering what you should do when something is still obviously wrong.

Regulators: If the regulator-to-cylinder connection still leaks after you have broken it, cleaned the seating surfaces, re-made and re-tested it, the odds are that the regulator inlet nipple is marred or deformed so that it will not make up leaktight to any cylinder. In that case, the nipple must be replaced. You can't do that on the spot. The regulator must be turned over to a qualified repairman or repair station.

When you close a torch valve, after setting regulator pressure for leak-test or operation, the delivery-pressure gauge hand "jumps" a few psi. This is normal. If it "creeps", however,—that is, moves up slowly but steadily for more than a second or two after the torch valve has been closed—the regulator valve is leaking and should be repaired. While it is true that a slight amount of such creep will have no effect on operation of the torch after it is lighted, it is most unwise to continue to use a regulator that creeps. It should be removed from service and sent to a properly-equipped repair station for overhaul.

All regulators are equipped with screens or filters designed to prevent particles of dust from reaching the regulator valve. In many regulators, the filter is located in the inlet nipple itself and is clearly visible. When using such a regulator, make it a practice to look and see that the filter is in place before connecting the regulator to the cylinder. If the filter is missing or if it appears to be clogged with foreign material, replace it before proceeding further. This will take very little time if you will remember to keep a spare filter on hand. NEVER remove a filter until you are prepared to replace it.

Torches: If either throttle valve on a welding torch handle will not shut off completely (as revealed by bubbling when the torch tip is placed in water, with pressure in the hose and both valves closed as tightly as possible) you should release all pressure from the system and remove the valve stem assembly from the torch. Wipe clean both the seating surfaces in the torch and on the valve stem. Reassemble and retest. If the valve still will not shut off tightly, either reseating of the valve body or replacement of the valve stem assembly will be required. For reseating, the torch must be sent to a properly-equipped repair station.

If the cutting oxygen valve on a cutting torch or cutting attachment will not shut off tight, replacement of the valve seat or valve stem, following instructions supplied by the torch manufacturer, is usually required.

If you detect leakage around the valve stem of a torch throttle valve (test must be made after the torch has been lit) you can usually stop the leak by tightening the valve packing nut. Occasionally, it may be necessary to replace a valve packing washer, or replace the complete valve stem assembly. Always follow the instructions supplied by the torch manufacturer. Leakage around the stem of a cutting oxygen valve can usually be repaired on the spot by replacement of a packing washer or O-ring, following instructions of the manufacturer. Do not use substitute materials; use only parts supplied by the manufacturer or his distributor.

If a torch flame is misshaped or irregular, cleaning of the orifice in tip or nozzle is required. Use of stainless steel tip cleaners made especially for this purpose is recommended. A twist drill of the proper size can also be used, but it should be pushed straight in-and-out, not twisted. Do not attempt to use any tool which might enlarge or bell-mouth the orifice.

Hose: In addition to testing for leaks at all hose connections, you should always inspect your hose carefully for external evidence of damage before starting work. If such evidence is found, test that section of the hose by dipping it in a bucket of water while there is pressure in the hose. If that discloses leakage, it is imperative that the hose be discarded, or that the leaky section be cut out and replaced. (Instructions for splicing will be found in the Appendix.) **Never attempt to repair welding hose with tape**.

★ ★ ★ ★ ★ ★ ★ ★ ★

Nothing stated above should be considered as contradicting specific instructions furnished by the manufacturer of the equipment actually in use. Always follow his instructions. Never attempt repairs which are not covered by the manufacturer's instructions or by the general suggestions given above. Above all, and we repeat, DO NOT USE APPARATUS OR HOSE WHICH YOU KNOW IS IN NEED OF REPAIR.

QUESTIONS–CHAPTER 6

1. What are the steps to be followed in setting up a welding or cutting outfit?
2. What special precautions should be followed when connecting an oxygen regulator to an oxygen cylinder valve?
3. What are the steps to be followed in connecting an acetylene regulator to an acetylene cylinder valve?
4. What should be done to the pressure-adjusting screw of a regulator before opening the cylinder valve?
5. How are hose connections put in place?
6. How should the connections be tested for leaks?
7. What should be done in case of leakage?
8. What are the general rules for adjusting pressures?
9. What should be done upon stopping work?
10. What should be done if connections do not fit exactly?
11. What is a backfire?
12. What is a flashback?
13. What should be done when a flashback occurs?

SAFE PRACTICES IN WELDING AND CUTTING OPERATIONS

In Chapter 3, on "Oxygen and Acetylene", we discussed the precautions which should be observed in the handling and storage of oxygen and acetylene. In Chapter 5, on "Equipment for Oxy-Acetylene Welding and Cutting", we covered some of the safe practices which should be observed in the connection with the use and handling of equipment and accessories. In Chapter 6, the safe practices which should be observed in setting up the equipment and lighting the flame were highlighted. In this chapter, we'll devote most of the space to talking about the precautions and safe practices which should be observed during the actual practice of welding and cutting. First, however, we'd like to restate a few of the points already made. These precautions are so important that they warrant repetition. Keep them in mind at all times.

General Precautions

CAUTION! IMPORTANT! USE NO OIL! Oil, grease, coal dust, and some other organic materials are easily ignited and burn violently in the presence of high oxygen concentrations. Never allow such materials to come in contact with oxygen or oxygen-fuel gas equipment, including hose. Oxygen-fuel gas apparatus does not require lubrication.

Always call oxygen by its proper name. Do not call it "air". Never use it as a substitute for compressed air. A serious accident may easily result if oxygen is used as a substitute for compressed air. Oxygen must never be used in pneumatic tools, in oil preheating burners, to start internal combustion engines, to blow out pipelines, to "dust" clothing or work, for pressure testing or for ventilation.

Never use acetylene at pressures above 15 psi. Using acetylene at pressures in excess of 15 psi gauge pressure, or 30 psi absolute pressure, is a hazardous practice. The 30 psi absolute pressure limit (absolute pressure is gauge pressure plus atmospheric pressure) is intended to prevent unsafe use of acetylene in pressurized chambers such as caissons.

Never use torches, regulators, or other equipment that is in need of repair. Treated with reasonable care, oxy-acetylene apparatus needs relatively little maintenance, but when a regulator "creeps" (indicating that its valve will not close completely), or a torch valve will not shut off tight, or you cannot make a leaktight hose connection to a regulator or a torch, get the apparatus to a qualified repair station.

Don't connect an oxygen regulator to a cylinder unless you are sure it is equipped with an inlet filter. Know where the filter is in your regulator. If it is mounted in the inlet nipple, always check visually to see that it is in place and intact before you attach the regulator to the cylinder.

Always use the operating pressures recommended by the manufacturer for the welding head or cutting nozzle in your torch. Using pressures higher than necessary not only makes flame adjustment more difficult, but can be a cause of flashback. In cutting, to use oxygen pressures higher than recommended can reduce cut quality as well as waste oxygen.

Always wear goggles when working with a lighted torch. Use only goggles supplied by reputable manufacturers for welding and cutting purposes. Use filter lenses of a shade dark enough to protect your eyes fully. Generally, shade 4 will serve for light cutting or sheet metal welding. For welding of plate or castings, or for heavy cutting, always use shades 5 or 6. (For more details, including recommendations for electric welding processes, refer to Sec. 7.2, ANSI Z49.1, "Safety in Welding and Cutting Operations", published by the American Welding Society.)

Do not use matches for lighting torches. Always use a friction lighter unless you have a stationary pilot flame, or some other reliable source of ignition that will keep your hand well away from the torch tip or nozzle.

Wear clothing suitable for the work to be done. Fire-resistant gauntlet gloves are recommended for all but the lightest type of welding. Wear woolen clothing if possible; wool is far more difficult to ignite than cotton or many of the synthetic materials. Try to keep the your outer clothing free from grease or oil. Don't have cuffs on your trousers to catch sparks. Avoid low-cut shoes when cutting; getting a drop of slag or hot metal in your shoes can be very painful.

Precautions During Work

Before you start to weld or cut, check the area to make certain that flame, sparks, hot slag or hot metal will not be likely to start a fire. Specific precautions which should be observed are given in the section on "Preventing Fires", which follows.

NEVER do welding or cutting without adequate ventilation. Standards for ventilation are set forth in Sec. 8 of ANSI Z49.1, "Safety in Welding and Cutting Operations", published by the American Welding Society. Standards covering allowable concentrations of toxic dust and gases are given in ANSI Z37, American National Standards Institute. The four paragraphs which follow are intended only to provide general guidelines for conditions frequently encountered. For complete information, it is imperative that ANSI Standards Z49.1 and Z37 be consulted.

When it is necessary to work in a confined space, make certain the space is adequately ventilated. If there are no overhead openings to provide natural ventilation, use an exhaust fan or blower. When screening an area, try to keep the bottom of the screens at least two feet above floor level. Do not take cylinders into a confined space. Test all equipment, including hose, for leaks before taking it into a confined space, and bring it out with you when your work is interrupted for any reason, even for a short time.

Never flow oxygen into a confined space in order to ventilate it, or to "clear the air". Remember that oxygen supports and accelerates combustion, and will cause oil, wood, and many fabrics to burn with great intensity. Clothing saturated with oxygen, or with oxygen-enriched air, may burst into flame when touched by a spark.

Do not weld brass, bronze, or galvanized steel except in a well-ventilated location. You must protect yourself against breathing the zinc oxide vapors usually generated when these materials are

ADEQUATE
FORCED
VENTILATION

Fig. 7-1. Adequate ventilation is essential when welding in confined places and when welding materials which give off fumes.

heated to welding temperatures. In open locations, it is usually sufficient to drive the vapors away by using a stream of air, or by suction, provided that does not send the vapors toward another person. In confined spaces which cannot be well ventilated, always use a mask which supplies clean air from an outside source.

When welding or cutting metals containing or coated with lead, cadmium, beryllium, or mercury, always wear a suitable air-line mask. No operator should be considered immune from the effects of these fumes. A straight filter-type mask is inadequate; nothing short of an air-supplied respirator is suitable. There must be sure protection against breathing fumes which occur when lead, mercury, beryllium, or their compounds are heated.

Use particular caution when welding or cutting in dusty or gassy locations. Dusty and gassy atmospheres in some mines and plants call for extra precautions to avoid explosions or fires from sparks, matches, or open flames of any type. Welding or cutting in any such "suspicious" location should be done only when proper precautions are taken, and only after a responsible official has inspected the situation and given approval for the work.

When welding or cutting is done underground, leak-testing of equipment set-ups should be performed carefully and frequently. Great care should be taken to protect hoses and cylinders from damage, and to protect timbers and other combustible materials from sparks and hot slag.

Never do any welding or cutting on containers that have held flammable or toxic substances until the containers have been thoroughly cleaned and safeguarded. Complete, detailed procedures are given in American Welding Society booklet A6.0-65 titled "Safe Practices for Welding and Cutting Containers That Have Held Combustibles". Here are some of the key points in that booklet:

1. Always start with the assumption that any used drum, barrel, or container may contain flammable (explosive) or toxic (poisonous) residue.
2. No work should be commenced until the container has been cleaned and tested sufficiently to assure that no flammable or toxic solids, liquids, or vapors are present.
3. Bear in mind that some non-poisonous substances can give off toxic (poisonous) vapors when heated.
4. Steam is usually an effective means of removing volatile or readily volatilizable materials from a container. Washing with a strong solution of caustic soda or other alkaline cleaner will remove heavier oils which steam may not volatilize.

5. Whenever possible, the container should be filled with water to within a few inches of the working area before attempting welding, cutting, or intense heating. Care should be taken to provide a vent opening for the release of heated air or steam.

6. When it is impractical to fill the container with water, an inert gas such as nitrogen or carbon dioxide may be used to purge the container of oxygen and flammable vapors. Maintain the inert gas during the entire welding or cutting operation by continuing to pass the gas into the container.

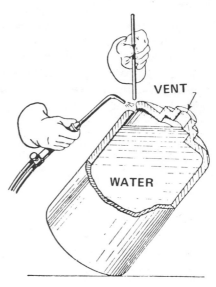

Fig. 7-2. Containers which have held flammable materials should be filled with water before welding or cutting. Be sure space above water level is vented.

VENT

WATER

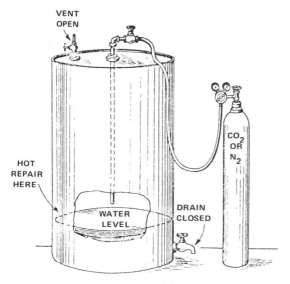

VENT OPEN

HOT REPAIR HERE

WATER LEVEL

DRAIN CLOSED

CO₂ OR N₂

Fig. 7-3. Nitrogen or carbon dioxide may be used to purge closed vessels before welding or cutting. Maintain flow of gas until work is completed.

Other Safe Practices to Bear in Mind

Make sure that jacketed or hollow parts are sufficiently vented before heating, welding, or cutting. Air or any other gas or liquid confined inside a hollow part will expand greatly when heated. The pressure created may be enough to cause violent rupture of the part. A metal part which is suspiciously light is hollow inside, and should be drilled to vent it before heat is applied. After work is complete, the vent hole can be tapped and plugged if necessary.

Bushings in a casting should either be removed or securely fastened in place before heating the casting. Bronze bushings expand more than cast iron when heated to the same temperature. If a bushing is left in place, the casting may be damaged, or expansion may cause the bushing to fly out, creating a definite hazard. If a bushing cannot be removed, it should be securely fastened in place. Bolting large washers or pieces of plate over the ends of the bushing is the suggested method.

Don't drop stub ends of welding rods on the floor. Put them in a suitable container. Aside from the fire hazard that may be created by carelessly dropping a hot stub end, a serious fall may result from stepping on one. A small container partly filled with water and within easy reach is a good place to dispose of these short ends.

Protect cylinders, hose, legs, and feet when cutting. Do not cut material in such a position as will permit sparks, hot metal, or the severed section to fall on or against a gas cylinder, or the gas hoses, or your legs or feet. A suitable metal screen in front of your legs will provide protection against sparks and hot metal.

Preventing Fires

Where welding or cutting has to be done near materials that will burn, take special care to make certain that flame, sparks, hot slag, or hot

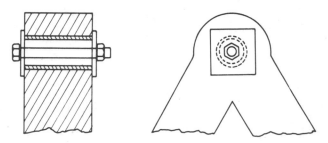

Fig. 7-4. If bushings cannot be removed before castings are heated, make sure they are restrained in some fashion, so that they cannot fly out.

metal do not reach combustible material and thus start a fire. This is particularly important in the case of cutting operations. Cutting produces more sparks and hot slag than welding, and locations where portable cutting equipment is used must, therefore, be thoroughly safeguarded against fire.

Refer to National Fire Protection Association Standard No. 51B, "Fire Protection in Use of Cutting and Welding Processes" for recommended practices.

Never use cutting or welding torches where sparks or open flame would be a hazard. Flames are a hazard in rooms containing flammable gas, vapors, liquids, dust, or any material that easily catches fire.

It is not safe to use cutting or welding equipment near rooms containing flammable materials unless there is absolutely no chance of sparks passing through cracks or holes in walls or floors, through open or broken windows, or open doorways. There is always the possibility that flammable vapors may escape from such rooms through doors or other openings, making it doubly necessary to keep sparks and flames away.

Before you cut or weld in a new location for the first time, always check with the nearest foreman or superintendent in authority. He may know of some serious fire hazard that might otherwise be overlooked.

If the work can be moved, take it to a location where there will be no possibility of setting fires. This must always be done when the metal to be welded or cut is in a place where open flames are barred. This practice may also be sensible in many other locations even if open flames are permitted.

If the work cannot be moved, materials that burn easily should, if possible, be taken a safe distance away. For cutting operations, this distance may be 30 to 40 ft. or more. Floors should be swept clean before the torch is lighted.

If flammable materials cannot be moved, use sheet metal guards, fire-resistant curtains, or similar protection to keep sparks close in to the work you are doing. Suitable protection to keep back sparks should always be used when it is not possible to move materials that will burn to a safe distance from the cutting or welding work. This also applies if sparks might lodge in wooden parts of the building, or drop through holes or cracks to the floor below.

Make sure that the guards are large enough and tight enough so that they do not permit sparks to roll underneath or slide through openings. Curtains should be weighed down against the floor or ground. For weights, use such things as angle iron, pipe, bricks or sand.

Use only fire-resisting guards. Do not use tarpaulins for shielding sparks since they may catch fire.

Fig. 7-5. When it is necessary to perform welding or cutting in the vicinity of combustible materials such as wood, set up screens to keep sparks from flying too far, and have water and sand available for use if needed.

Have someone stand by watch the sparks so that he can give warning if they begin to get beyond the protective guards. It is not reasonable to expect whoever is doing the welding or cutting to watch the sparks since his attention is on the work. In addition, the sparks cannot always be seen easily through goggles.

If welding or cutting over a wooden floor, sweep it clean and wet it down before starting work. Provide a bucket or pan containing water or sand to catch the dripping slag from any cutting that is done.

Before starting to cut off a piece of steel or iron, make sure it will not drop where there is any possibility of starting a fire. This is especially important when working in a high place where sparks or slag might be less apt to cause a fire down below than would a small piece of red hot steel. Pieces can be kept from falling by welding a rod or bar to the piece, and having a helper hold the rod or bar while the cut is made. Or the same thing might be accomplished by tying a chain or other suitable support to the piece.

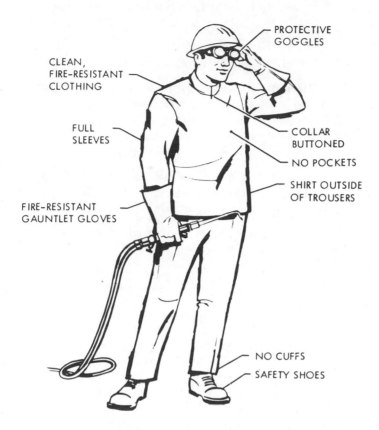

CLEAN,
FIRE-RESISTANT
CLOTHING

PROTECTIVE
GOGGLES

FULL
SLEEVES

COLLAR
BUTTONED

NO POCKETS

SHIRT OUTSIDE
OF TROUSERS

FIRE-RESISTANT
GAUNTLET GLOVES

NO CUFFS

SAFETY SHOES

Fig. 7-6. What the well-dressed welder will wear. Always select clothing materials which will provide maximum protection from sparks and hot metal.

When welding very close to wooden construction, protect it from direct heat. Wooden beams, partitions, flooring, or scaffolding should always be protected from the direct heat of the flame by sheet metal guards or asbestos. Protective guards should also be used to confine the sparks.

Use the correct oxygen pressure when cutting. An oxygen pressure greater than necessary will only cause extra sparks and increase the slag flow, to say nothing of increasing the oxygen expense.

Store extra cylinders away from important areas. Keep only enough cylinders near the work to insure an adequate supply of gases for the job at hand.

Be ready to put out any fire promptly with fire extinguishers, pails of water, water hose, or sand. When torches are to be used near wooden construction or materials that will burn, take every precaution to prevent fires, but always be prepared to put out fires that may start despite all precautions.

In hazardous locations, have a helper, or one or more extra men if necessary, on hand to watch for and be ready to extinguish a fire.

If there are sprinklers, maintain this protection without fail while cutting or welding is being done. It is of special importance to make sure that sprinklers are in working order during extensive repairs or building changes. If the sprinkler system must be shut down for a time, have this done when welding or cutting work is not in progress.

If there is a possibility that a smoldering fire may have been started, keep a man at the scene of the work for at least a half hour after the job is through. Have him look carefully for smoke or fire before leaving.

This is especially important when cutting torches have been used in locations where sparks may have started smoldering fires in wooden structures or in other slow burning materials.

Never forget that heavy cutting sparks sometimes fly 25 to 30 ft. or more and hold their heat for several seconds after landing.

When welding or cutting on bridges, structures, or at other outdoor sites, take care to avoid setting fire to grass or brush. Brush should be cleaned out or cautiously burned under or about structures before start of the work. Special care is necessary during a dry spell. A fire extinguisher and water or sand should be available to extinguish any fires started in the course of work. Before leaving the site, examine the premises thoroughly to be sure that sparks have not started smoldering fires.

QUESTIONS–CHAPTER 7

1. Why should oxygen never be used as a substitute for compressed air?
2. What should be done before starting to weld or cut?
3. What should be done when work must be performed in a confined space?
4. Should oxygen be fed into a confined space?
5. What should be done when working on materials that contain zinc?
6. What should be done if a sick feeling is experienced after working on material containing zinc?
7. What precautions should be taken when cutting iron or steel coated with lead or paint containing lead?
8. Is anyone immune from the effects of lead fumes?
9. What precautions should be taken before welding or cutting in dusty or gassy locations?
10. What precautions should be taken when welding or cutting is to be done on containers which have held a flammable material?
11. If a hollow part is to be welded or cut, what should be done first?
12. What kind of clothing should be worn for cutting work?
13. What are some of the ways in which possible fires from welding or cutting work can be prevented?

PHYSICAL PROPERTIES
OF METALS

What is a metal? Technically, it is an element which has the following properties:

— It is solid at room temperature (mercury is an exception)
— It is opaque (that is, you can't see through it)
— It conducts heat and electricity
— It reflects light when polished
— It expands when heated, contracts when cooled
— It usually has a crystalline structure

Some metals — gold, silver, copper, and zinc, for example — are often used in essentially pure form. However, most metals used for industrial purposes are actually *alloys,* not pure *metals.* An alloy is a metal to which another metal (or metals), or a non-metallic element such as carbon or silicon, has been added to modify the physical or mechanical properties of the pure metal. Iron, aluminum, titanium, and magnesium are used predominantly in alloy form. Pure iron, in fact, is something of a laboratory curiosity. Steel and cast iron are properly considered alloys of iron. Even though a low-carbon steel may contain more than 99% iron, and not more than 0.30% carbon, that little bit of carbon makes a lot of difference.

The distinction between "metal" and "alloy" is seldom observed in the everyday world, since alloys always have the general properties listed above as applying to metals. When we speak of "low-alloy" or "high alloy" steels we are not overlooking the fact that steel is an alloy of iron and carbon; instead, we are indicating that the low-alloy steel includes relative small percentages of other metals, and that high-alloy steels contain substantial amounts of other metals (most frequently, chromium or nickel).

This chapter will cover what are termed the *physical* properties of metal. Chapter 9 will be devoted to the *mechanical* properties of metals, with emphasis on steel. The physical properties of a material are properties not related to the ability of the material to withstand external mechanical forces, such as pushing, pulling, twisting, bending, etc. These properties include *density, melting point, specific heat, heat of fusion, thermal conductivity, thermal expansion, electrical conductivity,* and *corrosion resistance.*

Density. The measure of unit *mass;* in everyday terms, the weight of a unit volume. Density is variously expressed as grams per cubic centimetre (g/cm^3), kilograms per cubic metre (kg/m^3), pounds per cubic inch ($lb./in.^3$), pounds per cubic foot ($lb./ft.^3$). For comparative purposes, density is often expressed as *specific gravity*, the ratio of the density of the material to the density of water. The specific gravity of aluminum is 2.70 — in other words, it is nearly three times as heavy as water. Iron has a specific gravity of 7.86; for gold, the value is 19.3.

Melting Point. Every pure metal has a specific melting point. If you apply heat to a solid specimen, its temperature will rise until it reaches that melting point. It will then start to melt, and it will remain at the melting point temperature, even though the heating is continued, until the specimen is completely melted. Then, and only then, will the temperature of the liquid metal start to rise once more. The amount of heat required to melt a unit mass of metal includes the heat required to raise that mass to its melting point, and the additional quantity of heat required to accomplish complete melting once the melting point has been reached.

Melting Point of Alloys. Most alloys do not melt completely at a specific temperature. Melting starts when the material has reached a certain temperature, but is not completed until a somewhat higher temperature has been reached. This is a fact of great significance in the welding of steel; we'll get into this more deeply in Chapter 10, and when we get to talk about the practice of welding.

Specific Heat. The amount of heat required to raise a unit mass of solid metal one degree in temperature is termed *specific heat*. The lighter the metal, the greater the specific heat. In other words, it takes more heat to raise the temperature of one kilogram of aluminum one degree than it takes to raise the temperature of one kilogram of iron one degree.

Heat of Fusion. The amount of heat required to completely melt a unit mass of a metal once it has attained its melting point. Here again, more heat is required for a light metal, such as aluminum, than for a heavier metal such as iron.

Thermal Conductivity. As everyone knows, the handle of a sterling silver spoon left in a hot cup of coffee gets hot in a hurry, whereas a stainless steel spoon handle heats up only a little in the same period of time. Silver is an excellent conductor of heat, while stainless steel is a poor conductor. In fact, silver is twice as good a conductor as aluminum, and nearly 10 times as good as a conductor as low-carbon steel. Copper and gold are the only metals that come close to silver in thermal conductivity. In fact, the high conductivity of copper is quite a complication when it comes to welding.

Thermal Expansion. The increase in dimensions of a solid body due to an increase in temperature is termed *thermal expansion*. This property is of much significance in welding operations, since the metal close to the weld zone is heated to a higher temperature, and therefore expands more than the metal at a greater distance from the weld zone. Furthermore, the molten metal deposited during welding must shrink — or least try to shrink — as it cools down in the solid state. Mathematically, the term used to express the tendency of a metal to expand when heated is "coefficient of thermal expansion". By comparison with zinc, lead, and magnesium, this coefficient is relatively small for steel; an iron bar one metre long increases in length a little more than one millimeter when heated 100°C. The expansion and contraction of steel when heated and cooled are matters of great importance in welding, and will be covered in more detail in Chapter 12.

Electrical Conductivity. As stated earlier, a metal must be a conductor of electricity. Some are much better than others; generally, the metals which are the best conductors of heat, such as copper, silver and aluminum, are also the best conductors of electricity.

Corrosion Resistance. To some extent, the ability of a given metal to resist corrosion is a *chemical* rather than a *physical* property, since it is at least partially determined by purely *chemical* factors. However, we can properly mention it here because the corrosion resistance of an alloy is often determined as much by the physical crystalline structure of the alloy as by the chemical nature of its components. For example, stainless steel composed of about 74% iron, 18% chromium, and 8% nickel is virtually immune to attack by some liquids which would rapidly eat away low-carbon steel (99% iron). Why this is true is beyond the scope of this book. Let's be thankful, however, that it is and that for many purposes we can use an alloy which is largely iron and get almost the same corrosion resistance we could expect from more expensive pure nickel.

QUESTIONS – CHAPTER 8

1. What is meant by physical properties of material?
2. What is the difference between density and specific gravity?
3. What is the significant difference in melting temperature between pure and alloyed metals?
4. What is the difference between thermal conductivity and thermal expansion?
5. Is corrosion resistance of a metal really a physical property?

MECHANICAL PROPERTIES OF METALS

The *mechanical properties* of a material are those related to its ability to withstand external mechanical forces such as pulling, pushing, twisting, bending, and sudden impact. In general terms, we think of these properties as various kinds of "strength". However, the word "strength", used alone, doesn't tell us very much. Steel, cast iron, rubber, and glass are each "strong" in different ways.

Tensile Strength, Elasticity, and Ductility

In the field of metals, when the word "strength" is used alone (as in "high-strength steels") it almost always refers to the ability of the metal to resist pulling force; specifically, to what is termed its *tensile strength*. If we start by considering what happens when a bar of steel is subjected to a steadily-increasing pull, we cannot only define *tensile strength*, but also *yield strength, elasticity,* and *ductility*.

It's obvious that it will take more pull to break a steel bar with a cross-sectional area of 10 square centimeters (10 cm²) than to break one with a cross-sectional area of 5 cm², so we must start with a specimen having a precisely-determined cross-sectional area if the results are to yield useful data. This specimen is secured firmly in a *tensile testing machine* which is capable of applying all the pulling force needed to break it. The machine is equipped with gauges which will show both the force being applied and the increase in length of the specimen as force is applied. The *force* can be mathematically converted to *stress* by applying the known minimum cross-sectional area of the specimen. (*Stress* equals *force* divided by *area*.)*

---

*In the "English" system of measurement, *force* has been expressed in *pounds,* stress in *pounds per square inch* (psi). In the metric system, until recently, force was expressed in *kilograms,* stress in *kilograms per square centimeter* (kg/cm²). In the updated metric system (SI), force is expressed in *newtons (N),* stress in *pascals* (Pa). (One newton, acting across an area of one square meter, equals one pascal). Tensile strengths will usually be stated in *megapascals* (MPa) (millions of pascals).

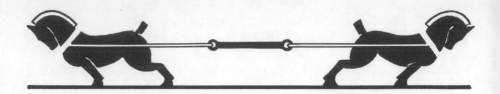

Fig. 9-1. Tensile strength is expressed in terms of the directly-applied pull required to break a part.

As the machine pulls the specimen, it stretches — not a great deal, but enough to register on the strain gauge. If we gradually increase the pulling force, the amount of strain will also increase. A force of 20 kilonewtons (4500 lb.) will cause twice the strain produced by a force of 10 kilonewtons (2250 lb.). The steel is *elastic.* Until the *elastic limit* of the specimen has been reached, the amount of strain will be directly proportional to the amount of pull, and the specimen will always return to its original length if the pulling force is released.

If we continue to apply pulling force at a gradually increasing rate, watching both the force and strain gauge hands closely, we reach a point where the strain gauge hand continues to move while the force gauge hand remains stationary, or even drops a bit. We have now reached the *elastic limit* of the steel. If at this point, the pulling force is released, the specimen will not return to its original length. It has undergone *permanent deformation.* The force required to produce a slight amount of permanent deformation, expressed as megapascals (MPa) or pounds per square inch (psi) of specimen cross-section, is termed *yield point* or *yield strength.*

If, instead of releasing the pulling force when the yield point has been reached, we continue to increase that force, the test specimen will stretch at a more rapid rate until the pulling force reaches a maximum point. Then it will begin to "neck down" or grow visibly narrower at some point; the force

Fig. 9-2. Tensile strength of a weld coupon can be determined by pulling the coupon until it breaks.

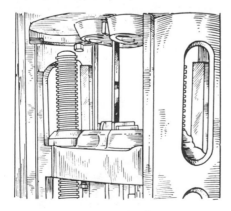

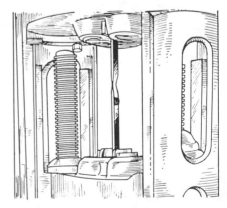

Fig. 9-3. This coupon has started to "neck down" outside the weld zone. The weld is good.

gauge hand will start to drop, while the hand on the strain gauge will continue to climb. Then the specimen will break, after "necking down" substantially. The value established by the highest reading registered on the force gauge is termed the *tensile strength* or *ultimate tensile strength* of the steel. To be more specific: The *ultimate tensile strength* is the maximum force registered on the testing machine divided by the *original* cross-sectional area of the specimen. The force registered at the instant of breakage, divided by the *final* cross-section area of the specimen *at the point of breakage*, is termed the *fracture strength.*

In steel, fracture strength, while of little practical significance, almost always has a higher value than ultimate tensile strength. Permanent deformation of steel increases its *unit* tensile strength. That's why steel wire, which is repeatedly deformed as it is drawn, is stronger (in terms of breaking force per unit of cross-section) than a steel bar from the same heat of steel, and why cold-rolled steel is stronger than hot-rolled steel.

Let's now try to define more precisely the several terms just introduced in describing the *tensile testing* of a steel bar:

Yield Strength. The tensile force required to cause a slight but well-defined permanent deformation.

Yield Point. The force level at which strain (elongation) takes place without any increase in stress (pull).

Elastic Limit. The force required to produce permanent deformation. For all practical purposes, when dealing with ordinary low-carbon structural steels, *yield strength, yield point,* and *elastic limit* have the same values.

Ultimate Tensile Strength. The maximum strength of the material in terms of its original cross-sectional area. For engineering purposes, this is the value that can be used to determine the maximum load which a structural member should withstand without breaking. For many purposes, *yield strength* is the more significant value, since appreciable permanent deformation (stretching) will usually occur before stress has reached ultimate strength value.

Elasticity. The linear relationship of *non-permanent* change in length to the *force* applied (in other words, the relationship of strain to stress). Rubber is extremely elastic; many metals are more elastic than steel in that a given pull will produce a greater increase in length. Cast iron, in this sense, is actually twice as elastic as steel. However, don't forget that the important value, when dealing with metals, is usually the *elastic limit,* not the *modulus of elasticity* (relation of strain to stress below the elastic limit).

Ductility. Elasticity deals with the relationship of non-permanent strain to stress. *Ductility* is a measure of the ability of a material to undergo permanent deformation without breaking. Copper and aluminum are extremely ductile, generally speaking. Most low-carbon steels are quite ductile. Some cast irons have virtually no ductility; to put it in simple terms, they break before they bend. All types of steel have approximately the same degree of *elasticity;* that is, up to the elastic limit, the stress-strain relationship is the same, regardless of composition. However, ductility varies greatly, depending not only on composition but on several other factors as well. Ordinary low-carbon steels are moderately ductile; high-carbon tool steels have little ductility.

Ductility is usually expressed as "per cent elongation in two inches" or as "per cent reduction in cross-section area". If, before we started the test just described, we had placed two marks on the test specimen, precisely five centimeters (5 cm) apart, we could establish the per cent elongation by fitting the pieces of the specimen together, after breaking, and then measuring the new distance between the two marks. In the case of low-carbon steel, we might find that the elongation was 30% (that is, from 5 cm to 6.5 cm). If the original cross-section of the specimen had been two square centimeters (2 cm^2) and the cross-section, remeasured at the point of the break, turned out to be 1 cm^2, we could state that the reduction in area was 50%

To check on the ductility of welds in steel plate, another method of arriving at "per cent elongation" is sometimes used. After the weld has been completed, it is ground flush with the surface of the base metal, and two small punch marks made in the actual weld metal. The specimen is then placed in a vise, and bent until the first crack appears in the surface of the weld metal between the two marks. By using a flexible steel rule, the distance between the punch marks is measured and compared with the original distance between the two punch marks.

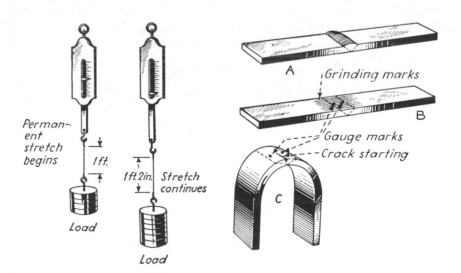

Fig. 9-4. A simple way to measure the ductility of wire.

Fig. 9-5. A way to measure the ductility of weld metal. (See description above).

While low-carbon steels exhibit relatively high ductility as measured by the methods described above, they are also subject to *brittle failure* under some conditions. A structural member may break suddenly when subject to stress which is below the expected yield point of the metal—that is, before any measurable permanent deformation has taken place. Such failure (fracture) always starts at a slight crack or notch in the metal. The ability of a steel to resist this type of fracture is termed *notch ductility.* Notch ductility is somewhat dependent on the composition of the steel. It is always related to temperature, (all steels lose notch ductility rapidly as temperatures drop below the 0-20°C range) and to the grain structures within the steel, especially the structures which are formed as the result of welding. *Stress-relieving*—the reheating of the weld zone to a temperature of not more than 600°C—is widely used to reduce the possibility of brittle fracture in welded structures.

Hardness

Where metals are involved, hardness is usually defined as the ability of the metal to resist indentation or penetration by another material. In itself, the exact hardness of a steel is not of great importance in most applications. However, hardness can be measured much more readily than can tensile strength, and there is a very close relationship between *hardness* and *tensile strength,* and between *hardness* and *ductility.* Usually, the harder the steel, the higher its tensile strength, and the lower its ductility. Three methods of hardness testing are widely used: The Brinnell method, in which a steel ball is forced against the surface of the specimen by a heavy load, and hardness determined by measuring the diameter of the impression left in the surface; the Rockwell method, in which a diamond cone is pressed into the surface, and hardness determined by a gauge, built into the testing unit, which registers the depth of the impression; and the Scleroscope method, in which a diamond-pointed cylinder of steel is dropped onto the surface of the material from a fixed height, and hardness determined by measuring the height of the rebound.

Fig. 9-6. The two methods most widely used to determine hardness of metal (Brinnell and Rockwell) measure the amount of penetration effected by a known force (by much more sophisticated means than illustrated here).

Other Kinds of "Strength"

Compressive Strength. This may be thought of as the opposite of tensile strength: in other words, the ability of a material to resist a gradually applied "push", rather than "pull". Most metals have at least as much strength in compression as in tension, so that exact values for compressive strength are seldom significant.

Fatigue Strength. Here is a property of great importance in the design of many parts and structures. All metals will fail under repeatedly changing load conditions at a lower stress than they will if the load is applied steadily in one direction. A wire that might support a continuous load of 5000 MPa indefinitely will probably fail in time if a load of 3000 MPa is alternately and repeatedly imposed and then released. The piston rod on a steam locomotive is subjected to tension for a half-cycle, then to compression for a half-cycle, thousands of times every day. Structural members in a bridge are constantly subject to changing load conditions. In all such applications, fatigue strength, which is always lower than tensile strength and sometimes *much* lower, must be considered by a designer.

In addition to factors in the internal structure of a metal which cause it to become weaker when subjected to repeated changes in load, metal surface conditions are closely related to fatigue strength. Fatigue failure usually starts with a small crack; any roughness in the surface of a metal which might make it easier for such a crack to start—even slight pitting from a corrosive atmosphere—can substantially reduce the fatigue strength.

Fatigue strength is usually expressed as *fatigue limit* or *endurance limit;* both terms mean the same thing: the stress to which the material can be subjected indefinitely, under *varying* load conditions, before failure. If someone says that the fatigue limit of steel from a certain heat is 140 MPa (about 20,000 psi) assume he means that the steel can be subjected to re-

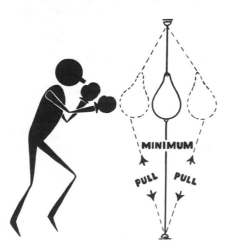

Fig. 9-7. The springs or elastic bands which secure this punching bag to floor and ceiling are being subjected to repeated, but not alternating, stress.

Fig. 9-8. The piston rod in this double air pump is being subjected to alternating stress. Each half of the rod is first pulled, then pushed. At some point in each cycle, stress in one half of the rod is zero.

peated alternation of stress, from 140 MPa tension to 140 MPa compression, for at least 10,000,000 cycles without failure. However, values for fatigue strength are often expressed in more limited terms; for example, that the material will withstand "100,000 cycles of 300 MPa tension to 0 tension", or "2,000,000 cycles of 125 MPa, reversed" (meaning that a complete cycle ranges from 125 MPa tension to 125 MPa compression).

Impact Strength; Fracture Toughness. Both of these terms refer to the ability of a material to withstand shock, or large forces suddenly applied. Neither property can be defined mathematically, for engineering use, in the same sense that tensile strengths can be defined. Impact strength is usually stated in terms of the energy absorbed by a metal when it is broken under carefully-defined and limited conditions. In the Charpy V-notch impact test, a specimen of fixed dimensions, which has been precisely notched, is broken by a blow from a pendulum hammer. The difference between the distance which the hammer travels after breaking the specimen, and the distance it would have travelled had there been no specimen to hit, is a direct measure of the energy absorbed by the specimen before it fractured. This energy, expressed as units of force, is correctly described as *impact energy,* rather than impact *strength.* Two steels which have equal tensile strengths at room temperatures may vary widely in their impact energies (strengths) especially when tested at low temperatures.

Fracture toughness refers specifically to the resistance of a material to rapid crack propagation (the *brittle fracture* mentioned earlier) when a slight crack already exists and a massive load is applied suddenly. For a homely example, think of a loaded grocery bag sitting on the floor. If the bottom of the bag has no holes or tears, you can usually yank it up suddenly without mishap. If there is a small break in the bottom of the bag, you can often lift the bag *slowly* and get your arm under it, but if you try to yank it up, you're likely to wind up with groceries scattered on the floor. Similarly, a very small crack in a metal member, which might reduce the strength of that member only slightly were high tensile stress to be created *gradually,* can sometimes spread with great speed, and destroy the member completely, when an equal load is applied *suddenly.* Fracture toughness depends on several factors which are not directly involved in the standard Charpy V-notch test, so the results of such tests are often considered only a rough measure of fracture toughness.

QUESTIONS – CHAPTER 9

1. What is tensile strength? How is it determined?
2. What part does the cross-sectional area of a tension test specimen have in the result?
3. What is elasticity? Are all metals elastic?
4. What is yield point?
5. What is yield strength?
6. What is the difference between elasticity and ductility?
7. How is ductility determined?
8. What is meant by brittleness?
9. What is hardness? How is it measured?
10. Is there any relationship between the mechanical properties of metals?
11. What are some of the other mechanical properties often considered important for determining the strength of material?

CHAPTER

10

THE STRUCTURE
OF STEEL

In opening Chapter 8, we said that one of the properties of a metal was a crystalline structure. This means simply that the atoms in the solid are arranged in regular, repeating patterns. The smallest group of atoms which defines the atomic arrangement in a crystal is termed a crystal lattice. Many different lattice structures are recognized. In pure iron, however, there are only two forms, one called the body-centered cube, the other called the face-centered cube. They can be represented like this:

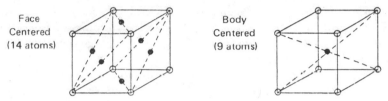

Face Centered (14 atoms)   Body Centered (9 atoms)

The Freezing of Pure Iron

In a liquid, there is no lattice pattern. All the atoms of the liquid are in constant, irregular motion. When the liquid has been cooled to its freezing temperature, crystals start to form. In the case of pure iron, at a temperature of 1530°C, something causes nine atoms to get together in the shape of a body-centered cube (one atom at each corner and one in the center) and other atoms then start to repeat the pattern around the cube. Hundreds of crystals start growing at about the same time. However, because each atom must give up its energy of motion as it joins a crystal, freezing cannot take place instantaneously. The mass of liquid must pass that surplus energy on to its surroundings, and that takes time. While that energy is being lost, competitive growth among the many crystals is taking place. Thus, when freezing is complete, and every atom of liquid has become part of a crystal, the crystals themselves are not arranged in any kind of an over-all pattern. Let pure iron freeze and cool, then cut it, polish and etch a cut surface, and examine that cut surface with a microscope. We can then make out an irregular collection of what are termed "grains". Each grain is essentially a single crystal.

When pure iron cools down from its freezing point to room temperature, something rather unusual happens—not once, but twice. At a temperature of 1400°C the crystal lattice pattern changes from its original body-centered form to the face-centered form. At 910°C the lattice reverts to the body-centered form. These temperatures are termed *critical* temperatures. As each of the crystal rearrangements takes place, heat is released without any change in temperature taking place.

The Freezing of Carbon Steel

Add carbon to iron — as little at 0.1% by weight — and many things change. The freezing temperature drops. Freezing starts at one temperature and is not complete until a lower temperature has been reached. In other words, we have a freezing temperature *range,* not *a* freezing temperature. Between the limits of this range, the metal is neither solid nor liquid; it is *mushy* or *pasty.* This is very important to the welder, since he can control the metal in the mushy state much more readily then he can control completely liquid metal.

Until the carbon content of the metal has reached 2%, the freezing temperature range gets broader as the carbon content increases. Beyond 2%, it starts to narrow, and finally disappears completely at 4.3%. An alloy of 95.7% iron and 4.3% carbon freezes completely at a temperature of 1130°C and is called a *eutectic* alloy. Think of "eutectic" as meaning "freezes completely at a fixed temperature" and you won't be mystified by that word.

At this point, we'd like to introduce you to what is known as the "iron-iron carbide equilibrium diagram". A simplified form of this diagram is shown as Fig. 10-1. The two heavy lines running across the upper part of the diagram define the freezing point range for all iron-carbon alloys from 0.2% carbon to 5% carbon.

Shown on the diagram are four words—*austenite, ferrite, pearlite, and cementite*—which we shall define shortly. First, however, we ask you to look at the vertical line which picks out the 0.8% carbon alloy. We shall start at the top of that line and work our way down, describing the changes which take place as the steel cools from the liquid state to room temperature.

This alloy starts to freeze at a temperature of about 1500°C. Crystals of almost pure iron form in the *face-centered* pattern. (In *pure* iron, the crystals first formed in the body-centered pattern, but changed over to the face-centered pattern at a temperature a bit above 1500°C.) Most of the carbon atoms keep moving around in the liquid until a lot of the iron has crystallized. As the temperature drops to a bit above 1389°C, all the liquid disappears. The carbon has gone into what is termed "solid solution" in the mass of iron crystals. Apparently the carbon atoms lodge themselves in the centers of the relatively open face-centered cubes. They remain there until the temperature of the solid metal has dropped to 723°C (1333°F), the transition temperature for almost all iron-carbon alloys. (The transition temperature for pure iron was much higher: 910°C.) At this temperature, the iron crystals change from the face-centered form to the body-centered form. In the body-centered form, there's not enough room for a carbon atom.

What happens to the carbon? Most of the carbon atoms link up with iron atoms to form a crystalline compound called iron carbide (Fe_3C). If cooling is slow, this iron carbide forms plates between plates of pure body-centered iron. If we cut, polish, and etch a specimen of this steel after it has cooled completely, and examine it under a microscope, we find that it is made up almost entirely of grains of *pearlite*. Each grain of pearlite has a layered structure, with layers of iron separated by layers of iron carbide.

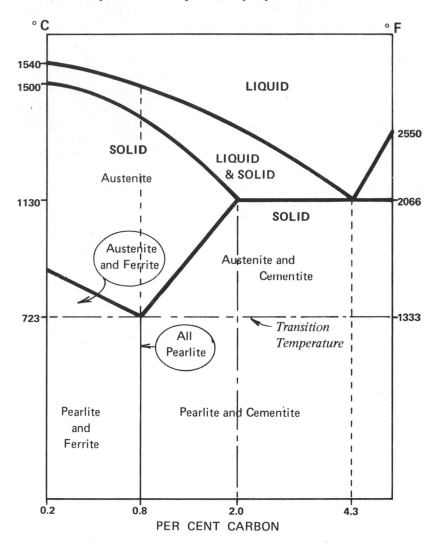

Fig. 10-1. In simplified form, a part of the standard "iron-iron carbide equilibrium diagram". The structures indicated below the transition-temperature line are those which normally exist in slowly-cooled iron-carbon compositions.

Now let's talk about the other three new words shown on the diagram. *Austenite* applies to the face-centered grain structure, with carbon in solid solution, that exists above the 723°C transition temperature. We cannot microscopically examine the austenitic structure in ordinary carbon steels (it's simply too hot to cut and etch at 723°C), but some alloy steels retain this structure at room temperature and in them it can be examined. *Ferrite* applies to the almost pure body-centered iron that occurs, along with pearlite, in any slowly-cooled steel with a carbon content *below* 0.8%. *Cementite* refers to crystalline iron carbide (Fe_3C) which forms between the grains of pearlite in a slowly-cooled steel which has more than 0.8% carbon.

Not shown on the equilibrium diagram is another word, *martensite,* which describes a structure formed in carbon steels when the steel is cooled *rapidly.* (Remember that we said we would describe what happened to an 0.8% carbon steel when it was cooled *slowly.*) Under slow cooling conditions, all the carbon in the steel appears as layers of iron carbide in grains of pearlite. The slower the cooling, the thicker the layers of iron carbide. Speed up the cooling rate somewhat, and the layers of iron carbide in the pearlite become thinner; the grains of pearlite appear to become larger, and any grains of ferrite become smaller. Speed up the cooling rate some more, by actually quenching the steel in water, brine, or oil from a temperature above the critical (723°C), and martensite forms. The apparent reason for the formation of martensite is this: That it takes time — many minutes—for the carbon in the face-centered crystals of iron (austenite) to move out of the face-centered crystals and form crystals of iron carbide. If the temperature of the steel is dropped rapidly from above 723°C to a temperature below 400°C the carbon cannot move out in orderly fashion. At some temperature below 400°C the forces operating to change the crystalline structure become so great that a rapid change takes place. The carbon is trapped in a new type of "solid solution" and the crystals of iron which retain carbon atoms are

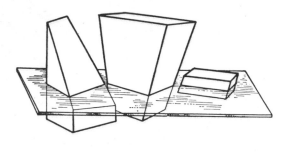

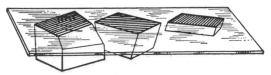

Fig. 10-2. Grains form in many shapes and sizes, which may appear alike when a piece of steel is cut and etched.

distorted into a lattice formation which is quite different from the normal body-centered cube. When a specimen of rapidly-quenched steel is examined under the microscope (after polishing and etching) it seems to be shot through with needles. There are no well-defined grains. This *martensitic* structure is much harder and stronger than the normal pearlite/ferrite structure; it is almost much less ductile.

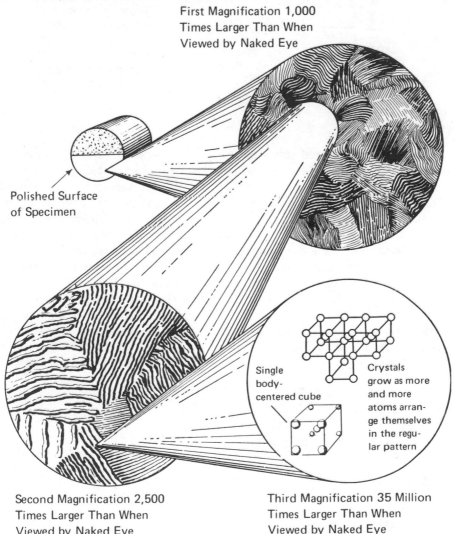

First Magnification 1,000 Times Larger Than When Viewed by Naked Eye

Polished Surface of Specimen

Single body-centered cube

Crystals grow as more and more atoms arrange themselves in the regular pattern

Second Magnification 2,500 Times Larger Than When Viewed by Naked Eye

Third Magnification 35 Million Times Larger Than When Viewed by Naked Eye

Fig. 10-3. A rough representation of what can be seen, under a microscope, when an etched surface of pearlitic steel is examined. The third magnification (incomplete) actually cannot be observed directly, even with an electron microscope, but indicates how the body-centered crystals of iron are linked together.

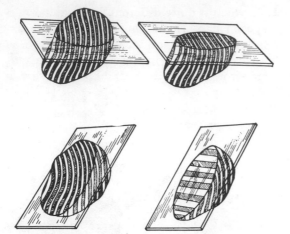

Fig. 10-4. A pearlite grain is made up of alternate layers of pure iron and iron carbide. When sectioned, polished, and etched it shows alternate light and dark lines. Width of lines depends partly on angle of section through the grains.

So far, we've covered only what happens when a carbon steel containing about 0.8% carbon is cooled slowly from the molten state, or is quenched rapidly from a temperature above 733°C. When it has been slowly cooled, the steel is made up almost entirely of grains of *pearlite,* which has a layered structure (termed "lamellar" by the metallurgist). If it is quenched rapidly from a high temperature, it usually has an entirely different structure, called *martensite.* We have noted that if the steel contains less than about 0.8% carbon, the cooled metal will contain grains of *ferrite* (pure iron) as well as pearlite, and that if it contains more than 0.8% carbon it will contain *cementite* (iron carbide) around or between the grains of pearlite.

However, a steel containing 0.8% carbon is classified as a high-carbon steel, and is seldom encountered by a welder. The metallurgist terms such a steel *eutectoid;* it can form a structure that is 100% pearlite. (Don't get *eutectoid* confused with *eutectic,* which applies to the 95.7% iron -4.3% car-

Fig. 10-5. A martensic structure, formed when medium- or high-carbon steel is quenched, looks something like this when examined under the microscope.

bon composition which melts completely at a fixed temperature.) A welder is almost always working on *hypoeutectoid* steels, containing less—usually much less—than 0.8% carbon. (The steels with more than 0.8% carbon are termed *hypereutectoid*.) It would be wrong to close this chapter without looking a bit more closely at the hypoeutectoid steels, and without discussing the various types of heat treatment (other than simple rapid quenching) which are used to modify the structure and the properties of carbon steels.

Most of the steels used to form sheet (thickness less than about 0.5 cm or 1/8 in.) contain 0.13% carbon or less; extra-low-carbon sheet may contain as little as 0.03% carbon. Steels in the upper part of this range (0.08 to 0.13% C), when allowed to cool slowly, usually contain some grains of pearlite, although the grains of pearlite are much smaller than the grains of ferrite. Steels in the lower part of the range (below 0.08% C) seldom contain pearlite. The carbon usually winds up in particles of iron carbide (cementite) scattered between grains of ferrite. The mechanical properties of the finished steel are affected by the size of the ferrite grains, the shape of the ferrite grains (if the steel is cold-rolled the grains will be distorted and elongated by the rolling process), and by the size and shape of the iron carbide (cementite) particles, which may be large and irregular, or small and more-or-less round in cross-section (spheroidical).

The carbon steels used to form steel plate (thickness greater than 0.5 cm), and most steel pipe and tubing, usually contain more than 0.13% carbon. Unless it has been given special heat-treatment at the steel mill after rolling, carbon steel plate will usually show a mixture of ferrite and pearlite grains, with the pearlite grains smaller than the ferrite grains. However, this structure can be modified greatly by heat treatment.

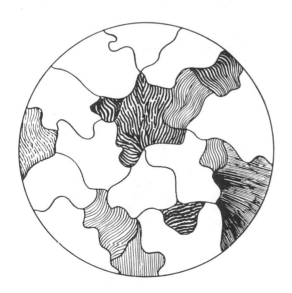

Fig. 10-6. A photomicrograph of a piece of steel containing about 0.3% carbon will look something like this, showing a mixture of ferrite grains (white) and pearlite grains.

Types of Heat Treatment

The four terms most frequently used in connection with the heat treatment of steel are *annealing, normalizing, quenching,* and *tempering.* We'll take them up one at a time.

Annealing. Steel is annealed by heating to a temperature above the critical (733°C), so that all the iron will return to the face-centered form called austenite, and then allowing it to cool slowly through the *transformation range* (from just below to about 50°C below the critical temperature). The heating part of the process is termed *austenizing;* the precise temperature to which the steel is heated, and the time it is held at that temperature, are both carefully controlled. Annealing is almost always performed at the steel mill. Sheet and strip steel are usually annealed to reduce the hardness acquired in rolling, and to make cold forming easier. Annealing is also done to improve the machinability of steel. By precise control of the heating and cooling cycles, several different types of final structures can be achieved, ranging from the lamellar (where the carbon is in grains of pearlite) to the spheroidical (where virtually all the carbon winds up in small particles of cementite between grains of ferrite). *Process annealing* is a different process, performed for a different purpose. It is applied to parts which have been undesirably hardened by cold forming, to remove stresses locked up in the metal by the cold forming and to restore the ductility of the steel.

Normalizing. Normalizing is a simpler process than annealing. The steel is heated to a temperature above the transformation range (that is, above the critical) and then allowed to cool in still air. (In annealing, cooling usually takes place in an annealing furnace, under precise control.) Normalizing may be performed to make steel softer (after casting, forging, or cold-working), or to make it harder (after annealing), or merely to improve the grain structure (in castings, for example.)

Quenching. This is defined as the rapid cooling of steel from an elevated temperature, usually by immersion in oil or water. The purpose of quenching is always to harden the steel; usually that implies the transformation of the steel to the *martensitic* structure previously described. Quenching is usually followed by *tempering.*

Tempering. Steel is tempered by heating it to a temperature below the transformation range and then allowing it to cool at a controlled rate. The purpose of tempering is always to improve the toughness and ductility of steel which has been hardened by quenching, or even by normalizing. Usually tempering reduces the hardness of the steel, although some alloy steels can be tempered without loss of hardness. Tempering is seldom applied to the low-carbon steels.

Surface Hardening. Several processes are used in industry to produce a hardened surface on a tough, unhardened steel core. Some of these are *carburizing* processes, whose aim is to increase the carbon content, and therefore the hardness, of the steel surface. Flame-hardening, which will be covered in more detail in a later chapter, has a similar aim, but does not depend upon a change in the carbon content of the surface. Surface-hardening processes are applied to finished parts, usually forged or machined, and hence are of no direct interest to a welder.

Hardness vs. Hardenability

In closing, we'd like to call attention to the distinction between two terms widely used in talk about steels: *hardness* and *hardenability.* To a considerable degree, the hardness of a carbon steel depends on its carbon content; any high-carbon steel is naturally hard, no matter how it is cooled. It is usually heat-treated to give it the best combination of hardness and toughness required for a particular application. *Hardenability* usually refers to the ability of alloy steels to form martensite through heat treatment, and thus acquire higher strength. This ability is often not directly related to carbon content; to put it another way, an alloy steel with relatively low carbon content may be more *hardenable* than another alloy steel containing two or three times as much carbon.

QUESTIONS – CHAPTER 10

1. What is the effect of increase carbon content on melting point of iron?
2. What is eutectic alloy? eutectoid?
3. What is pearlite? Ferrite? Austenite? Martensite?
4. In what form is the carbon present in steels at ordinary temperatures?
5. What are hypoeutectoid and hypereutectoid steels? Which is the most common encountered by a welder?
6. What are the four heat treating processes commonly used for changing the properties of steel? Describe each.
7. What is meant by hardenability?

11

HOW STEELS ARE CLASSIFIED

Steels are classified in several different ways. The primary method of classification is by carbon content, or by content of alloying elements other than carbon (which is present in every steel); in short, by *chemical* composition. Let's take a look at steels from that standpoint first.

Classification by Composition

Carbon Steels. When we refer to "carbon" steel, we mean steel which contains iron, carbon, less than 1.65% manganese, less than 0.6% copper, and small amounts of silicon, sulphur, and phosphorus. The sulphur and phosphorus are considered impurities, and not more than 0.05% of either is allowed by specifications, except in the case of some grades designated as "free-machining". The amount of manganese may range from as little as .35% to as much as 1.65%.

The family of carbon steels (it is a large family, with nearly 50 standard grades) is usually sub-divided into four sub-families: the low-carbon steels, which contain no more than 0.30% carbon; the medium-carbon steels, which range from 0.30 to 0.45% carbon*; the high-carbon steels, from 0.45 to 0.75% carbon; and the very-high-carbon steels, which range up to 1.50% carbon. The low-carbon steels, often termed "mild" steels, are more widely used than the grades with higher carbon content. They are quite ductile, can be machined or formed with relative ease, and can be welded by any process. As the carbon content increases, tensile strength and hardness increases, but ductility declines, and machining of the steel may become more difficult. The very-high-carbon steels are used principally for springs and for tools which are used to cut or form metals. High-carbon and very-high-carbon steels are seldom welded; when welding must be used, the metal must be heat-treated before, during, and after welding if sound welds are to be obtained, and the desired mechanical properties of the steel retained.

Alloy Steels. Any steel which contains more than 1.65% manganese, or 0.60% copper, or a guaranteed minimum amount of any other metal, is termed an "alloy" steel. The metals most frequently used for alloying purposes are nickel, chromium, molybdenum, vanadium, and manganese.

---

*Some metallurgists refer to the medium-carbon range as "0.25 to 0.50%".

In one group of alloy steels, usually termed "high-strength" or high-strength, low-alloy'', the addition of small amounts of nickel, chromium, or molybdenum (less than 1%) raises tensile strength appreciably. Although these steels cost more (per pound or per kilogram) than plain carbon steels, steel costs for structures specifically designed to utilize their higher strength are less than the steel costs for equally strong structures designed in terms of plain carbon steels. (In fact, several of the "high-strength" steels are not truly "alloy" steels at all; their extra strength is achieved at least partly by holding the phosphorus content below the normal limits for carbon steels.) These steels are readily welded by almost any process.

Even stronger than the "high-strength, low-alloy" steels are the structural steels generally termed "high-strength, heat-treated alloy". Such a steel may contain somewhat more than 1% nickel, about 1% copper, and 0.5% or less molybdenum. These steels, which must be heat-treated after rolling, have yield strengths 50-100% higher than the yield strengths of straight-carbon steels of comparable carbon content. They usually cannot be welded without some sacrifice in mechanical properties.

Beyond these structural steels there lies a very large group of steels generally termed simply "alloy steels". In such steels, the nickel or chromium content may reach 3.75%, with up to 0.30% molybdenum specified for many grades. In very few of these steels does the total alloy-metal content exceed 5%. In this group, chromium is the most frequently encountered alloying metal. It generally adds both strength and ductility, and is especially useful in alloys designed for heat treatment. Nickel contributes to both greater strength and greater shock resistance. Chromium and molybdenum are used in combination (in "chrome-moly" steels) for their ability to retain strength and resist creep under stress at elevated temperatures.

High-Alloy Steels. Metallurgists do not often use the term "high-alloy" but we shall use it here to mean steels which contain more than 5% alloying metals. Most "high-alloy" steels are formulated for corrosion resistance or heat resistance or a combination of both, and use chromium or nickel or a combination of the two as the principal alloying ingredients. Many of these steels are classified as "stainless steels" and virtually all are produced in electric furnaces. The grades most widely used for corrosion resistance are the "18-8" stainless steels, which contain approximately 18% chromium and 8% nickel. In addition to being totally resistant to atmospheric corrosion, and to many corrosive chemicals, the 18-8 grades are both strong and ductile. They cannot be hardened by heat treatment, and can be welded by many different processes.

Not all stainless steels are "18-8". Stainless steel kitchen knives will usually be made from a high-chromium steel containing little or no nickel, since such steel can be hardened by heat treatment, and will take a much better edge than an 18-8 steel.

AISI and SAE Numbering Systems. Most standard steels, both carbon and alloy, are given number designations within a system originally set up by the American Iron and Steel Institute (AISI) and later adopted, with some modifications, by the Society of Automotive Engineers (SAE). In both the AISI and SAE systems, the same four-digit numbers are used to identify the compositions of carbon steels and most standard alloy steels. The first digit represents the general class of steel, based on its major alloy ingredient; the numbers for all steels classed simply as "carbon" steels start with "1"; the numbers for all alloy steels categorized as "nickel" steels start with "2", for "chromium" steels with "5", etc. The second digit gives a general indication of the percentage of the principal alloy ingredient, and the last two digits indicate the approximate amount of carbon in the composition, expressed as "points". (A "point" of carbon is 0.01%.) Thus a 1013 steel (either AISI 1013 or SAE 1013) is a carbon steel containing approximately 0.13% carbon; 2511 is a nickel steel containing about 5% nickel and about 0.11% carbon.

In the AISI system, most stainless steels carry three-digit numbers (such as 302, 347, etc.). The same three digits are used in the current SAE system, but are preceded by "30", in the case of the non-hardenable nickel-chromium alloys, or by "50", for the hardenable alloys. Thus "AISI 304" refers to the same composition designated by SAE as "30304".

ASTM Specifications

AISI and SAE specification numbers always relate to the chemical composition of steels, with prefix or suffix letters used for special distinctions. (For example, the AISI system provides for prefix letters to indicate the type of furnace in which the steel is manufactured; "B" for basic open-hearth, "E" for electric, etc.) An entirely different series of specifications is published by the American Society for Testing and Materials (ASTM).

An ASTM steel specification usually covers steel in a particular form (sheet, plate, pipe, tube, forging, casting, etc.). (For example, ASTM Specification A 210 covers "Seamless Medium-Carbon Steel Boiler and Superheater Tubes".) It may cr may not cover chemical composition. When it does not cover composition specifically, the purchaser then specifies composition by reference to SAE or AISI grade. An ASTM specification typically covers such things as test requirements, forming operations, marking, packaging, etc. It may be cross-referenced to several other ASTM specifications. The system appears complex, but is extremely useful to industry. All ASTM specifications applying to steel start with the letter "A", followed by three digits. The complete specification number also includes two additional digits at the end (as in "A 210-73") which indicate the year in which the specification was issued or revised. In the 1974 "Annual Book of ASTM Standards", steel specifications alone (5 volumes out of a total of 47) ran to about 3000 pages!

Rimmed vs. Killed Steel

Some low-carbon steels are available in three grades: "rimmed", "semi-killed", and "fully-killed". The terms themselves are derived from the action of the steel when it is poured into an ingot mold after leaving the furnace. In terms of welding, they indicate whether or not there is oxygen in the steel which may cause weld porosity when certain welding processes are used. *All* carbon steels contain some oxygen. The very nature of the furnaces in which they are made makes this inevitable. It's what happens to the oxygen when a weld is made that is significant. When a rimmed steel is welded, some of the oxygen will usually combine with some of the carbon to form bubbles of carbon monoxide (CO). These will cause weld porosity if they cannot escape from the molten weld metal before it solidifies. In oxyacetylene welding, these minute bubbles of gas always have time to escape. In some other processes, such as tig welding (GTAW), however, they may be trapped in the solidified metal. To make a killed steel, aluminum (which has a stronger affinity for oxygen than carbon, manganese, or silicon) is added to the molten steel before it is poured. The aluminum locks up the oxygen, in the form of aluminum oxide, so that it cannot form gas bubbles during welding. In a semi-killed steel, silicon may have been used, with or without aluminum, as a deoxidizing addition, and there may be some bubbles of carbon monoxide gas formed during welding.

QUESTIONS – CHAPTER 11

1. How are the carbon steels classified?
2. What is an alloy steel? What are some of the major elements used for alloying purposes?
3. What is the difference between the AISI and the SAE numbering systems?
4. What does each digit indicate in the AISI and SAE systems?
5. What does the ASTM system cover?

EXPANSION AND CONTRACTION

All metals expand when heated, contract when cooled. Put a steel bar into a furnace and heat it up to a temperature of 500°C. It will get longer. Take it out and cool it. It will return to its original length. Further, if you can find a way to precisely measure the width of the bar while it is hot, and again while it is cold, you'll find that width also increased during the heating process. To put it another way, expansion and contraction are "three-dimensional". If the length of the bar increased one per cent, both dimensions of the cross-section increased one per cent.

Now suppose that this steel bar, instead of being placed in a furnace so that it could expand in all directions, is mounted between two immovable objects, such as two five-ton blocks of granite, and then heated with a torch until the center of the bar reaches a temperature of 500°C. The granite blocks will effectively keep it from getting longer as it heats up. As a result, it will get "fatter" than it would had it been free to increase in length. In fact, if the bar is now allowed to cool down to its original temperature, it may wind up a bit shorter than it was at the start, and also a bit "fatter".

Let's try one more example to show what can happen if normal three-dimensional expansion or contraction is restrained. Take a steel rod exactly five feet long, and heat it up to 500°C or so with no restraint on its movement. Then, while it is hot, clamp the ends in some way so that the bar can't get shorter as it cools. Let it cool down. Then measure it. You'll find that it's a bit longer than five feet, and, somewhere along its length, a bit "skinnier".

These are key points to remember about expansion and contraction: First, that changes in dimension, if there is no restraint, will be of the same proportion in all directions. Second, that if restraining forces prevent a change in one dimension, changes in other dimensions will be greater, and often *permanent*.

In welding operations, the "three-dimensional" forces of expansion and contraction are seldom unrestrained. Heating and cooling are usually more-or-less localized. You generally apply heat to an *edge*, not to the entire piece of metal. While the conductivity of the metal will carry heat away from the edge and back into the body of the part, the edge will reach a temperature of well over 1000°C (in the case of steel) while the metal only a few inches away from the edge may be heated only to 300°C. The cooler metal acts as a restraint to prevent *uniform* increase in dimensions of the hot section. When welding has been completed, and the metal is cooling, the cooler section acts as a restraint against uniform contraction of the metal in, or close to, the weld itself. Let's explore some of the practical aspects of this problem.

Expansion and Contraction in Sheet Metal

If we take a piece of sheet metal and rapidly heat it with a torch along one edge, that edge will get "wavy", as illustrated, with exaggeration, in Fig. 12-1. Why? Because the cooler metal away from the edge will not expand as much as the edge itself, which therefore can increase in length only by "buckling" a bit. If we then allow the piece to cool down, most of the "buckling" will disappear. However, if the edge is carefully measured before heating and after cooling, it will be found that it has shortened a trifle. During the period of expansion, there was some thickening, or "upsetting" of the metal in the edge, in addition to the buckling.

As a practical matter, the upsetting of the metal at the very edge, and the slight decrease in edge length, are of little significance. The buckling, however, can create major problems, with respect to both the welding operation and to the appearance or utility of the finished product. In production operations, when it is essential that the finished weld be perfectly flat, the usual procedure (regardless of the welding process used) is to clamp the metal so firmly, and so close to the actual weld zone, that only "upsetting" can take place, with all other movement of the pieces completely restrained. We'll be talking more about that subject in Chapter 13.

For another example of the effects of restrained expansion and contraction in sheet metal, look at Fig. 12-2. Here a piece of sheet has been cut

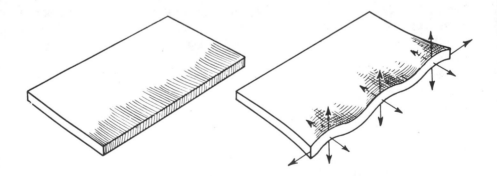

Fig. 12-1. When the edge of a piece of sheet steel is heated, expansion will cause the hot edge to warp or wave. (The effect shown here is much exaggerated). After cooling, however, the heated edge, is likely to be a bit shorter than it was originally.

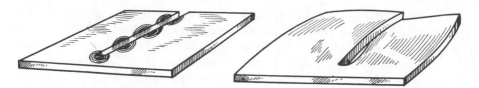

Fig. 12-2. Because of what may be termed the "hinge effect", heating and cooling will tend to close the gap between parts unless some method is provided to prevent that from happening.

nearly in two by a slit. Then (as in A) spots along the edges of the slit are heated rapidly, with a torch. Not too much seems to happen. The cold part of the metal restricts any general expansion, so that the forces tend merely to "upset", or thicken the edges, at the spots most strongly heated. However, when the piece is allowed to cool, the slit closes at its open end, and one end may even slide past the other, as indicated in B. The forces of contraction, rather than eliminating the "upsetting" that took place during the heating, have shortened both sides of the slit, and the metal in the uncut end of the sheet has had sufficient elasticity to allow it to act as a hinge. The point we'd like to make is this: that what happens during the cooling period is seldom the reverse of what happens during the expansion period.

Expansion and Contraction in Welded Joints

In welding, we must consider both the expansion and contraction in the parts being welded together, and the contraction which takes place, as it cools, in the metal actually melted during the operation. Usually, the latter is the more significant. The weld metal will always tend to shrink. In a simple "V" joint between two small pieces of steel, unrestrained, as illustrated in Fig. 12-3, there will be both bending and shrinkage. If we clamp the two pieces firmly to prevent bending, one of two things will result. Either the weld will crack, across the top, as it cools, or bending will occur (although to a more limited degree) as soon as the clamping force is released. In ordinary steels, which have a great deal of ductility, cracking will seldom occur, but some bending cannot be avoided.

Fig. 12-3. Because there is more hot metal at the top of a single-V weld than at the root, distortion is likely to occur when the metal cools.

Look now at Fig. 12-4, which represents a simple fillet weld between two pieces of steel. Here we wind up with a change in the angle between the pieces and a bend in one of the pieces. If we now make a weld on the other side, the error in angle will be largely corrected after cooling, but the bend in the bottom piece will almost certainly be increased.

In both Figs. 12-3 and 12-4, the effects produced by contraction have been exaggerated somewhat. As a practical matter, the amount of distortion will depend on several factors, including the skill of the operator and the speed with which he welds. Further, it should be evident that when we are dealing with two small pieces of steel, and can anticipate the amount of distortion likely to occur, we can take steps in advance to "nullify" the distortion. In the simple "V" joint, we can start with the surfaces of two pieces at a slight angle, rather than in the same plane (that is, perfectly flat). In the case of the fillet joint, we can pre-bend the bottom piece along the line of the future joint, and position the vertical piece at something other than a 90-deg. angle before we start the weld.

Let's look at a more practical example of how we can counteract the effect of weld contraction by anticipating it. Fig. 12-5(A) represents a rather odd-shaped piece of steel which has cracked in the middle. We've opened up the crack so that we can weld it properly. If we now make the weld and let it cool, the whole piece will be distorted, as indicated with exaggeration in sketch B. However, if before or during the welding operation, we heated the centers of both the other spans cherry red with heating torches, as indicated in sketch C, we could eliminate most or all of the final distortion. Another way to counterpart the distortion would be to place a jack parallel to the center span before we started to weld, and operate the jack to increase the opening in the weld area, while distorting the rest of the unit. If, immediately after welding, we slacked off the jack, we might again wind up with a minimum of distortion in the completed job.

In itself, Fig. 12-5 isn't a very practical example. But it illustrates a principle. Superimpose the outline of that part on the outline of a huge cracked gear, as in Fig. 12-6, and see how the principle might be applied to a real-life repair job. If it is necessary to weld one of the spokes in this gear, you must be sure to preheat certain sections strongly before you weld, assuming it is

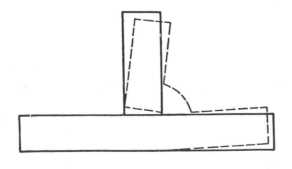

Fig. 12-4. In tee or fillet welds, distortion similar to that shown here in exaggerated form will usually result.

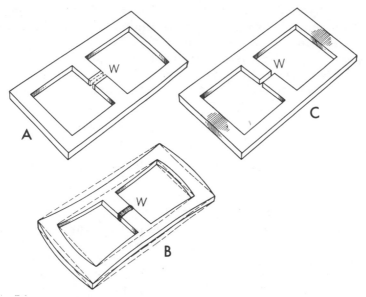

Fig. 12-5. Use of heat to counteract distortion due to weld contraction. If the crack shown in (A) is welded without preheating, the result will be a warped part, as indicated in (B). But if the parallel sections are strongly preheated before welding starts, as indicated in (C), distortion should be negligible.

Fig 12-6. Illustrating a way in which the principles sketched In Fig. 12-5 might be applied to welding a cracked spoke in a large gear.

not feasible to preheat the entire gear to a rather high temperature. If you don't, you'll wind up with a cracked weld (quite likely in this case), or a cracked gear, or an out-of-round gear.

There are other ways to minimize or eliminate distortion. When two thick plates must be joined, weld from both sides (a double-V joint) instead of from only one. In fillet welding, weld a little on one side, then a little on the other, then a little more on the first, etc.

Residual Stress

We said that the weld metal always *tends* to shrink. If the sections being joined are locked into a structure so securely that they cannot move during the welding period, or during the cooling-down period, what happens? The weld metal stretches while it is cooling. Steel, at elevated temperatures, is quite ductile, so it can stretch quite a lot. (Cast iron, which is not very ductile, would probably crack.) Most of that stretch will represent *permanent deformation*. But some of that stretch will take place within the *elastic limit*. It is stretch that would disappear if the structural forces restraining the welded joint should suddenly be released. In place of that theoretical stretch, we have a "residual" or "locked-up" stress. That sounds alarming. Don't let it worry you too much. Almost all welded structures contain residual stresses. Unless a residual stress in one section tends to reinforce the residual stress in another section, it's not likely to cause trouble. When it seems necessary to get rid of residual stresses of considerable magnitude, they can be largely eliminated by post-heating the entire assembly, or the weld zone, and allowing it to cool slowly.

In modern welding practice, residual stresses are often minimized by using "multi-pass" instead of "single-pass" welds in heavy sections. Each pass eliminates or reduces the residual stress created by previous passes.

Coefficient of Thermal Expansion

All metals expand when heated, but not to the same degree. The measure of expansion is termed the *coefficient of thermal expansion*. Most steels have a coefficient of about 0.000011 per degree Celsius. In metric terms, that means that an unrestrained steel bar, one metre long, will increase in length 11 millionths of a metre, or 11 thousandths of a millimetre, for each 1 degree C rise in temperature. A temperature rise of 1000°C will cause a one-metre bar to increase 11 mm in length. In "English" measure, you can calculate that a one-foot steel bar will increase in length about 1/8 inch when heated 1000°C.

Thermal Conductivity

Some metals are much better conductors of heat than others. The *thermal conductivity* of copper is eight times that of carbon steel; some stainless steels have only one-fourth the conductivity of carbon steel. In practical terms, this means that if you weld copper, the metal four inches away from the weld zone will get much hotter than it would if the material were carbon steel. If you weld stainless steel, the metal four inches from the weld zone will not get as hot as it would if the material were carbon steel. Since the degree of expansion, or internal stress created when expansion is restrained, depends on temperature rise, thermal conductivity has a very real bearing on the "expansion-contraction" problem. The differences between steel, copper, and aluminum need not concern the oxy-acetylene welder greatly, since he is likely to weld carbon steels most of the time, and all carbon steels have about the same coefficient of expansion and about the same rate of heat conductivity. However, the variation between different metals with respect to these two temperature-related properties, and the substantial differences between metals in their strength at elevated temperatures, are matters of considerable significance to the welding engineer, especially in the design of fixtures for mechanized welding.

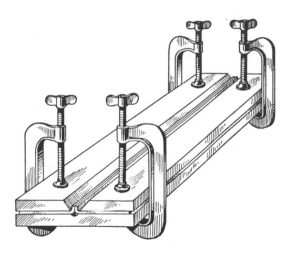

Fig. 12-7. Here is a simple jig which can be constructed from pieces of steel plate and several C-clamps to permit making either a butt weld or a flange weld in sheet steel without undesirable distortion. Note the groove in the bottom plate, provided to eliminate the possibility of welding the sheet metal to the jig. With a jig like this, there is no need to make tack welds, or to provide extra space between the parts at the finishing end of the seam, both of which must be done when unjigged pieces are to be welded (as directed in Chapter 14, which follows.)

QUESTIONS – CHAPTER 12

1. If a part is freely supported and uniformly heated and then cooled, does the amount of expansion upon heating equal the amount of contraction upon cooling?
2. If thermal expansion is prevented or reduced along one or two axes of a specimen, what will be true of the expansion along the remaining axes or axis?
3. If expansion is restrained along one axis of a specimen uniformly heated, what change in shape of the part will result upon uniform cooling?
4. What distortion occurs when the edge of a piece of sheet metal is heated?
5. How can the waviness often produced in sheet metal be avoided?
6. What may happen if a strip in a heavy mass of metal is heated to a high temperature and then allowed to cool?
7. What distortion occurs when a single-vee weld is made in plate material?
8. How can the distortion in a single-vee weld be corrected?
9. What causes the gap between sheet metal parts to close before welding is completed?
10. What is upsetting?
11. How can uneven heating and cooling be used to correct distortion?
12. What is the most important metal property from a standpoint of expansion and contraction effects?
13. What importance does the coefficient of thermal expansion have in welding?
14. Of what importance in welding is the rate of heat conduction?
15. What is the coefficient of thermal conductivity?
16. How can the welding operator use tables of coefficients of thermal expansion and thermal conductivity to advantage?

PREPARATION FOR WELDING

In the broadest sense, "preparation for welding" would include the design of a structure — deciding where the welds should be placed, what type of joint design should be used for each weldment, and what sequence should be followed in making the welds. However, full treatment of structural design for welding is beyond the scope of this book; moreover, oxy-acetylene welding is seldom used for all the welds in a *structure*, other than by the hobbyist or home craftsman. This chapter will thus be limited to describing different *configurations* of welded joints, methods for *shaping and cleaning* the edges of the parts to be welded, and ways in which the parts to be joined can be *preheated*, when such preheating is required.

Joint Configurations

Square Butt Welds. The simplest of all joint designs is the square butt weld, in which pieces with squared edges are merely brought quite close together, as illustrated in Fig. 13-1. In the oxy-acetylene welding of steel, the square butt weld can be used with material as thin as about 20-gauge (0.04 in. or 1 mm) sheet to as thick as 3/16-in. (5 mm) plate. (By trade prac-

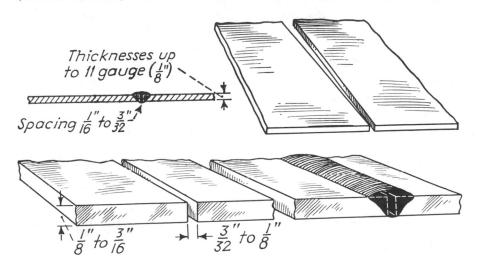

Fig. 13-1. Square butt weld specifications for sheet steel or thin plate.

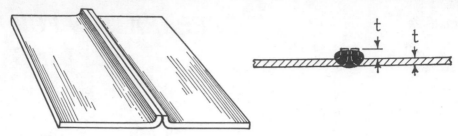

Fig. 13-2. The flange weld for sheet metal. When it is possible to flange the metal, this is the ideal way to make full-strength welds in thin sheet. (See Fig. 12-7 for a jig which can be used with this design.)

tice, rolled metal in thicknesses up to ⅛-in. is termed "sheet"; in thicknesses above ⅛-in. it is termed "plate".) Filler metal, in the form of welding rod, is almost always used in making square butt welds. It is seldom possible to make a satisfactory, full-strength weld by merely butting the pieces tight together, without spacing, and then melting the edges together.

Flange Welds. A simple way of making a variant of the butt weld in sheet steel is to roll up, or flange, the edges of the pieces to be joined, as shown in Fig. 13-2. The thinner the sheet, the easier it is to flange the edges, and the more useful this design becomes. Using this joint design, a skilled operator can make good welds in sheet thinner than 20-gauge. Further, the rolled edges, which are melted during the welding, eliminate the need for using filler metal. The height of the flange should normally be about the same as the thickness of the sheet, or slightly greater.

Lap Welds. The lap weld, single or double (as illustrated in Fig. 13-3), is not recommended for oxy-acetylene welding. The single lap weld is not a strong weld. While the double lap weld has more strength, it is certainly no better than a single butt weld, properly made, and requires twice the time and twice the filler metal needed for the butt weld. The double lap weld is sometimes used in arc welding sheet with covered electrodes because of the difficulty of making good butt welds in thin sheet with that process.

Single-V Butt Welds. To weld steel plate in thicknesses above ³⁄₁₆-in. (0.5 cm), and up to about ½-in. (1.2 cm), the single-V butt weld, shown in Fig. 13-4, is used both in oxy-acetylene welding and in most electric welding processes. The plate edges are beveled to form an included angle of between 50 and 90 degrees. Filler metal is always required. The beveled edges should normally be squared off a bit at the bottom to produce a "nose", as shown,

Fig. 13-3. The single lap weld (left) and double lap weld (right). For oxy-acetylene welding, the square butt weld or single-V is almost always preferred to the lap weld.

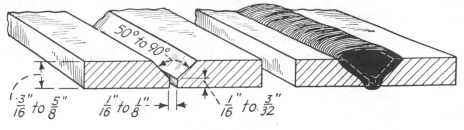

Single-V Butt Weld

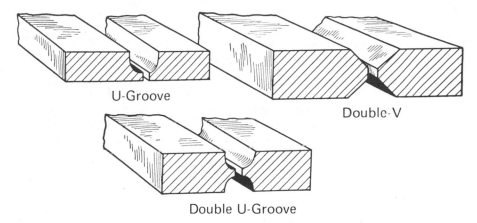

U-Groove

Double-V

Double U-Groove

Fig. 13-4. The single-V butt weld is used almost exclusively for all oxy-acetylene welds in metals thicker than 1/8-3/16 in. (3-5 mm). The square nose at the base of the V is not always required. The double-V and U-groove joint designs are frequently used for electric welding of material thicker than 1/2 in. (12 mm).

although a skilled operator can often work without the nose if the beveling has been properly performed. The included angle should be held to less than 90 degrees whenever feasible, since with a smaller angle less filler metal is needed and welding speed can be greater. The ideal included angle for carbon steel is about 65 degrees.

Other Butt Weld Designs. To familiarize you with terminology, several other butt weld designs are illustrated in Fig. 13-4. These are usually applied only to plate thicker than 1/2-in., and are almost never used for the range of work likely to be done with the oxy-acetylene torch.

Fillet Welds. Fillet welds, as illustrated in Fig. 13-5, are seldom made by oxy-acetylene welding today, although a great deal of fillet welding is performed, especially in construction work, by various arc welding processes. You can make a fillet weld with the gas torch, but it is well to steer clear of the design if possible.

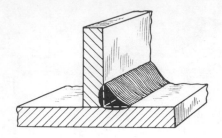

Fig. 13-5. The fillet weld, widely employed in electric arc welding, is seldom executed with the oxy-acetylene torch. The double fillet has a weld on each side of the upright member.

Corner Welds. There are several ways to make a corner joint, each of which is similar to one of the other joint types previously described. These are illustrated in Fig. 13-6. If the metal is thick enough to allow it, the design which is equivalent to the 90-deg. single-V butt joint is probably the best.

Shaping and Cleaning Edges

For square butt welds, no cutting or beveling is required, as long as the edges of the two pieces are reasonably straight, so that there will not be variations in spacing of a degree which will cause difficulty during the actual welding. The edges need not be perfectly square. They can be cut with shears, or with the oxy-acetylene cutting torch.

Flanging the edges of sheet metal is easy enough if the pieces are small, and you have a large vise in which to hold them. However, flanging the edges of large pieces will usually call for specialized forming equipment, or considerable ability to improvise.

Beveling of edges for single-V butt welds can be done mechanically or with the oxy-acetylene cutting torch. On steel plate, mechanized oxygen cutting, followed by grinding to form the "nose" (if required) and to remove ox-

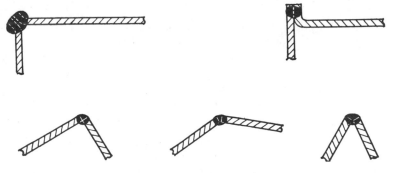

Fig. 13-6. Several ways to make corner welds. The two examples at the top are essentially flange welds; the lower examples are all variations of the single-V weld.

ides, is probably the most effective and economical method. With reasonable care and skill, steel can also be beveled by hand torch cutting. With cast iron, it will be found difficult to get a reasonably accurate job with the oxygen cutting torch, although a skilled operator may be able to do it. Grinding, followed by filing or wire-brushing, is usually preferred.

Regardless of the method used for cutting or forming the edges of the pieces to be welded, cleaning before welding should never be overlooked. All traces of paint, grease, or loose dirt should be removed. A wire brush usually will do the trick. If the edges have been oxygen-cut, all bits of adhering slag should be knocked off, chipped off, or ground off. Heavy grinding to remove all traces of oxide from oxygen-cut edges is not necessary, however.

Preheating

While preheating is seldom necessary in the oxy-acetylene welding of steel, other than a light amount with the same torch which will be used to do the welding, it is usually essential in the welding of cast iron. Steel castings may also require preheating, not so much to avoid cracking as to limit the amount of distortion which might take place due to uneven heating and cooling.

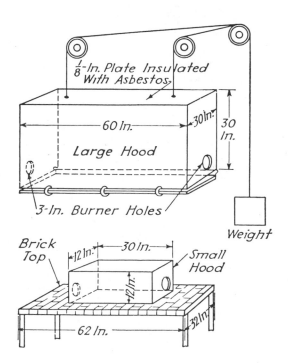

Fig. 13-7. Here are two ideas for hoods which can be fabricated in the shop for use in preheating castings before welding.

There are several methods of preheating; the choice will depend on many factors, including the size and shape of the part, cost of fuel, and the need for slowest possible cooling after welding has been completed. Many types of *preheating torches* are available which burn relatively inexpensive fuels such as kerosene or natural gas. They can be used for local preheating on large castings, or for general heating of smaller pieces under a hood such as illustrated in Fig. 13-7. It is not too difficult to build a temporary preheating furnace of firebrick, as shown in Fig 13-8. Such a furnace is best heated with charcoal. If the casting is properly positioned in the furnace, welding can be done without removing it from the furnace, and it can be allowed to cool slowly, under an asbestos paper cover, after welding.

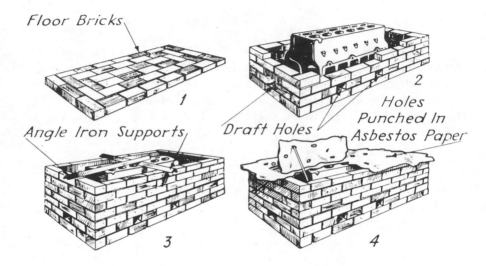

Fig. 13-8. How to construct a temporary preheating furnace out of loose fire brick and asbestos paper.

QUESTIONS – CHAPTER 13

1. In general, what thicknesses of metal are considered sheet?
2. What are the fundamental joint designs used in welding sheet metal? Plates?
3. To what height are the edges turned up for the flange-type joint design?
4. What thickness of material is usually considered plate?
5. Why must plate material be beveled for welding?
6. What is the maximum thickness of plate material that can be welded without beveling?
7. What is a fillet weld?
8. In what ways can preheating be done?
9. What fuels are frequently used for preheating?

CHAPTER

14*   *WELDING CARBON STEEL*

Low-carbon mild steel is not only the most widely used metal; it is also the easiest to weld. Although most steel welding is done today with coated electrodes, or by one of the consumable-wire arc welding processes, oxy-acetylene welding of steel, especially in thicknesses of ¼ in. (6 mm) or less, is still widely employed. A well-trained oxy-acetylene welder, working on steel ⅛ in. (3 mm) thick, can usually make welds of better quality than can the average arc welder, and make them almost as rapidly.

Once you have mastered the art of welding steel, you are ready to tackle some of the metals which are more difficult to weld. Steel should always be the starting point.

In this chapter, the specific instructions for welding will be given in the form of captions accompanying Fig. 14-1 through 14-19. Fig. 14-1 through 14-4 deal with welding of sheet, Fig. 14-5 through 14-12 with the welding of plate, Fig. 14-13 through 14-19 with the welding of pipe. If you are teaching yourself to weld from this book, without the aid of a good instructor, we urge you to work your way through Fig. 14-12, in sequence, then decide whether or not you wish to tackle pipe. However, if you are definitely interested in learning to weld steel pipe, and feel that you are doing well after getting through Fig. 14-6, you may properly skip from Fig. 14-6 to Fig. 14-13, assuming that you can secure an adequate supply of properly-bevelled pipe, 2 to 4 in. in diameter.

---

*In previous editions of this Handbook, the welding of steel sheet, steel plate, and steel pipe were covered in separate chapters. For two reasons, we have elected to treat the welding of steel in one continuous chapter in this edition. The first is this: In previous editions, the technique of flame and rod movement recommended for welding sheet was quite different from that recommended for welding plate and pipe. That technique is still valid, especially for the welding of the thinnest sheet (less than ¹/₁₆ in., or 16-gauge), and will be covered at the close of this chapter. In most situations, however, the same technique used for welding plate and pipe can be used for welding sheet, and it is easier to master. The second reason concerns pipe welding: Earlier editions of the Handbook treated pipe welding chiefly in terms of rather large-diameter pipe, which is seldom oxy-acetylene welded today. Oxy-acetylene welding of pipe is today largely restricted to pipe sizes ranging from ¹/₂ in. to 4 in. The technique used for welding pipe in those sizes is essentially no different than that used for welding plate or sheet of equivalent thickness.

Equipment and Material Requirements

Equipment: To do all the work covered in this chapter, you need a complete welding and cutting outfit, as described at the start of Chapter 5. At least two or three different welding heads (tips) are needed. For welding $1/16$-in. sheet, you need one which is rated to consume about 4 cfh (cubic feet per hour) of each gas. For welding $1/8$-in. steel, a head one or two sizes larger (consuming 6-9 cfh) is needed; this size will also be suitable for 2-in. or smaller pipe. For welding $1/4$-in. plate, or 4-in. pipe, a head rated to consume 15 cfh of each gas is recommended. For bevelling plate or pipe with your torch, a cutting nozzle with cutting oxygen orifice drill size 60 or a little smaller is recommended. In addition, you need a suitable welding table (slotted cast iron or fire brick top), some C-clamps, and pliers or tongs for handling hot metal. For pipe-welding practice, two useful work-holding devices which you can make for yourself are pictured in Fig. 14-20.

Materials: For practice on sheet steel, we recommend that you secure several pieces of sheet, at least 4 in. by 4 in. (10 cm by 10 cm) in size, and not thinner than 16 gauge ($1/16$ in. or 1.5 mm). (Sheet as thick as $1/8$ in. will also be satisfactory.) For practice on plate, several pieces 6 x 9 in. (15 x 22 cm), about $1/4$-in. (6 mm) thick, are suggested. For pipe welding practice, we suggest short lengths (or one length, 4-6 feet, which you can cut yourself) of standard (Schedule 40) seamless steel pipe, 2 in. to 4 in. diameter. (The larger size is preferable, if you can secure it.)

You will also need a supply of steel welding rod. For sheet metal practice, $1/16$-in. diameter rod is suggested. For plate and pipe welding, either $1/8$-in. or $3/32$-in. diameter rod will be satisfactory. Two types of steel rod which will serve your purposes are generally available. One is sometimes termed "drawn iron" because it is more than 99% iron; it falls into A.W.S. Class RG45. (OXWELD No. 7 rod is an example of this type.) The other is usually designated as "No. 1 HT", contains about one per cent manganese, and falls into A.W.S. Class RG60.

General Instructions

Flame Adjustment: All the work described in this chapter should be done with the *neutral* oxy-acetylene flame. To secure a neutral flame, always start with an excess of acetylene, then increase the flow of oxygen (or decrease the flow of acetylene) until the excess acetylene feather just disappears. Check flame adjustment frequently. An excess of acetylene is easy to spot, but an excess of oxygen is not always evident to the eye, although it will usually cause the molten metal to spark excessively.

When starting steel welding practice, do not use the strongest flame which your welding head can produce. (The strongest flame is the one which would separate slightly from the tip if the flow of each gas were increased only slightly.) Use the regulator delivery pressures recommended by the maker of your torch for the tip size in use, but do not hesitate to cut back the flame length slightly by adjustment of the torch throttle valves. Too *harsh* a flame will make it hard for you to control the weld puddle until you have acquired some skill. Better to have a flame which is a bit too *soft* than one which is too *harsh*. You will not be able to weld as fast, but you will have better control. Experiment with flame size as you move along, but start out on the soft side.

Welding Positions: The four primary positions, as shown in the various sketches which follow, are described as:

Flat — Surfaces of the work lie in a plane parallel to the ground.

Vertical — Both the surfaces of the work and the line of the weld are perpendicular to the ground.

Horizontal — The surfaces of the work are perpendicular to the ground, but the weld line is parallel to the ground.

Overhead — Same as flat, except that welding is performed from below the work rather than above it.

In pipe welding, if the axis of the pipe is vertical, the welding is done in the *horizontal* position; if the axis of the sections is horizontal, and the pipe cannot be rotated as the welding proceeds, a single weld involves the *flat, vertical,* and *overhead* positions, as defined above. In the piping trade, however, joint positions are officially described in terms of the pipe direction; thus, what a pipe man may term a "vertical" position calls for welding in the *horizontal* position.

Forehand and Backhand Techniques. For a right-handed operator, *forehand* welding means that the welding proceeds from right to left, when working in the flat or horizontal positions. (The left-handed operator will do forehand welding from left to right). The flame is angled toward the unfinished end of the weld, the filler rod is angled toward the completed section. *Backhand* welding is the opposite of forehand. The right-handed operator works from left to right, with the flame angled toward the comleted portion, the rod angled toward the unfinished end. Most oxy-acetylene welding is done by the forehand method. There are times when backhand welding may be used effectively, but beginners should stick to forehand welding until they have mastered it. (For more about backhand technique, see the caption for Fig. 14-8.)

Flame and Rod Motions. If you watch an experienced oxy-acetylene welder at this work, perhaps the first thing you will notice is that he keeps both the flame and the end of his filler rod in almost constant motion. The flame moves back and forth across the line of the weld, edging forward almost imperceptibly. The end of the rod moves back and forth too, from one side of the puddle to the other. However, the motion of the rod is opposite to the motion of the flame, and often less pronounced. The inner cone of the flame is not pointed directly at the rod for more than a small fraction of each cycle. The neat little ripples that form on the surface of the solidified weld metal are in large part the result of puddle movement generated by the rod. You will also note that if the welder withdraws the end of the rod from the puddle momentarily, he does not draw it away from the puddle very far, but keeps it within the outer envelope of the flame.

Flame and Rod Angles. In the sketches which follow, we have tried to indicate, as clearly as possible, the relative angles of the flame and rod with respect to the work. The sketches were made by a skilled artist, observing a skilled welder. The captions for the sketches, especially those covering welding in positions other than flat, will have more to say about flame and rod angles.

Puddle Control. One of the nice things about carbon steel is the fact that it has a melting point *range,* not a fixed melting point. At temperatures within that range (approximately 1400-1435°C) molten steel has a pasty or mushy consistency and is quite easy to control. The welder's aim must be to hold the molten steel within that range. If he does his work correctly, he adds heat to the puddle with the flame, withdraws heat from the puddle with the filler metal rod. While it may seem a bit far-fetched to describe the operation in this way, he has a *heating* device in one hand, a *cooling* device in the other.

Flame-to-Work Distance. As a general rule, the tip of the flame's inner cone should be kept about 1/8 in. (3 mm) from the surface of the work piece or weld puddle. Try to maintain that separation as well as you can, especially during your first practice sessions. As you gain experience, you will find that there are times when you can deliberately break that rule, to let the flame "dig in" to the puddle for a specific purpose, or to hold the flame farther from the work in order to weld a bit more slowly in a difficult position.

When the Rod Freezes to the Work. Until you gain good control over the motion of the welding rod, it is almost certain that at some point the end of the rod will "freeze" to the workpiece because it entered the very edge of the puddle, not the center of the puddle. When that happens, resist the impulse to pull it loose. Pulling simply won't help. *Melt* it loose with the flame.

Put a Bend in the Rod. For work in most welding positions, it is desirable to put a bend in the welding rod before you start work. Heat up a spot on the rod, about 8 in. from the end, and bend it by stubbing the end against the work table or the work itself. Bending the rod will generally give you better control, and keep your rod hand out of the path of hot air downstream of the flame. The angle of bend depends on welding position and personal preference. For work in some positions (see Figs. 14-10 and 14-11) the bend is not required or helpful.

Eliminating Stub Ends. The arc welder, using stick electrodes, must discard part of each electrode. The economical oxy-acetylene welder can eliminate "stub ends" almost completely. When a length of rod gets too short for comfort, he can weld on another full length immediately (see Fig. 14-11) or he can set the short piece aside, and later weld it to other short pieces to make up another full length of useful rod.(text continued on page 142)

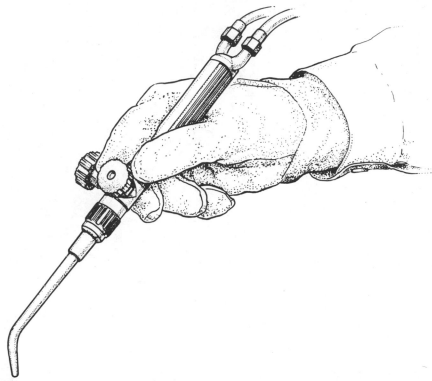

Fig. 14-1. First find a way to hold your torch comfortably with good control over tip movement. If you have a small torch, with valves at the front end of the handle, holding it much as if it were a large pencil is a good idea. With a larger torch which has valves at the rear end of the handle, you will probably find it necessary to modify this grip somewhat. Try to find a way to support the hose so that it interferes with free torch movement as little as possible. Some welders bring the hose over their right shoulder.

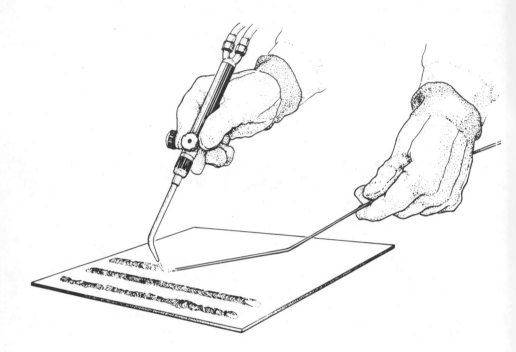

Fig. 14-2. Running a bead of weld metal across the surface of sheet steel. Before trying this, light the torch and practice running a puddle across the sheet without using welding rod. Start by holding the torch still, with the inner cone of the flame about 1/8 in. (3 mm) from the surface of the metal, until a small pool of molten metal has formed. Then start to move the flame back and forth in a series of short arcs or semi-circles, advancing the puddle as steadily as possible from right to left. You may find it difficult to avoid melting a hole through the sheet. If necessary, cut back on flame size, increase clearance between inner cone and work, or move puddle forward at a faster rate. Practice until you can run a reasonably uniform bead for a distance of several inches.

Now take a length of 1/16-in. welding rod and try to do what the operator in this sketch is doing. Bend the rod so that you can hold it comfortably. Keep the end of the rod within the outer envelope of the flame, but about a half-inch from the inner cone, until you have formed a puddle with the flame. Move the rod into the puddle enough to melt off a drop or two of metal. Withdraw the rod slightly, advance the puddle again. Repeat this sequence until you have crossed the sheet. Try again, and yet again, until you can run a bead which stands above the sheet surface for its full length, and is quite uniform in width. Experiment with rod and flame angles; those indicated in the sketch may not be best for you. When you melt a hole through the sheet, practice filling in that hole by adding filler metal, a bit at a time, first to one side and then to the other side, until the gap has been bridged.

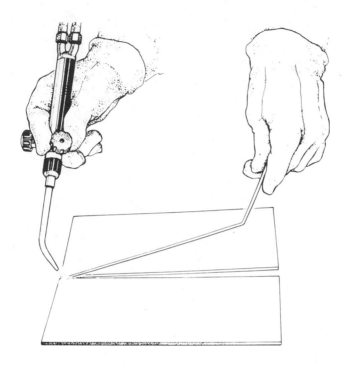

Fig. 14-3. Place two pieces of sheet side by side on the work table, spacing them 1/16 in. (1.5 mm) apart at the weld starting end, 3/16 in. (5 mm) at the other end. Make a tack weld at the starting end. Play the flame in small circles, heating each side evenly until first evidence of melting appears near the corners. Then add a little metal from the welding rod (already heated in the outer flame envelope) to bridge the gap. Do not build up the tack above the sheet surface. Allow the metal a few seconds to cool, then swing the pieces around so that you can make the finishing-end tack weld from the same position you used for the first tack. Because of the greater gap, the second tack-weld will be harder to make. A little metal must be added to each side, and allowed to cool slightly while the flame is directed toward the other side, before the gap can be bridged. After bridging the gap, make this tack-weld definitely larger than the first one.

Return sheets to original position. Melt a small puddle on top of the first tack-weld, add filler metal to build it up above the sheet surface. Start moving the flame back and forth, in a series of short arcs, adding filler metal regularly by moving the end of the rod into the puddle, then retracting it slightly. Advance the puddle with the flame as you move it back and forth across the joint line.

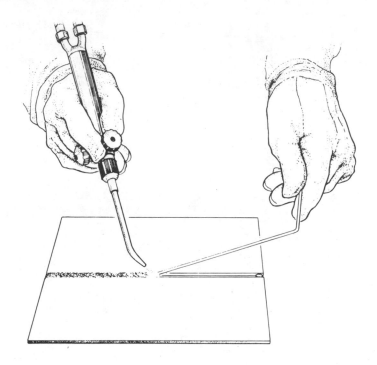

Fig. 14-4. Here we are at the middle of the weld. By now, it has become quite evident that making a weld between two pieces isn't as easy as running a bead across the surface. But a rhythm should be developing. You learn that the flame must linger a bit at each end of each arc, to avoid overheating the center of the puddle, and you get the feel for the timing of the movement of the rod in and out of the puddle. (Later, you will do work which calls for keeping the rod in the puddle at all times, but you can't do that with sheet metal.) In this first weld, do not worry too much about appearances. Try to avoid adding more filler metal than necessary to bridge the gap. The first aim should be to get complete fusion at the bottom of the weld. To achieve this, the metal ahead of the puddle must be brought to melting point before the puddle itself reaches it. That's not easy to accomplish without getting frequent burn-through.

After you have completed your first weld, turn the piece over and examine the bottom of the weld carefully. If it appears that you have achieved rather complete penetration (if you have, there will be a definite "droop" all the way along the weld line) make a second weld and pay more attention to the top surface. Keep at it until you make a weld that looks good on both top and bottom. Then test it (see Fig. 14-22).

If you are working on sheet that's thinner than ¹⁄₁₆ in., you may find it very difficult to avoid melt-through, or excessive sagging of the weld, when using the flame motion recommended at the start of this chapter. If that is the case, move forward in this chapter to Fig. 14-23, where a quite different (but more difficult) technique is described.

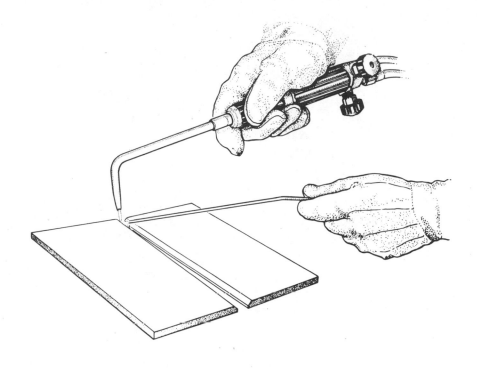

Fig. 14-5. Making the first tackweld between two pieces of ¼-in. steel plate. Each piece of plate should have a bevel of about 45 degrees, and the lower edges should be ground to produce square shoulders about ¹⁄₁₆ in. deep. (Later, when you have acquired more proficiency, edges can be bevelled to produce a smaller included angle—perhaps 60 degrees instead of 90 degrees—and the squared-off shoulders can be dispensed with, but at the start the 90-degree included angle and the squared-off lower edges are recommended.) Space the two pieces of plate, if they are about 9 in. long, so that they are separated by about ⅛ in. at the starting end, at least ³⁄₁₆ in. at the finishing end. Using ⅛-in. welding rod, make the starting-end tack much as you make it on sheet, heating both sides of the joint evenly until melting just starts, then carefully adding filler metal, a drop at a time, until the gap has been bridged. Do not build this tack up to the level of the plate surface. Allow it to cool for a few seconds, swing the pieces around with tongs or pliers, make the finishing-end tack, which, because of the greater gap between the plates, will take a bit more patience and care. Reverse the plates again, and start to make a root pass which will be only about one-half the thickness of the completed weld.

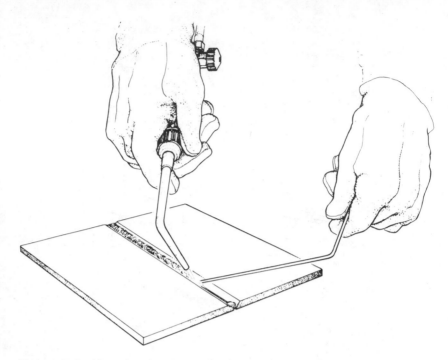

Fig. 14-6. At this point, the root pass is approaching completion. Note that the top corners of the two pieces are still sharp and unmelted. The objective of this first pass is complete root penetration, little else. The puddle can be kept relatively small, with attention largely directed toward making sure that the squared-off lower edges of each piece are brought to melting temperature before the puddle advances across them. Take care not to add too much filler metal at one time. Move the end of the rod in and out of the puddle as necessary to control the rate of filler metal addition. Move the flame back and forth across the joint in relatively short arcs, trying to melt the sides of the vee a bit more than half way to the top edges.

In recommending that you weld ¼-in. plate in two passes—a root pass and a finishing pass—we do not intend to rule out the possibility of making the weld in one pass. Many skilled welders prefer to weld steel of this thickness in a single pass. Others do it in what has been termed "layer welding sequence". They run a root pass for perhaps 2 in., then back up and finish off that section while the metal is still hot, then make another root pass section, and so on, until the weld has been completed.

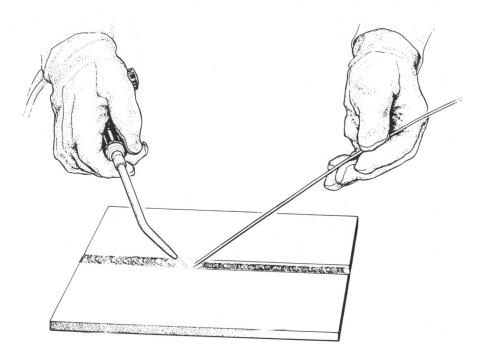

Fig. 14-7. This sketch shows the finishing pass in the same 1/4-in. plate joint. After completing the root pass, the welder has returned to the starting end, formed a new puddle, and proceeded to fill the joint completely. In making this pass, much more filler metal is required that in making the root pass. Try to keep the end of the rod in the puddle at all times, actually rubbing the end against the solid metal below the puddle, and keeping it in constant back-and-forth motion across the joint line. The flame must describe longer arcs than were needed for the root pass, and must linger briefly at each end of each arc to make sure that the top edges of the plates are actually melted before the puddle, which is being moved backward by the rod motion, can reach those edges. In making this pass, the filler rod is largely melted by heat transferred through the puddle, rather than directly by the flame. The motions of rod and flame must be carefully controlled, so that when the flame is concentrated on the left side of the joint, the rod is pushing the puddle on the right side. The arcs described by the flame need not be as wide as the arcs described by the end of the rod. If rod motion is insufficient, the weld will almost surely be "undercut"; that is, along each side of the completed weld there will be places where the weld metal has not reached the level of the plate surface.

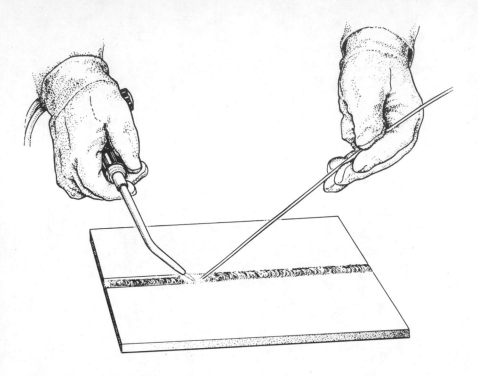

Fig. 14-8. At first glance, this sketch may appear to be a duplicate of the previous sketch. Look again, however, and you will see that this finishing pass is proceeding from right to left (as you look at the sketch) rather than from left to right. The operator is using backhand technique. The flame is angled toward the completed section of the weld, the rod is angled toward the finishing end. As noted in the text of this chapter, most oxy-acetylene welding is performed using the forehand technique shown in all the other illustrations, but some welders find backhand technique faster in certain situations. If you wish to try your hand at backhand welding, we suggest that you first deposit a root pass by forehand technique, then make a backhand finishing pass. You will find that motion of both rod and flame must be quite different that those which work best in forehand welding. Both must describe ovals along the weld line, with rod moving backward as the flame moves forward. The finished weld will have somewhat coarser ripples than a good forehand weld.

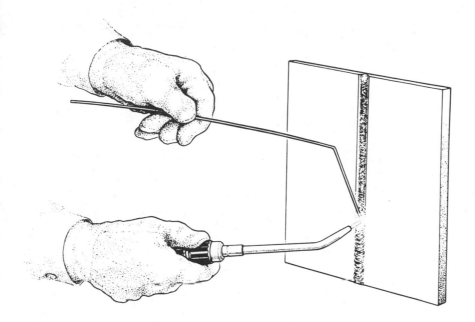

Fig. 14-9. This sketch shows welding in the vertical position. The operator is making a finishing pass, after completing the root pass. Vertical welding is not difficult once you have learned how to keep the weld puddle from "running away" under the force of gravity. Note that the flame-to-work angle is quite different from that illustrated previously. The flame must be directed so that the gas stream tends to push the puddle uphill. The puddle must be kept as small as possible. The key to making a vertical weld between two pieces of steel plate, as pictured here, lies in getting off to a good start. You must work rather slowly, adding filler metal a bit at a time, in order to build a starting "shelf" of solidified weld metal which will act as a support for the puddle. Once that has been accomplished, the balance of the weld should proceed smoothly if you don't try to rush the work and get too large or too fluid a puddle. Keep the puddle in the mushy or pasty state, never let it get "runny". In making the second pass, take especial care to move the puddle so that it fills the vee completely. It will probably be difficult to avoid some undercutting on the first attempt at a vertical weld.

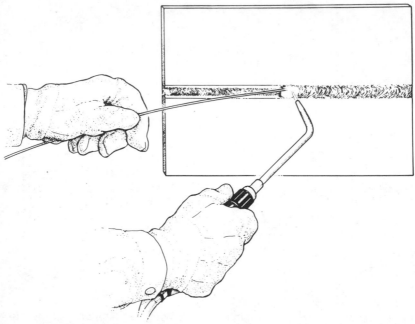

Fig. 14-10. Making the root pass in the horizontal position presents no particular problems if puddle size is held to a minimum. However, making the finishing pass requires a different technique than that used in the flat or vertical positions. The flame must move back and forth diagonally across the weld line to maintain a puddle which is also somewhat slanted across the line. The rod is added near the top of the puddle. The flame, as well as the rod, must play a part in pushing the puddle up in order to avoid undercutting at the upper edge of the weld. Therefore, it must be angled upward. As in vertical welding, the aim must be to maintain the puddle in the mushy or pasty state, not let it get so fluid that it will spill over and run down the lower piece of plate. Be careful not to melt the corner of the upper section any more than absolutely necessary to secure fusion. Considerable practice will be required to learn just the right way to direct the flame on the rod so as to supply enough metal for the upper part of the weld without letting the puddle get so large or fluid that it will run out of control.

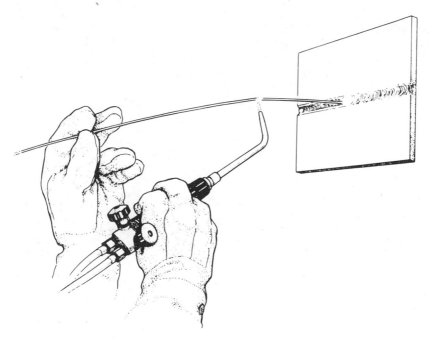

Fig. 14-11. Here's a good trick to learn. When your rod gets too short for comfortable manipulation, let it freeze in the puddle. Bring a fresh length up against the free end, and weld it to the short piece. Then reform the puddle, melting the rod free in the process of doing so, and continue your work. This works especially well in the horizontal position, as illustrated in this sketch, because in horizontal welding it is seldom necessary to put a bend in the rod in order to work comfortably, since both flame and rod are angled upward somewhat. However, you can do this in any position, first welding on the new piece of rod, then removing the bend in the original section and adding a bend in the new section.

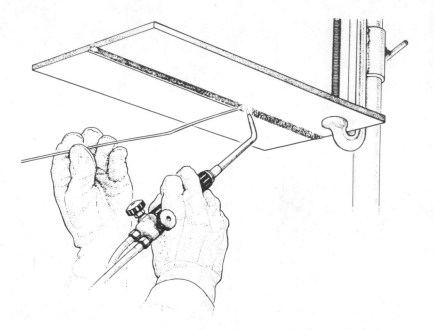

Fig. 14-12. Welding in the overhead position looks difficult. Actually, it is easier than welding in the horizontal position, if you can achieve a reasonably comfortable position for the work. For practice purposes, first tackweld the two pieces of plate together and then clamp them securely several inches above head level. Put a small bend in your welding rod. Direct the flame almost straight up, angling it only slightly toward the finishing end. Then move flame and rod very much as though you were welding in the flat position. Keep the puddle in the pasty state, so that it cannot form a drop, and the work will proceed with surprising ease. Position the work and stand in such a way that you don't need to bend your neck too much. Even the best position will prove somewhat tiring at first, so don't be reluctant to take a break every so often.

When welding in this position, it is absolutely essential that the flame be held at the edges of the puddle a little longer than at the center, in order to spread the puddle and keep it from accumulating molten metal at the center in a large, heavy drop. It is also essential that the rod be rubbed in the puddle, and that heat from the puddle, rather than direct heat from the flame, be used to melt the filler metal.

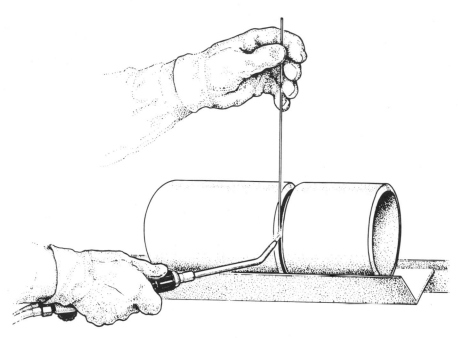

Fig. 14-13. This sketch, and the five which follow, picture the welding of 4-in. steel pipe. The ends of the pipe sections have been bevelled about 35 degrees off the vertical, to produce an included angle of 70 degrees. No squared-off shoulders have been provided on the pipe ends; the bevelled edges are sharp. If you have acquired the ability to do hand cutting with some precision, you can bevel the pipe yourself with a cutting torch or attachment. (See Fig. 14-21 for pointers on how to position torch and hands for pipe bevelling.) However, first practice in pipe welding will be easier if the pipe edges have been bevelled by the pipe supplier.

A pipe rest formed by welding a piece of angle iron to a couple of pieces of flat scrap will prove extremely helpful for tackwelding purposes. The same rest can be used from much of the actual welding practice. However, for working on the bottom of a joint, an extemporized rig such as that shown in Fig. 19 will be needed.

Pipe of 4-in. size should be tackwelded in four spots. Space the two pieces 1/8 in. apart before tackwelding; shrinkage of tacks will bring the final spacing down to about 3/32 in. Make the tackwelds in rapid succession, the second directly opposite the first, to minimize the possibility of misalignment of the joint due to contraction of the tackwelds. Use 1/8-in. welding rod. (For 2-in. pipe, 3/32-in. welding rod is recommended.)

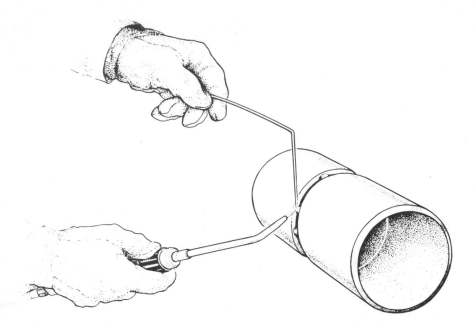

Fig. 14-14. After making four tackwelds, the operator is beginning his root pass. Note that he is not starting at one of the tackwelds, but about an inch away from one. This is important, if the joint is to be kept in good alignment.

In actual field work, pipe welds are made, whenever possible, by rotating the pipe during welding so that work can be done entirely in the flat position. If these pipe sections had been placed in a fixture that permitted rotation, welding would have been started close to the top of the pipe, although still at least one inch from a tack weld.

While it is relatively easy to improvise a fixture which will allow pipe welds to be made on a "rotating" basis (a discarded pair of roller skates can be useful for the purpose) the person who hopes to become a reasonably proficient pipe welder must be able to work in all positions. Completing this weld, if the pipe is not rotated, will involve welding in the flat, vertical, and overhead positions. (However, the professional pipefitter will refer to this entire joint as being in the 5G "horizontal" position!). The exact point at which to start the weld, and the points at which the welder should change his own position relative to the pipe, are matters of personal preference. To weld the entire joint in one continuous operation is almost impossible.

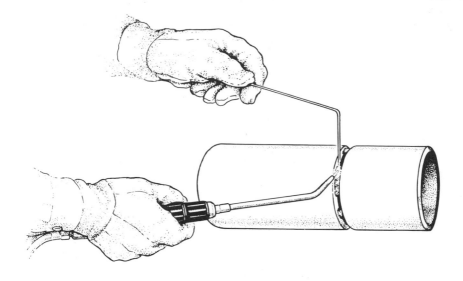

Fig. 14-15. Here the root pass has been well started. (If the pipe wall is more than 1/8 in. thick, two passes are recommended. For thinner-wall pipe, only one pass is needed.) In both this sketch, and Fig. 14-14, note that the torch flame is pointed almost, but not quite, toward the centerline of the pipe, while the filler rod is held approximately tangent to the pipe surface. These are the normal angles for pipe welding, regardless of the welding position, except when adjustment of flame angle is required for puddle control in the horizontal and overhead positions.

When a tackweld is reached, always be sure to melt it out completely, right down to the root. Tacks are made quickly, often without sufficient attention to securing of full penetration. To weld over a tack without melting it completely is a serious error. In order to melt out the tack completely, it may be necessary to withdraw the filler rod from the puddle for a few seconds.

Unless the pipe ends have been perfectly prepared, there will be variations in the width of the joint gap at the root. This may make it necessary to do some careful bridging, by concentrating first on one side of the joint, then on the other. One of the big advantages in oxy-acetylene welding is that heat input and filler metal input can be separately controlled. Gaps that can give the arc welder trouble are no problem at all to the experienced oxy-acetylene pipe welder.

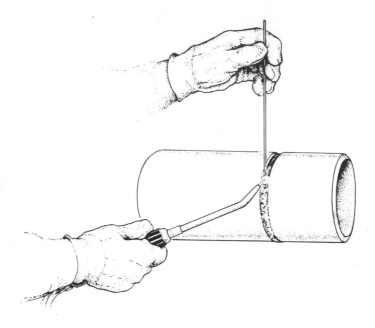

Fig. 14-16. Putting in the finishing pass in a pipe weld is essentially no different than putting in the finishing pass on a plate weld. Proper rod movement is the key factor. The rod must rub in the bottom of the puddle, and bump against the edges of the joint. The flame must linger a bit at each end of each arc, and be concentrated on the puddle, never on the filler rod. Movement of flame and rod must be in opposite directions.

At the instant caught by this sketch, the welder is working in what may be termed the vertical position. The flame is pointed somewhat away from the centerline of the pipe in order to hold the puddle against the force of gravity.

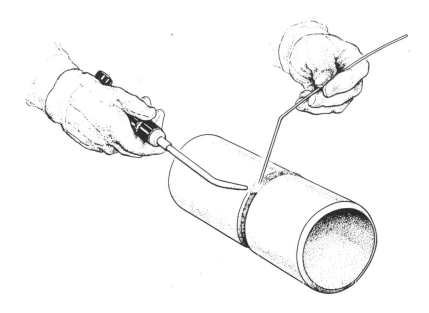

Fig. 14-17. The thing to note about this sketch (as in Fig. 14-8) is that the welder is using backhand technique. In pipe welding, when the pipe cannot be rotated, there are many occasions when the ability to switch easily from forehand to backhand technique can save time for the welder. With backhand technique, it is quite easy to make a vertical weld from top to bottom, rather than from bottom to top. The flame is still used to "support" the puddle, but in this case its aim is to keep the puddle from running ahead onto metal which has not yet reached melting temperature. As noted in the caption for Fig. 14-8, the relative movements of flame and rod are quite different from those used in forehand work. It would be wise to experiment with backhand work on pieces of plate, trying it in both the flat and vertical positions, before employing the technique on pipe.

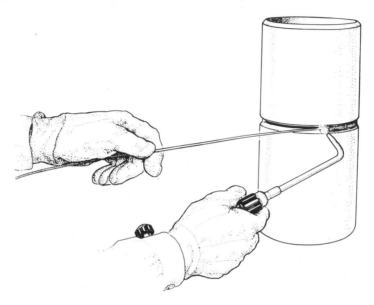

Fig. 14-18. Here the root pass is being made in the horizontal welding position. (To the pipefitter, this is the 2G "vertical" position.) If you have been successful in making horizontal position welds in plate, pipe should present no new problems. In making the root weld, keep the puddle as small as possible, angle the flame a bit toward the upper side of the joint. The rod should be held in what is considered the normal position for all pipe work—approximately tangent to the circumference of the pipe. In putting in the finishing pass, remember that the puddle must be slanted a bit, with its lower end leading its upper end, and that the rod must be manipulated to push molten metal up against the top edge of the joint.

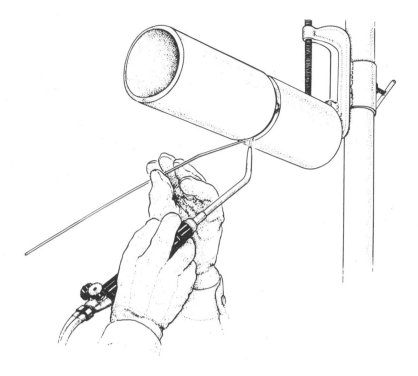

Fig. 14-19. When the joint is at a comfortable position above your head, as depicted in this sketch, making an overhead weld in pipe is no harder than making one in plate. On the other hand, if you must lie on your back to do it, you may find it more difficult at first.

Note that if you wish to weld the entire joint with forehand technique, you must start at the bottom of the joint, work up one side of the pipe, then change your position, and work up the other side of the joint, starting at the bottom once more. However, if you have mastered backhand technique, you can start at one side, work down to the bottom using backhand technique, then switch to forehand and work up the other side. The ability to switch from forehand to backhand, or vice versa, can sometimes be a real timesaver when welding fixed joints in horizontal pipe runs.

This sketch shows how you can easily make an adjustable support rig for pipe welding practice, using a pipe upright and an improvised sliding clamp to which an ordinary C-clamp has been welded.

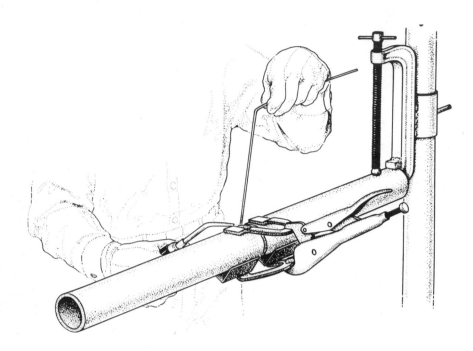

Fig. 14-20. This shows another tool which can be improvised for holding small-diameter pipe in position for tackwelding. It is based on ordinary wrench-grip pliers.

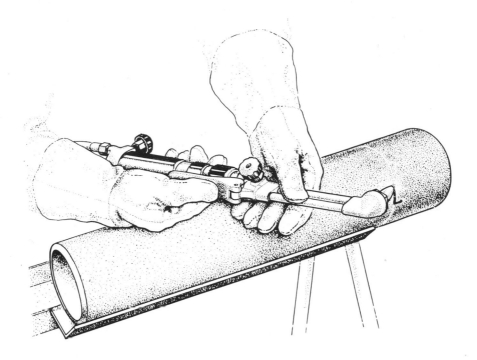

Fig. 14-21. Bevelling pipe with a hand cutting torch or attachment is largely a matter of learning how to place your hands and the torch. Here the pipe is supported by the same angle-iron rest shown in Fig. 14-13. The operator has started his cut in the scrap end, moved the cut a short distance, and then started his bevel. He will now be able to make a continuous cut halfway around the pipe before he must stop, rotate the pipe section 180 degrees, and then complete the bevel cut.

Testing Sheet Metal Welds. To test a sheet metal weld that appears satisfactory to the eye, clamp the specimen in a vise, with the weld metal parallel to the jaws and just above them. Then hammer the top portion of the specimen to bend it 90 degrees away from the bottom side of the weld. Remove the specimen and reverse it so that the lower half can be similarly bent. The "folded" specimen should then be placed in the vise so that the ends can be pulled up flush against each other, with the weld just above the jaws of the vise. If the weld has normal ductility, and the work has been done well, there should be no visible cracks in the weld metal, or between the weld metal and the balance of the specimen.

Alternative Sheet Metal Technique. On sheet steel less than $1/16$ in. (1.5 mm) thick, the torch and rod motions described earlier in this chapter may give trouble. It may be hard to avoid frequent melt-through if flame motion is limited to arcs described back and forth across the weld line. If that proves to be the case, an alternative technique, sketched in Fig. 14-23, should be used. This technique is not easy to master, but with it a skilled welder can handle sheet steel as thin as $1/32$ in. (less than 1 mm). The flame must be moved chiefly up and down, in a series of overlapping ovals, while the end of the rod is moved up and down in opposite sequence, so that rod and inner cone are close to each other at one point in each cycle. There must be some slight motion of the flame from side to side—enough to bring the edges of the metal to fusion temperature—but the dominant flame motion must lie in the vertical plane. Before attempting to use this technique to make a weld, use it to deposit beads on thin sheet, practicing until you can put down a bead of uniform width and contour.

Testing Practice Plate Welds. After completing what appears to be a satisfactory weld between two pieces of steel plate, cut three specimens from

Fig. 14-22. To test a weld between two pieces of sheet metal, place specimen in vise, with weld just above jaws of vise, and hammer it 90 degrees away from the back of the weld, as shown at left. Then bend the other side as far as possible (not shown). Finally, as shown at right, bring the two halves of the specimen together.

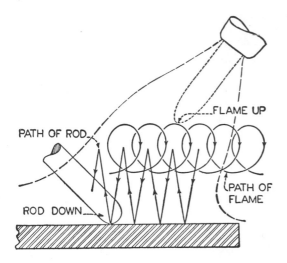

Fig. 14-23. This sketch shows the way flame and rod should move when welding sheet by the alternative technique described in the text.

FLAME UP

PATH OF ROD

PATH OF FLAME

ROD DOWN

the weld as shown in Fig. 14-24. Grind the top of the weld flush with the surface of the plate. Place the specimen in a vise and bend it 15-20 degrees at a point midway between the weld and the end of the specimen. (See Fig. 14-25). Reverse the specimen and put a bend in the other side. (Be sure to bend *away* from the back side of the weld.) Then place the specimen in a large vise and apply pressure until the ends of the specimen make contact. If the welding has been done quite well, two out of three specimens taken from a single weld should withstand this test without evidence of cracking.

Review

To close this chapter, perhaps the most important in the book from the standpoint of the beginner, a brief summation seems in order. This cannot cover everything stated in the preceeding pages, but will highlight the most important aspects of steel welding.

1. **Flame.** Keep it neutral. If the weld metal seems to be sparking more than usual, check your flame. It may have become slightly oxidizing.

2. **Penetration and Fusion.** You can achieve what appears to be complete *penetration* (when you take a quick look at the back side of your weld) without having achieved complete *fusion*. "Cold shuts"—places within the weld, between root pass and finishing pass, or between weld metal and the original surfaces of the base metal—are difficult or impossible to spot visually. (For "nick-break" testing which will often disclose cold shuts, see Chapter 26.)

3. **Keep the filler metal rod in the flame.** By that, of course, we mean in the outer envelope of the flame, not necessarily close to the inner

Fig. 14-24. To test plate welds, cut specimens as shown here, using cutting torch. Cut end specimens at least 1/2 in. from end of plate.

Fig. 14-25. After grinding weld flush with plate surface, given each end of the specimen about a 15-degree bend, bending away from the back of the weld.

Fig. 14-26. In a large vise, bend each specimen until the ends meet. Fully-bend specimens can be seen on the back of the vise in this photo.

cone. The outer envelope preheats it *and* protects it from undue oxidation.

4. **Use both flame and rod to control puddle size.** If the puddle gets too large or too fluid, withdraw the flame slightly, but generally keep the rod in the puddle and keep it moving.

5. **When making a fresh start, get the puddle formed before you add filler metal.** That also applies to working over tackwelds. For a few seconds, withdraw the rod and make sure the tack is melted. Haste can lead to cold shuts.

6. **Take time to make tackwelds right.** Unless the tackweld is thoroughly fused to both sides of the vee, it's worse than useless.

7. **Don't yank the rod if it sticks unexpectly. Melt it loose with the flame.**

8. **Practice, practice, practice.** Few people become proficient welders in one day—even a full eight-hour day. (But if you stick with it, you have a good chance to become proficient within a week.)

9. **Test your work as you practice.**

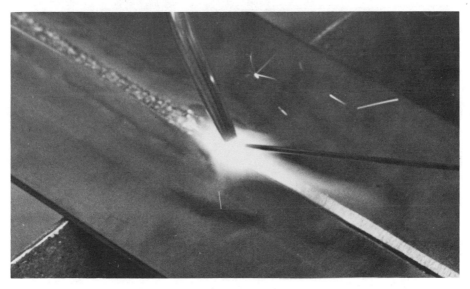

Fig. 14-27. This photograph covers the same operation as the Fig. 14-6 sketch—putting in a root pass on 1/4-in. mild steel plate. It is worth noting that the welder is making no attempt to achieve a uniform ripple on the surface of the deposited weld metal. In making this pass, his key objective is to achieve full penetration. He will concentrate on uniform contour and reinforcement when he makes the finishing pass.

Fig. 14-28. This photograph shows the making of a root pass with backhand technique. It takes a bit more skill to be sure of complete fusion of the root pass using this technique, and both flame and rod must be moved in patterns somewhat different than those used in forehand welding, but some welders find that they can work a little faster, using larger rod.

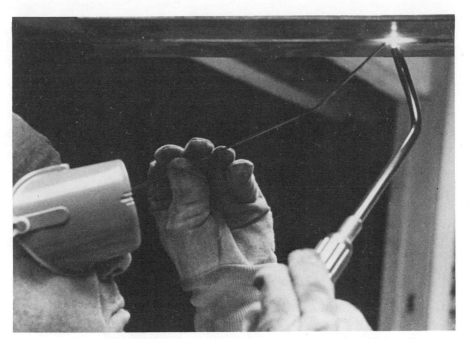

Fig. 14-29. This shows, better than the Fig. 14-12 sketch, the ideal position for the operator when doing welding in the overhead position.

1. What is the proper flame adjustment for most steel welding?
2. What are the usual names for the various positions of welding?
3. What is the backhand technique?
4. What factors contribute to the control of the molten puddle?
5. What is the proper position of the welding torch with respect to the metal surface?
6. How far away from the surface of the metal should the tip of the inner cone be?
7. If the base metal is in the mushy stage and molten metal is added from the welding rod, does thorough fusion occur?
8. What can be done with the stub ends of welding rods?
9. What are the purposes of tack-welds?
10. Does an even ripple mean that a good weld has been made?
11. What happens when the welding puddle is moved forward too slowly? Too rapidly?
12. What happens if the molten puddle is allowed to flow forward over metal which has not been brought to the mushy stage?
13. Does it mean that a good weld has been obtained if the top surface of the weld is uniform in width and height?
14. If you can still see the edges of the sheet when the underside of the weld is examined, what is wrong?
15. How should butt welds in sheet metal be tested?
16. What is a good test of butt welds in steel plate?
17. What factors are most important in vertical welding?
18. Is it possible to weld overhead?
19. What is the main factor which is used to prevent the puddle from falling when welding in the overhead position?
20. Why are tack-welds always used when welding pipe?

BRAZE WELDING

Up to this point, we have been talking about the *fusion welding* of carbon steel, and in the chapters immediately following this, we shall talk about the fusion welding of cast iron, of stainless steel, and of non-ferrous metals. In fusion welding, the filler rod always has a melting point approximately the same as the melting point of the metal to be joined, and both the filler metal and the base metal are actually melted and fused together. *Braze welding* is a process of almost equal importance to the user of an oxyacetylene welding outfit. It closely resembles fusion welding in several important respects. It is used to produce joints of excellent strength in steel, in cast iron, and in copper and some copper alloys. However, in braze welding, the filler metal always has a melting point well below the melting point of the base metal, and the base metal is never melted.

Years ago, the process we now term "braze welding" was commonly known as "bronze-welding". Ever since the process was renamed "braze welding", there has existed a degree of confusion between the terms "brazing" and "braze welding". The American Welding Society definitions for "brazing" and "braze welding" both stipulate that the filler metal must have a melting point above 425°C (800°F). However, the definitions state that in *brazing* the filler metal is drawn into a tight-fitting joint by *capillary attraction;* in *braze welding* the filler metal is deposited in the joint by *other* than capillary attraction. We shall talk about the use of the flame in brazing operations in another chapter.

The basis for the braze welding process is that both brass and bronze* will flow onto properly prepared surfaces of higher-melting-point metals or alloys to form a bond or molecular union which has excellent strength. The base metal is never melted. It is merely raised to the temperature at which the filler metal will *tin* — form a smooth film — on the surface of the joint. Although the temperatures involved are much lower than those required for the fusion welding of steel, braze welding is primarily an oxy-acetylene process. The intense heat of the oxy-acetylene flame quickly raises the base

---

*Traditionally, "bronze" was considered an alloy of copper and tin, "brass" an alloy of copper and zinc. Today, while all alloys designated as "brass" contain a lot of zinc, several alloys commercially labeled "bronze" also contain zinc, and some contain no tin.

metal to the proper temperature for *tinning*. The welder can control every variable factor involved: the temperature of the base metal, the melting of the filler rod, and the condition (neutral or slightly oxidizing) of the flame.

Filler Metal and Flux for Braze Welding

The filler metal used for most braze welding is a copper alloy containing roughly 60% copper, 40% zinc, and small amounts of tin, iron, manganese, and silicon. OXWELD No. 25M bronze welding rod is an example of a material formulated specifically for braze welding. It tins readily, flows freely, forms weld metal with excellent strength and high ductility. For bronze-surfacing — a process used for building up wearing surfaces rather than making up joints — a filler metal of slightly different composition, designed to achieve greater hardness at some sacrifice in ductility, is frequently specified. OXWELD No. 31T rod is an example of such a material. Silicon bronze, which contains only copper and silicon (no zinc), and phosphor bronze (a copper-tin alloy) are also sometimes used for braze-welding steel.

Whenever a copper-zinc filler metal is used for braze welding, a flux must be used. Without flux, proper tinning action, even on the cleanest steel or cast iron surfaces, is virtually impossible to attain. The flux also serves other purposes, such as reducing the amount of fuming which occurs because of the rather low boiling point of zinc. The flux can be precoated on the welding rod, or transferred to the rod by dipping the heated end of the rod in a can of powdered flux. A vapor flux, which is picked up by the acetylene on its way to the torch, is sometimes used in production braze welding applications. Precoated rod (such as OXWELD Flux-Coated 25M) is the choice of many welders, since it eliminates the need to interrupt the actual welding operation in order to pick up flux on the rod.

The Nature of the Braze Welded Bond

Braze welding works because a molten metal with low surface tension will flow easily and evenly over the surface of solid metal which has been well cleaned and heated to the right temperature. You can compare the action to the even flow of water over a truly clean glass surface. If the glass is not perfectly clean, the water will form a series of puddles or drops. Similarly, if the metal to be welded isn't really clean, or cannot be made clean enough by the action of the welding flux, and if the metal is not at the right temperature, the brazing filler metal will not flow, or tin, properly.

Whenever proper tinning has been achieved, the bond between the base metal and the brazing alloy, after the weld has cooled to room temperature, should have a strength at least equal to the strength of the brazing metal deposit itself, and equal to the strength of the base metal in many cases. Although we say there is no true "fusion" of the two metals, there is actually a very narrow zone, observable only at high magnification under a microscope, in which mixing of the atoms of the base metal and brazing alloy has taken place.

Braze Welding Technique

Successful braze welding requires careful attention to three factors:
1. Preparation and mechanical *cleaning* of the joint.
2. Proper *tinning* of every bit of the joint surface, which results from the combination of chemical cleaning of the surface by the flux and maintenance of the proper metal temperature.
3. *Complete fusion* between layers of weld metal when the weld is made in two or more passes.

Joint Preparation. In general, the joint design for braze welds is the same as for fusion welds in base metals of like thickness. Square edges may be used if the base metal is sheet not thicker than about 3-4 mm (1/8 to 3/16 in.) Bevelled edges should be used with all thicker material. Generally, avoid using an included angle of less than 90 degrees.

In all cases, that part of the base metal on which tinning action is to take place must always be cleaned thoroughly of all rust, scale, paint, oil or grease, or any other foreign substance. Clean the metal back from the edge of the joint for at least a half-inch if possible.

Welding Technique. For braze welding steel or cast iron, select a welding tip at least one size smaller than you would use for fusion welding steel of equivalent thickness. Adjust the flame to be *slightly* oxidizing. (First, arrive at a neutral flame which is relatively soft; that is, less than maximum size. Then throttle the acetylene flow just enough to cause a perceptible shortening of the flame's inner cone.) Heat the base metal, moving the flame back and forth over a generous area, until it just starts to glow. While you are doing this, heat the end of the filler rod and dip it in the flux to get it well-coated. When you think the base metal is hot enough concentrate the flame on the rod until a bit of it melts off onto the hot base metal. If the melted bronze flows evenly and smoothly on the surface of the metal, spreading over a surprisingly large area, you have hit the right temperature. If it merely rests on the surface as a large drop, the base metal temperature is too low. If the bronze spreads, but seems to bubble and separate into small drops, the base metal temperature is too high. (It is never necessary to raise the base metal temperature above the melting temperature of the bronze.)

Once good tinning action has been established, completing the weld should not be difficult. You must be careful not to melt rod into the puddle faster than the base metal ahead of the puddle has reached tinning temperature. You must avoid overheating the base metal or the puddle. You must learn to move the rod and flame in such a fashion as to secure adequate reinforcement and a uniform ripple effect. It is suggested that you start braze welding practice by merely laying down a bead on the surface of a piece of steel plate. Then try making a braze weld between two pieces of 6-mm (¼-in.) steel plate, each piece bevelled to a 45 deg. angle. Tackweld the pieces, as you did in preparation for fusion welding; however, spacing at the root of the weld, after the tackwelds have been made, need be no more than 2mm (¹⁄₁₆ in.)

Advantages and Disadvantages of Braze Welding

Braze welding is faster than fusion welding, since the heat input required is much less. The rod normally used for braze welding has a melting point of about 875° C (1600°F). In the braze welding of steel, the base metal must be

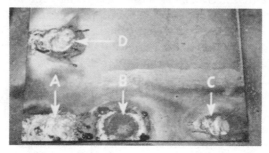

Fig. 15-1. Examples of good and bad starts in braze welding. For A, conditions were right. At B, the plate was too hot, so that the bronze ran to the edge of puddle, with an oxidized area in center. At C, the plate was too cold, so the bronze built up instead of spreading well. At D, the plate surface had not been properly cleaned.

Fig. 15-2. A poor braze weld which illustrates several faults. At A, the rod was dipped too far ahead of the puddle. At B, the bronze was allowed to drip from the end of the rod, forming globules. At C, the base metal was too hot, so the bronze spread out too much and ran ahead too far.

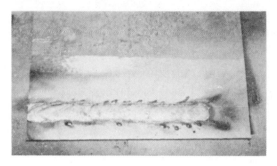

Fig. 15-3. This is a well-deposited layer of bronze. Note the even ripple, uniform width. The black spots are melted flux.

heated only to a temperature of about 900°C, rather than to a temperature of more than 1500°C. The saving in time and the saving in gas consumption may frequently be more than enough to counterbalance the substantially higher cost of the filler metal.

The reduction in heat input has other advantages, especially in the welding of cast iron, which will be covered in the next chapter. It minimizes the amount of preheating required. Since the bronze filler metal is extremely ductile, it can absorb stresses created during cooling which might, in the case of a cast iron fusion weld, cause cracking of the base metal or the weld. When used on steel, braze welding reduces distortion of the base metal due to forces of contraction and expansion.

When mild steel or cast iron are properly braze welded, the strength of the joint, at *normal temperatures,* is likely to be equal to, or even superior to, the strength of the base metal.

Braze welding can sometimes be used to join dissimilar metals which cannot be successfully fusion welded together. Steel can be braze welded to cast iron. Copper can be joined to brass by a braze weld. However, the joining of dissimilar metals by any welding process is something to be approached cautiously. The fact that you can turn out what appears to be a good-looking weld is no proof that the overall result is satisfactory. Essential properties of one or both of the metals joined may have been adversely affected by the act of welding.

So much for advantages. What are the disadvantages? One is quite obvious, although often of no significance; you can't match the color of the weld to the color of the base metal. Another, less obvious, is that bronze loses strength at relatively low temperatures. At 500°C, steel and cast iron are nearly as strong as they are at room temperature (20°C). Any bronze has lost a great deal of its strength at 500°C. Never use braze welding to repair parts that must operate at temperatures above 200°C.

In Chapter 22 we shall talk more about the technique and advantages of *bronze-surfacing,* which is very closely related to braze welding.

QUESTIONS – CHAPTER 15

1. How is brazing defined?
2. What is braze-welding?
3. What is the basic theory of the braze-welding process?
4. What heat source is used for braze-welding?
5. What are the important points in the metallurgy of the all-weld metal for braze-welding?
6. What are the characteristics of the bond between the bronze weld metal and the base metal?
7. What is meant by tinning?
8. Is there any melting of the base metal in braze-welding?
9. What are the three most important factors in the braze-welding technique?
10. What is the usual joint preparation for braze-welding?
11. What is the purpose of flux in braze-welding?
12. What are some of the ways in which the proper temperature for braze-welding can be determined?
13. What are some of the advantages of braze-welding?

WELDING OF CAST IRON

Cast iron is an extremely versatile material, used in thousands of industrial products. It is hard, wear-resistant, and relatively inexpensive. Like steel, it is available in many different grades and compositions. While we usually think of cast iron as being *brittle* (having low ductility), this is not true of all cast irons, as we shall see shortly.

Cast iron, like steel, is an iron-carbon alloy. In composition and structure, and in some of its properties, it is quite different from steel. While many grades of cast iron can be welded successfully, not all cast iron is weldable, and welding of any cast iron presents problems not usually encountered in the welding of steel.

Composition and Grades of Cast Iron

Cast iron is by no means pure iron. In fact, there is less iron in any grade of cast iron than there is in a low-carbon steel, which may be 98% iron. Almost every cast iron contains well over 2.0% carbon; some contain as much as 4.0%. In addition, cast iron usually contains 1.2 to 2.5% silicon, 0.5 to 0.8% manganese, and (as in steel) small percentages of sulphur and phosphorous.

It is the high percentage of carbon that make cast iron different from steel in many of its properties. In a finished steel, all the carbon is combined with iron in the form of iron carbides, whether those carbides are in grains of pearlite, in grains of cementite, or in scattered small particles of carbide. In cast iron, most of the carbon is usually present in uncombined form, as graphite. (Graphite is one of the two crystalline forms of carbon; diamond is the other). The differences between the general types of cast iron most widely used arise chiefly from the *form* which the graphite assumes in the finished iron.

Gray Iron. Of the general types of cast iron, gray iron is by far the most widely used. The term "gray iron" was adopted originally to distinguish it, by color of the fractured metal, from *white iron*, a form of cast iron in which all the carbon *is* combined. We'll have more to say about white iron later. At this point, we wish to stress the point that *gray iron* is a very broad term. All gray irons contain graphite in the form of flakes. This makes the gray irons readily machinable. All gray irons have almost no ductility, again because of the flake form of the graphite, which causes the metal to break before any appreciable amount of permanent elongation has occurred. However, not all gray irons are equally strong, or equally hard. As in steel, tensile strength and hardness are closely related. In gray irons, tensile strength ranges from about 14 MPa (20,000 psi) to more than 35 MPa (50,000 psi). The hardness of the strongest grades is double that of the weakest grades. All gray irons have high compressive strength — three to four times their tensile strength.

While all gray cast irons contain free carbon (graphite) in flake form, they also contain combined carbon (iron carbide) in almost every case. This combined carbon is often present in pearlite grains, such as found in most carbon steels. It may also be found as cementite or martensite. The composition of the cast iron, the rate at which it cooled after casting, and heat treatment after casting all have a bearing on the structure. Small amounts of alloying elements are used in the strongest gray irons; they tend to prevent the formation of pearlite. While the hardness and strength of steel almost always increase as carbon content rises, in the case of gray cast iron the strongest, hardest grades have less carbon than some of the lower-strength, less expensive grades.

Gray iron is usually cast in sand molds, and allowed to cool normally in the mold. Heat treatment after casting is not always necessary, but is frequently employed, either to increase or to decrease hardness. Almost all gasoline and diesel engine blocks are gray iron castings. Whenever industry desires an intricate form which can be machined to close tolerances, and must withstand abrasive wear, gray iron gets consideration. Only when it is essential that the finished item have some ductility and good shock resistance is some other material — such as nodular cast iron or cast steel, both more expensive — likely to be substituted.

White iron, mentioned above, is about the same as gray iron in composition, but has been cooled rapidly so that graphite does not have time to form, and all the carbon winds up in the combined form, as pearlite, cementite, or martensite. Many white iron castings are subsequently converted to malleable iron, which we shall take up next. However, some gray iron castings are made with white iron wearing surfaces, since white iron is much harder than gray iron, although extremely brittle. This is accomplished by inserting metal or graphite chill blocks at appropriate places in the mold. The molten metal that solidifies against those chill blocks cools so rapidly that white iron surfaces are created. Plowshares, railroad car wheels, and various types of dies are often made with such chilled white iron surfaces.

Gray cast iron can usually be welded without loss of essential properties. For fusion welding, preheating of the casting is absolutely essential. Since a higher level of preheat is required for oxy-acetylene welding then for arc welding, arc welding is likely to be chosen where fusion welding is essential (as it is whenever good color match is desired). For many repair jobs, however, oxy-acetylene braze welding is the ideal method. Much less preheating is required; in many cases, preheating can be done with the torch. If the work is properly done, the braze-welded joint will have a strength equal to that of the base metal, and excellent machinability.

Welding of gray iron castings which have chilled white iron surfaces is seldom attempted, since the desirable properties of white iron will always be affected by welding temperatures. Welding of white iron generally is limited to malleable iron foundries, where castings may be reclaimed by welding before conversion to malleable iron takes place.

Malleable iron. The chemical composition of malleable cast iron is much the same as that of a typical gray iron, but its properties are much different. It is tough; it can resist shock; it has ductility approaching that of mild steel. How is such a remarkable change achieved? By cooling the original casting so rapidly that white cast iron, with no free carbon, is formed; then heating the casting to about 800°C and holding it at that temperature for several days. Under those conditions, virtually all the carbon is released from the iron carbide to form fine rounded particies of graphite (sometimes called *temper carbon*) scattered among grains of ferrite. Malleable iron has good wear resistance, and is widely used for parts where the toughness of steel is required, and the economy of casting (instead of forming or machining) will result in lower cost. However, malleable iron is substantially more expensive to make than gray iron, and is usually selected only where its toughness and ductility are essential.

Malleable iron cannot be successfully fusion welded and retain its unique properties; to put it another way, you can weld malleable iron as easily as you can weld gray iron, but in the act of welding you will convert some of the malleable iron casting into a gray iron casting. Seldom will that yield a satisfactory result. However, malleable iron castings can usually be braze welded successfully.

You may wonder how to tell a malleable iron casting from a gray iron casting. There's one almost infallible method: use a high-speed grinder to make a spark test. The difference between the spark streams produced by gray iron and malleable iron is quite pronounced. Spark testing is covered in the Appendix.

Nodular Iron. Nodular cast iron, sometimes called *ductile iron*, has many of the properties of malleable iron. Nodular cast iron is made by *inoculating* the molten metal, just before casting, with a small amount of *magnesium* or *cerium*. This causes the free carbon in the finished casting to appear as rounded *nodules* of graphite, rather than as flakes. Each nodule is surrounded by a zone of ferrite (carbon-free iron) with the balance of the metal usually in the form of pearlite. Nodular iron has less ductility than malleable iron (which can have almost as much ductility as mild steel) but far more than ordinary gray iron, which has virtually none. It usually has high strength; in fact, the yield strength of a nodular iron is almost always greater than that of mild carbon steel. All nodular irons have one property which clearly sets them apart from most gray irons; they have a high *modulus of elasticity.* In simpler terms, they have excellent *stiffness*, a property much desired in parts like propeller shafts or forming rolls. Where most gray irons are much more elastic (less stiff) than steel, nodular cast iron is nearly as stiff as cast steel.

Like malleable iron, nodular iron cannot be fusion welded and retain all of its original properties. This is especially true of nodular iron castings which have been heat-treated after casting. A fusion weld made in nodular iron may not cause loss of tensile strength, but will almost always reduce the shock resistance of the part. Braze welding can be used on nodular iron if some sacrifice of tensile strength can be tolerated.

Alloy Cast Irons. Alloying ingredients — chromium, nickel, molybdenum, and, occasionally copper or aluminum — are added to cast iron for three principal purposes: to increase wear resistance, to increase resistance to scaling in high-temperature service, and to increase corrosion resistance. In some alloy cast irons, the silicon level is also increased substantially. Some of the extra-hard, abrasion-resistant alloy irons are *white* irons; they appear almost white when fractured because they contain virtually no free carbon. Others may have the general appearance of gray cast iron. The range of compositions is so great that no general statement about the weldability of alloy cast iron can be made. So far as the oxy-acetylene process is concerned, fusion welding is not recommended; braze welding will not permit retention of all the properties for which the alloy iron was originally specified.

The Importance of Preheating

For Fusion Welding. If you are called on to weld cast iron, the material to be welded will almost always be gray iron. Gray iron is brittle; it has virtually no ductility. If the forces of expansion or contraction, as generated during the welding operation or in cooling after welding, are concentrated in one area of the casting, cracking of the casting, or of the cooling weld, will almost certainly occur. Even at elevated temperatures, gray cast iron has little "give"; it will break, rather than stretch, when the force of expansion or contraction exceeds its yield strength. Therefore, whenever a casting must be fusion welded, it is usually necessary to preheat the entire casting, slowly and evenly, before welding is started, and then allow the casting to cool slowly after welding has been completed. This will permit all sections of the casting to expand and contract at a reasonably uniform rate.

The temperature to which a casting must be preheated depends somewhat upon the welding process to be used. Oxy-acetylene fusion welding puts more heat into the casting than does arc welding, and therefore requires a higher level of preheat, usually to about 600°C (1100°F). The preheat temperature level is also somewhat dependent upon the size and form of the casting. Rather simple castings, without major variations in section thickness, usually require less preheat than complex castings.

If a suitable furnace is not available for preheating a casting, one can be improvised out of fire brick, as suggested in Chapter 13. If the casting is preheated in a furnace, and then withdrawn for welding, it is essential that as much of the casting as possible be insulated during the welding operation, to hold the preheat as well as protect the welder. Asbestos paper will be found almost indispensable during the fusion welding of cast iron.

For Braze Welding. When a casting is to be braze welded, some preheating is usually required, but the level of preheat temperature can be much lower, and many jobs can be done without preheating the entire casting. In braze welding, there is no danger of weld cracking. Bronze weld metal has extremely high ductility, and is capable of absorbing any contraction stresses to which it may be subjected. Because the temperature of the casting itself, even in the metal immediately adjacent to the weld metal, need never exceed 900°C, changes in the physical properties of the casting metal will seldom occur. That is why malleable iron castings can often be braze welded. However, even the heat input involved in braze welding may be enough to cause cracking of a gray iron casting (or leave the casting with residual stresses which might cause cracking at a later time) if some preheating is not performed. If preheating of the complete casting is feasible, it should be done, although the temperature need not be raised to more than 300-400°C. In most cases, thorough preheating of the metal adjacent to the weld zone, using the welding torch, will be sufficient.

Braze Welding Practice

If you have already braze welded pieces of steel plate, as suggested in the preceding chapter, the braze welding of cast iron should present no new problems. If possible, get some coupons of cast iron, about 13mm (1/2 in.) thick, which some foundries cast especially for welding practice. If not, locate some pieces of a broken casting and use them. Prepare the edges of the joint carefully. The included angle of the weld vee should be a full 90°, and the edges must be thoroughly cleaned. Grinding, followed by filing, is recommended. (The file will remove any loose particles left by the grinding wheel, as well as any graphite flakes which might interfere with proper tinning of the metal.) Be sure to remove all traces of grease or paint from the metal surface immediately adjacent to the weld vee.

For braze welding cast iron about 13mm (1/2 in.) thick, we suggest that you use a welding tip which consumes 15 cfh of acetylene, and a slightly oxidizing flame. (To secure that, adjust the flame carefully to neutral, then throttle the acetylene flow enough to shorten the flame inner cone *slightly*.) You must also have a good braze welding flux, such as OXWELD BRAZO flux or OXWELD Cast Iron Brazing Flux. (The latter is more expensive, but contains bits of bronze "spelter" which help you to determine when the casting has reached the proper temperature for tinning.)

Since tackwelding will seldom be called for in actual repair work on castings, we suggest that you merely space the two pieces of cast iron so that there is a gap of about 1.6 mm (1/16 in.) at the starting point of the weld, and a gap of 5 to 6 mm (3/16 to 1/4 in.) at the finishing point. If you are using a welding table with a cast iron top, be sure to raise the finishing end of the joint a bit above the table, lest you actually weld the specimens to the table.

If the cast iron coupons or the pieces of casting are at least 13 mm (1/2 in.) thick, we suggest that you plan to make your weld in three passes.

After lighting the torch, pass the flame back and forth along the entire length of the weld zone several times, holding the tip of the inner cone at least 13 mm (1/2 in.) away from the metal surface. Then concentrate the flame in an area about 8 cm (3 in.) in diameter at the starting end. The cast iron will be ready for tinning just as it starts to turn a very dull red color. (To spot this point in a brightly lighted room, through the dark lenses of welding goggles, isn't always easy. It will take practice to acquire the knack of instantly recognizing that first glow.) You should have heated the end of the welding rod and dipped it in flux while you were preheating the metal. Now melt just a little of the bronze onto the surface of the vee. If it balls up and tends to roll down the surface, the metal isn't hot enough. Withdraw the rod and continue heating for a few seconds. Dip the rod in flux again and make a fresh start. If the molten rod tends to bubble up on the cast iron surface, and run around likedrops of water on a fairly hot stove top, the cast iron is too hot. You must withdraw the flame and let the iron cool down a bit before trying to deposit more filler metal.

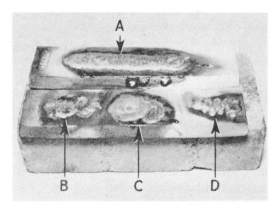

Fig. 16-1. Good and poor deposits of bronze on cast iron coupons. At A, results were first-class. At B, surface of cast iron had not been ground, so tinning was uneven. At C, too much heat was used, while at D too little heat was used.

Once proper tinning action has been started, continuing the first pass is largely a matter of maintaining the tinning action and melting in the right amount of bronze. Always try to get tinning action which extends a good halfway up each side of the vee, but deposit no more bronze than necessary to achieve a *concave* weld contour. If you do not tin the sides of the vee enough, and then try to melt in too much metal, you'll arrive at a *convex* weld metal surface and find it very hard to make the second pass without running molten bronze onto parts of the iron surface that have not been properly tinned.

On the second pass, tinning action should be carried to the top of each side of the vee, and enough bronze melted to secure another concave surface, not a convex surface. Be sure that the additional filler metal added in this pass in is completely fused to the bronze deposited in the first pass. If there is not complete fusion between the first-pass bronze and the second-pass bronze, what appears to be a good weld may actually be less than full strength.

In making the third pass, try to achieve a good ripple and a good shape for the top surface of the weld. Carry the weld just a bit past the top of the vee on each side, making sure that the cast iron surfaces tin before the puddle passes the top of the vee.

Testing a Practice Weld. If your first weld looks good, and the underside of the weld shows complete penetration without too many unsightly protrusions, you should find a way to test it. The methods suggested for test-

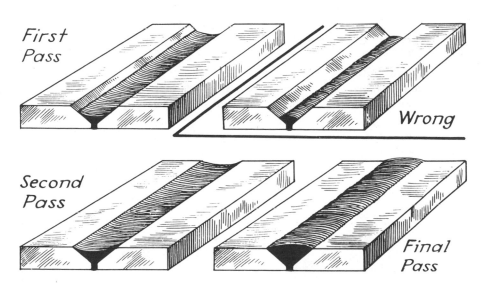

Fig. 16-2. Sketches to illustrate proper contours for successive passes with bronze rod. Except when making the final pass, try to achieve a concave surface on the weld metal.

ing welds in steel sheet and plate are not really suitable for braze welds. For one thing, you can't cut out a coupon with your cutting torch or attachment. More important, any test which involves hammering the specimen is likely to cause the cast iron to fracture, even if the weld is less than perfect. For a very rough test (if welding was done on flat pieces) you can place the specimen in a heavy vise, with the centerline of the weld parallel to the vise jaws and level with the top edge of the jaws. Then strike the specimen, above the weld line, with a heavy hammer. If you can break the specimen, and the break occurs in the cast iron, not along the weld zone, you know that the weld was at least passable. A far better method of testing, if you have the means for doing it, is illustrated in Fig. 16-3. If a steadily increasing force is applied, the specimen will ultimately break, and if you have made a really good weld, it will break through the cast iron, with no evidence of bronze on either side of the fracture. If one surface of the fracture shows bits of bronze, indicating that the weld broke through the bronze-cast iron bond at that point, it indicates that you did not attain complete tinning of the cast iron during the welding operation. On your first weld, lack of proper fusion at the bottom of the vee will usually be the result of overheating the cast iron, rather than underheating it.

Tips on Braze Welding. A cast iron surface that has been exposed to fire may prove hard to tin, even after thorough mechanical cleaning. Spreading a strong oxidizing agent, such as powdered potassium chlorate, on the well-heated surface, just ahead of the weld puddle, will often help. The chlorate will foam; once foaming starts, tinning will proceed normally.

A cast iron surface which has been exposed to oil and grease for a long period will actually absorb some of that material, and normal cleaning methods will not remove it. The answer to that problem is to heat the surface bright red before any attempt is made to weld it. That will usually vaporize and burn the grease out.

Before repairing any casting, take time to study the job in advance, and decide how to clamp it or support it so that welding can be done most easily. If there are a series of cracks, try to plan the welding sequence so that welding one crack isn't likely to create expansion forces which will enlarge another crack.

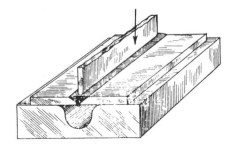

Fig. 16-3. A method for testing a braze weld in cast iron is illustrated by this sketch. A steady force should be applied in the vertical direction, as indicated by the arrow.

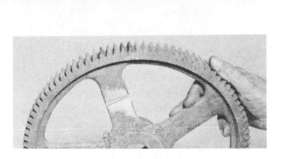

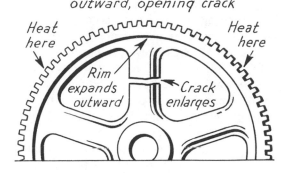

Heat causes rim to bow
outward, opening crack

Heat
here

Heat
here

Rim
expands
outward

Crack
enlarges

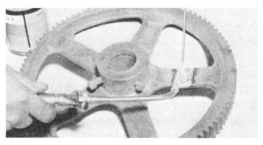

Fig. 16-4. Three steps in the repair by braze welding of a
cracked spoke in a cast iron gear. First, the crack should be
bevelled on each side, leaving at least 1/16 in. of metal in the middle, between the two vees. Then the rim of the gear should be
heated strongly, as illustrated by the sketch in the center. This
will cause the rim to expand and will open up the crack somewhat. Finally, without delay, the weld area should be preheated
with the torch and bronze deposited, first on one side of the
spoke, then on the other.

No matter how you preheated a casting for braze welding, always do
everything possible to permit slow, even cooling. Frequently it will help to
play the torch flame gently over the surface of the metal for a considerable
area surrounding the weld, to bring the piece as a whole to a more even heat
level. Whenever possible, cover the part with asbestos paper, or, if it is
small, bury it in dry slaked lime. Always protect the part from drafts.

Fusion Welding

The general rule for the oxy-acetylene fusion welding of gray iron castings is that the entire casting be preheated in a furnace to dull red heat (about 800°C), that the actual welding be done under conditions which will allow the retention of most of the preheat, and that the casting be allowed to cool *slowly* after the welding. Whenever possible, the casting should be reheated to a uniform temperature of about 750-800°C after welding, and cooling to room temperature should require at least one full day. When these conditions can be met, the results should be good.

In some cases, depending on the size of the casting, and the thickness of its various sections, fusion welding can be done successfully with only local preheating to a dull red color. However, it would be unwise to attempt fusion welding without full preheat unless you have had considerable experience in the fusion welding of cast iron, and feel thoroughly competent to assess the effects of expansion and contraction on the whole casting. Few oxy-acetylene welders get the chance to acquire that kind of experience.

You do not, however, require previous experience, or a preheating furnace, to acquire the basic skills involved in making a fusion weld. The welding action is quite different from that with which you are familiar (if you have previously welded only steel, or braze welded cast iron) so we suggest that you make a few practice welds in small pieces of cast iron.

Materials Required for Practice Welds. You will need two or more pieces of 13mm (1/2-in.) cast iron, about 3 by 6 in. in area, with edges bevelled to an angle of 45 degrees (the same as suggested for braze welding practice). Torch tip size should be the same as that you used for braze welding 13-mm (1/2-in.) cast iron. Filler metal should be cast iron rod especially formulated for welding (either gray iron or nodular iron). A flux designed specifically for fusion welding of cast iron is required, such as OXWELD Ferro Flux. (Do not attempt to use a brazing flux. It will not serve this purpose.)

Practice. The bevelled edges of the pieces should be filed thoroughly. If the bottom of the bevelled edge is sharp, it should be filed to give you square edges, at least 2 mm (3/32 in.) deep, at the root of the weld. The pieces should be positioned so that there is a gap of about 1.6 mm (1/16 in.) at the weld starting point and about 5 mm (3/16 in.) at the finishing point.

For fusion welding of cast iron, a neutral flame should be used, not the slightly oxidizing flame suggested for braze welding.

First preheat the entire weld zone thoroughly with the torch flame. Try to reach dull red heat along the entire length of the welding vee. Then heat the bottom of the vee, at the starting end, until the actual melting has started. Angle the torch flame as you did in steel welding; keep the inner cone at least 3 mm (1/8 in.) from the metal, however. When a small puddle has formed at the base of the vee, move the flame from side to side to melt down the sides of the vee gradually. Only after you have a fair-sized puddle should the rod, which has been preheated in the flame and dipped in the flux until it is well-coated, be introduced into the puddle.

From this point on, your aim must be to keep the rod in the puddle, and to allow the heat from the puddle, not the flame itself, to do the actual melting of filler metal. Try to avoid withdrawing the rod from the puddle except when more flux is needed on the rod. Never hold the rod above the puddle and allow it to melt into the puddle drop by drop. Direct the flame against the puddle, and against the sides of the vee. You must make the weld in one pass, not two or three. Therefore, you must not allow the puddle to advance too rapidly along the root of the vee. Keep the rod in the puddle, fill the vee completely for a length of perhaps one inch, then redirect the flame to melt the lower edges of the vee and allow the puddle to advance. You will find the puddle more fluid than the puddle you handled in steel welding, since cast iron does not have the fairly wide "mushy" range which make steel welding quite easy. Therefore, extra care to avoid letting the puddle run ahead and roll onto metal which has not yet reached fusion temperature is required.

While making the weld, you may see gas bubbles or white specks in the puddle. During your first weld, we suggest that you ignore them. Thereafter, you must take pains to work them out as you go along, by adding flux to the rod, and by playing the flame around the specks until they float to the very top of the puddle. Once they float to the top, skim them off with the tip of the welding rod, and tap the end of the rod gently on the welding table to dislodge them. Removal of such visible particles (usually dirt, or impurities in the base metal) is essential if a full-strength weld is to be secured.

Once the weld has been completed, reheat the entire weld with the torch until it glows faintly. Then place the welded specimen between sheets of asbestos paper to allow it to cool as slowly as possible.

After the weld has cooled completely, wire brush the surface of the weld on both sides, and examine it carefully. Note particularly the appearance of the underside. If thorough fusion between the bottom edges of the vee has not been obtained, the defect can be clearly seen. The bottom of a good weld will show little round beads of weld metal protruding through.

Test your weld by clamping the specimen in a large vise, with the centerline of the weld flush with the tip of the jaws. Strike the upper part of the specimen with a heavy hammer until the part breaks. If you have made a good weld, the break will probably occur in the base metal, not in the weld.

If it breaks through the weld, examine the fracture carefully for inclusions, gaps, or blowholes. If the break occurs in the base metal, remove the specimen from the vise, nick it with a hacksaw, on both sides of the weld zone, then return it to the vise and break it across the weld. Examine the fractured weld metal carefully to see whether it appears sound, with no slag or oxide inclusions or blowholes.

Practical Hints

If you are preheating a casting with the torch, or in an improvised furnace, watch carefully to make sure that you do not overheat any part of the casting. It should never get more than dull red. If it gets too hot, it may warp from its own weight, and become completely unrepairable. Try to keep the thinner sections farthest from the heat source if an improvised preheating furnace is being used.

Just as the foundryman must rely on experience, and the use of correct foundry practices, to feel quite sure that a finished casting with no visible defects is sound, so a welder must follow correct procedures, with emphasis on proper preheating and cooling, if he is to feel confident that a good-looking fusion weld in cast iron will stand up in service. Of course, he can leak-test a weld in a water jacket. A weld which must be leaktight, but cannot be tested under pressure in the repair shop, can be checked rather well by applying kerosene to one side of the weld. Kerosene will work its way rapidly through even a slightly porous weld. But such tests cannot be conclusive as to the overall soundness of the weld, and the final condition of the repaired casting.

QUESTIONS – CHAPTER 16

1. What is cast iron?
2. How is white cast iron made?
3. What are the properties of gray cast iron that make it popular for so many uses?
4. What is malleable iron? Nodular iron?
5. What mechanical operations can be performed on cast iron?
6. What are some of the uses of cast iron?
7. Why are the expansion and contraction effects so important when working on cast iron?
8. How does the ductility of cast iron affect the welding procedure?
9. What are some of the ways in which the effects of expansion and contraction can be cared for when welding cast iron?
10. What welding techniques can be used to join gray cast iron parts?
11. How should malleable iron be welded?
12. What are some of the advantages of braze-welding when applied to cast iron?
13. What should be done to prepare cast iron parts for welding?
14. What is a good test of the quality of a braze-weld in cast iron?
15. What are some of the things which can be done in the commercial application of braze-welding cast iron to make the results better or the work easier?
16. Why must preheating be more extensive for fusion welding cast iron than for braze-welding this metal?
17. What are some of the things that must be done to insure the proper structure in a fusion weld in cast iron?
18. What property of cast iron makes puddle control more difficult than in steel welding?
19. What is the preferable joint design for fusion welding cast iron?
20. How extensively should preheating be done for fusion welding cast iron?
21. What are the essential properties that are required for a cast iron welding rod?
22. What is the purpose of flux in cast iron fusion welding?
23. What flame adjustment should be used for fusion welding cast iron?
24. What are some of the important points in the welding technique for cast iron?
25. What is the recommended treatment after cast iron has been fusion welded?

WELDING OTHER FERROUS METALS

In the preceding chapters, we've been talking chiefly about the welding of the two kinds of ferrous materials (iron alloys) most frequently encountered: low-carbon mild steels, and gray cast iron. Now let's take a look at the problems involved in the oxy-acetylene welding of several other ferrous materials, specifically:

Cast Steel   Stainless Steels
High-Carbon Steel   Wrought Iron
Galvanized Steel

Cast Steel

Many castings are made from steel, rather than cast iron, in order to arrive at finished parts which have high shock resistance and good ductility, properties in which cast iron is generally deficient. Cast steel can often be distinguished from cast iron by its surface color. The "gray" color of steel is so distinctive that the term "steely" is often used to describe the color of other materials. When surface identification isn't possible, the color of a freshly fractured surface will distinguish cast steel from cast iron. If necessary, use a cold chisel on the surface of the casting, and attempt to cut off a thin chip. From steel, you can cut a curling chip of some length; from cast iron, even a short continuous chip is unusual. Finally, the behavior of the two materials when raised to melting temperature by the torch flame is quite different. The steel appears to be nearly white-hot before it melts; cast iron starts melting at a red heat. A puddle of molten steel is straw-white in color; a puddle of cast iron is reddish-white.

Most cast steels are similar to low-carbon or medium-carbon rolled steels in composition, and can be welded with ease. In fact, the welding of rolled (wrought) steel to steel castings is often a production application. When welding cast iron, the major problem is to avoid cracking the cast iron, or leaving it with locked-in stresses that might cause cracking in service. When welding cast steel, you normally need not worry about cracking, but you must be concerned about distortion, since steel will *stretch* — become permanently elongated — before it will *break*. Distortion can often destroy the utility of a casting just as completely as cracking.

Preparation for Welding. When faced with the problem of welding a broken steel casting, first consideration should be given to correcting any permanent distortion the casting may have suffered before it broke. Any heating and bending required to restore a casting to its original shape and alignment should be done before beveling and welding.

Small steel castings usually require no more preparation than beveling of the edges to be welded, and good cleaning of the surfaces. Beveling can be done with a chipping hammer, portable grinder, or cutting torch. Follow oxy-acetylene beveling with grinding or wire-brushing.

Large or intricate castings will often require preheating before welding, in order to eliminate the chance of permanent distortion. So much depends on the shape of the casting and the location of the place where welding must be done that it is impossible to provide guidelines which can be broadly applied to determine whether general preheating, local preheating, or no preheating is required. If general preheating is done, the casting should be heated bright red, and allowed to cool slowly after welding is completed.

Welding Technique. Welding the casting, whether preheated or not, should usually be done in a series of passes, following the normal practice for heavy steel plate. If you are repairing a break which occurred in service, watch closely for evidence of sand holes or inclusions which may have been the primary cause of the break. These will show up as bright spots or unexpected craters in the molten metal. Work on these with the flame so that any inclusions (sand or slag) will be brought to the surface of the puddle, and then worked over to the edge of the puddle with the welding rod.

When a break between a thin section and a thick section is being welded, take pains to direct more of the heat from the flame onto the heavier section.

Building-Up and Filling-In Operations. Welding on steel castings often falls into two categories rarely encountered in work on rolled steel: the building up of lugs or bosses which may have emerged incomplete from the mold, or the filling-in of holes which cropped up unexpectedly. (These defects are more common in cast steel than in cast iron, because molten steel isn't quite as fluid as molten cast iron; on the other hand, they can be corrected far more easily in cast steel than they can in cast iron.)

The building up of a lug, a small boss, or an incomplete edge is something of an art, but an art that any welder can master with experience. The trick is to keep the molten metal in the mushy range, not let it get really fluid, and to learn how to control the puddle with the flame. As in normal welding try always to let the puddle do the actual melting of the filler metal.

Before trying to fill a hole which extends all the way through a section of the casting, always find a way to shape the sides of the hole, either by countersinking or actual melting, so that at the bottom of the hole you have something sharper than a square corner to start work on. Then run a bead around that bottom edge, and add weld metal in progressively narrowing circles until the hole is closed at the bottom. Then add metal, a layer at a time, until the hole is completely filled. Always make certain that every layer is thoroughly fused to the layer below.

When the hole goes all the way through a thick section, and it is possible to work on it from both ends, countersink or shape it from both sides, and then fit a small piece of steel into the center of the hole. Finally, weld from each side, making sure, when starting the second side, that the steel insert is completely melted.

High Carbon Steels

Almost every item made from high-carbon steel must be heat-treated after forming or fabrication to achieve the right combination of hardness and toughness required in service. Welding high-carbon steel by the oxy-acetylene process, even when filler metal of high carbon is employed, will always result in substantial modification of those properties in the base metal. Therefore, high-carbon steel items can seldom be repaired by welding unless facilities for *correct* heat-treating after welding are available. If, in an emergency, you ever feel the need to weld something which is probably made of high-carbon steel (such as a knife blade or spring) use the best steel filler metal you have, use an excess acetylene flame (to cause carbon pickup by the molten metal), and try to work as fast as you can, melting no more of the base metal than is absolutely necessary to insure complete fusion.

Galvanized Steel

Galvanized steel (frequently called "galvanized iron") is steel which has been coated with zinc to protect it against corrosion. Most coating is done by immersing the steel sheet, pipe, or wire in a bath of molten zinc. The thickness of such hot-dip coating ranges from about 0.025 mm (0.001 in.) to 0.125 mm (0.005 in.) Galvanizing can also be done by electroplating; the thickness of the zinc coating on electroplated material will often be less than 0.025 mm (0.001 in.)

AVOID INHALING ZINC FUMES! Zinc has a low melting point, about 420°C, and vaporizes (become gas) at a temperature (900°C) far below the melting point of steel. As it vaporizes, it reacts with oxygen to form fumes of white zinc oxide. If you inhale many of these fumes, you are likely to feel sick. While the sickness will pass, leaving no known lasting after-effects, it can be quite unpleasant. Therefore, when you weld galvanized steel, do it only in a well-ventilated location. If good ventilation cannot be assured, wear a respirator.

Fusion Welding. Fusion weld galvanized steel exactly as you would ungalvanized steel. Be sure to clean the surfaces thoroughly. If beveling is necessary, do not hesitate to use the cutting torch, since that will remove no more zinc than will the welding operation.

Fig. 17-1. Before welding galvanized steel indoors, always provide for forced ventilation to remove zinc oxide fumes. Here, a roomy hood with overhead exhaust fan is in use.

Braze Welding. The technique for braze welding galvanized steel is exactly the same as for braze welding ungalvanized steel. Where a color match is not essential, braze welding is perhaps preferable to fusion welding, since the lower temperature of the braze welding operation removes less zinc. Generally, braze welded joints will give excellent service without any finishing, but aluminum paint may be used where a more uniform appearance is desired.

Corrosion Resistance of Welded Galvanized Piping. While it might appear that welding would reduce the corrosion resistance of galvanized piping, experience has shown that this is not the case. In fact, welding is clearly superior to threading when it comes to galvanized pipe. Threading

Fig. 17-2. This attractive fence was fabricated by a talented welder from galvanized steel pipe. Joints were all braze welded.

removes the zinc coating—in addition to reducing wall thickness—and always leaves some unprotected steel. In the case of welding, the surfaces from which the zinc has been vaporized are left with a black iron oxide layer which is usually an excellent barrier against further oxidation of the steel.

At one time, it was felt that braze welding of galvanized piping, especially buried piping, might lead to corrosion due to galvanic action, which is sometimes a problem when dissimilar metals are joined. Actually, experience in many different fields has shown conclusively that accelerated corrosion due to galvanic action does not take place when brass, bronze, or copper are in contact with steel or cast iron. In the case of buried piping, where electrolytic corrosion due to stray electric currents may be a possibility, welded joints (either fusion welded or braze welded) are clearly superior to threaded joints, since there is no loss of electrical conductivity at the joint. The way to protect uninsulated buried piping from electrolytic corrosion due to stray currents is to provide good ground connections designed to lead stray currents out of the piping without causing corrosion.

Stainless Steels

Very little welding of stainless steels (or other high-alloy steels) is currently done by the oxy-acetylene process. Shielded arc welding processes — notably the inert-gas-shielded tig and mig processes (GTAW and GMAW) — have become standard for the welding of such steels. Nonetheless, there may be an occasion when a stainless steel part must be welded, and the equipment for tig or mig welding is unavailable. Here are some things you should know before you attempt any stainless steel welding:

1. There are three general types of high-chromium "stainless" alloy steels: the hardenable high-chromium steels which usually contain 0.15% carbon (maximum) and up to 14% chromium; the non-hardenable straight-chromium steels which contain 14-27% chromium; and the austenitic chromium-nickel steels, also non-hardenable, which contain 18-20% chromium, 8-20% nickel. All are weldable, but the straight-chromium steels, whether hardenable or non-hardenable, require preheating and post-weld heat-treating, if the original properties of the metal are to be retained.

2. The austenitic stainless steels ("18-8" and "25-20") can be oxy-acetylene welded without great difficulty, and without preheating, whenever a suitable filler rod (such as OXWELD No. 60 rod) and welding flux (such as OXWELD CROMALOY flux) are available. The problem with these steels is that they are usually chosen for maximum corrosion resistance, and welding may substantially reduce that corrosion resistance. Unless these steels are especially formulated to have extremely low carbon content, or contain *stabilizing* elements (columbium, titanium, or tantalum), chromium carbides precipitate along the grain boundaries in the steel when it is cooled slowly through the 1100-450°C temperature range. This precipitation may later lead to *intergranular corrosion* unless it is removed by post-weld heat treatment.

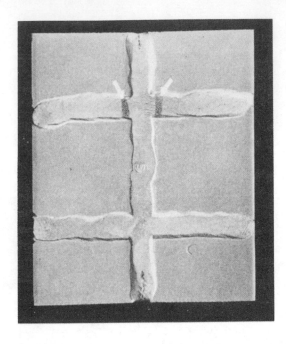

Fig. 17-3. Crossed weld beads, ground and then dipped in acid, on a plate of columbium-stablized 18-8 stainless steel. The upper cross was made with unstabilized welding rod. Note the evidence of intergranular corrosion indicated by the arrows.

3. Austenitic stainless steel should always be welded with filler metal which contains the stabilizing element columbium (found in OXWELD No. 60 rod). This eliminates any possibility of later intergranular corrosion in the joint itself. However, the welding process will always raise the temperature of the base metal, in a zone close to the weld, to a temperature well above 1100°C, and the cooling of that zone, after welding, will be slow enough to permit precipitation of carbides. If the base metal is not stabilized or extra-low-carbon stainless steel, post-weld heat treatment to restore the original metal structure is essential. The metal should be raised to a uniform temperature of about 1100°C for at least fifteen minutes, and then cooled to a temperature of 450°C in a period of less than three minutes. (In the case of thin sheet, air-cooling will usually accomplish this.)

Welding Technique. As noted above, you need a suitable filler metal and a flux specifically formulated for stainless steel welding. The flux should be mixed with water to form a thin paste, and then painted on the surfaces to be welded. Because stainless steel has much lower heat conductivity than ordinary carbon steel, the welding tip selected should be one or two sizes *smaller* than the size you would use with carbon steel of the same thickness. Adjust the welding flame to have a *slight* excess of acetylene. (A truly neutral flame will be satisfactory, but any excess of oxygen will cause trouble; a slight visible excess of acetylene is suggested to guard against the possibility of excess oxygen.)

Since the austenitic stainless steels have a much higher coefficient of expansion than mild steel, particular attention must be paid to the expansion/contraction problem. For sheet metal, careful jigging, with chill plates designed to conduct heat out of the metal at a point close to the weld zone, is strongly recommended. In material thicker than 2 mm (16-gauge) sheet, when a weld longer that 30 cm (1 ft.) must be made, it's a good idea to tack-weld both ends in normal fashion, but then keep a wedge in the joint, 15-20 cm ahead of the weld puddle, and move the wedge periodically as the weld progresses.

While welding, try to avoid moving the filler rod any more than is absolutely necessary. Keep the weld puddle as quiet as possible, trying to melt both rod and base metal almost simultaneously. This will minimize the chance of excessive oxidation of the molten metal, with resultant loss of chromium. While the standard forehand welding technique is preferred for welding sheet, the backhand method is probably better for heavy material, since that technique makes it easier to melt both rod and base metal together.

Wrought Iron

Wrought iron, widely used a century ago, is no longer made in the U. S., but you may be called on to weld it, since a great deal of wrought iron piping is still in service.

Wrought iron has properties much like those of mild steel, but is chemically and structurally much different. It is essentially a mixture of rather pure iron and a slag made up chiefly of iron oxides and iron silicates. The slag is distributed through the iron in the form of very fine particles which have been stretched, by rolling, into threads or fibers so small that there may be 250,000 or more per square inch of metal cross-section. This structure not only gives the metal high ductility, but also improves its corrosion resistance.

You can weld wrought iron with any good low-carbon steel rod (such as OXWELD No. 1 H.T.) and without using flux. However, the iron component, which is virtually carbon-free, melts at a higher temperature than carbon steel, while the slag component melts at a much lower temperature. The slag will melt first and give the surface of the welding vee a greasy appearance. With most base metals, this greasy look is a signal that the metal is ready for fusion with the filler metal, but in the case of wrought iron this is not true. Considerably more heat must be applied before the metal really begins to melt.

In welding wrought iron, you can concentrate the flame more on the rod than you should when welding steel, and let the puddle build up to a fair size before moving the flame from side to side to fuse the base metal with the puddle. Try to keep the motion of the rod to a minimum, and to melt as little of the base metal as possible.

QUESTIONS – CHAPTER 17

1. What is meant by cast steel?
2. What are some of the properties of cast steel?
3. What are some of the ways in which cast steel can be recognized?
4. What welding operations are most frequently performed on cast steel?
5. What are some of the factors that should be considered in preparing a steel casting for welding?
6. What are the steps in the technique for building up edges?
7. What are the steps in the technique for filling holes in casting?
8. What is meant by high-carbon steel?
9. What are some of the important factors to bear in mind before welding high-carbon steel?
10. What is galvanized iron?
11. What are the properties of zinc that require special consideration when galvanized steel is welded?
12. What is the recommended joint design for galvanized iron?
13. How should the material be prepared for welding?
14. How is the galvanized coating affected by the heat of fusion welding?
15. What is the effect of heat on the galvanized coating when the braze-welding technique is used?
16. What effect does welding have on the corrosion resistance of galvanized piping?
17. Which has more effect on the corrosion resistance and mechanical strength of galvanized iron piping, threading or welding?
18. How are stainless steels grouped with respect to their welding characteristics?
19. What flame adjustment is used for welding stainless steels?
20. Should preheating or annealing be used for stainless steels?
21. What is wrought iron?
22. What are the two characteristics of wrought iron which are of importance to the welding operator?

18

WELDING ALUMINUM

Before the inert-gas-shielded arc welding processes were introduced, most fusion welding of aluminum was done with the oxy-acetylene torch. Today, either tig welding (GTAW) or mig welding (GMAW) is preferred if the necessary equipment is available. However, aluminum is widely used, and thousands of shops and individuals possess oxy-acetylene welding outfits but do not have tig or mig welding equipment. Therefore we devote an entire chapter to the welding of aluminum, believing that many readers will find the information helpful. Welding aluminum is quite different from welding steel, but not extremely difficult once you understand the basic differences between steel and aluminum, and acquire a bit of actual welding experience.

Key Properties

Aluminum and its alloys have three properties which make welding of these materials quite different from the welding of steel:

(1) Not only do they have low melting points (around 700°C) but there is no visible color change to warn you that the metal is approaching its melting point.

(2) They are extremely weak at elevated temperatures, even temperatures well below the melting point. The term often used to describe this property is "hot-short". In welding aluminum, adequate support for heated base metal must be assured. Because aluminum is an excellent conductor of heat, sections well removed from the weld zone may be quite weak.

(3) Aluminum oxidizes very rapidly. On cold metal, a thin film of surface oxide provides an excellent barrier to further oxidation. Molten aluminum reacts with any available oxygen, and forms an oxide with a melting point much higher than that of the metal itself. A flux which will react with this oxide to form a lower-melting-point slag is absolutely essential in oxy-acetylene welding. The slag will then rise to the surface of the weld puddle, and can be removed after the weld has cooled.

Aluminum Alloy Classification

As in the case of steels, aluminum alloys are assigned four-digit numbers, with the first digit representing the most significant alloy component. The

"1xxx" series all contain at least 99.00% aluminum; the 1100 grade, commonly called "commercially pure" contains not more than 1% total of all other components, such as silicon, iron, manganese, and zinc (which are considered as impurities). Members of the "2000" series contain up to nearly 7% copper; in the "5000" series, magnesium is the key alloy ingredient. The "4000" alloys, used principally as filler metal for welding many different alloys, contain substantial amounts of silicon. Except in the "1000" series, the last two digits in a number have no significance; they are assigned in sequence to alloys as they reach the commercialization stage.

In the case of aluminum, the heat treatment or cold-working which the metal receives at the mill or foundry is extremely significant. An alloy heat-treated or cold-worked to give it maximum tensile strength and hardness may have five times the yield strength of the same alloy when it is annealed to give it maximum ductility. The aluminum industry uses a rather complex system of letter and letter-digit suffixes (following the basic four-digit composition classification number) to indicate the treatment given to the alloy. The "0" suffix means that the metal has been annealed for maximum ductility and formability. An "F" means that the material has received no special treatment after normal rolling or casting. The letter "T" indicates that the alloy has been heat-treated, and the digit or digits after the "T" designate the type of heat treatment. "H1" indicates that the material has been cold-worked to increase its strength and hardness, and a second digit (for example, in "3003-H14") indicates the degree of hardness.

In the aluminum industry, all these different suffixes are said to designate the "temper" of the material. This represents a far broader use of that word than is customary in the steel industry, where "tempering" almost always refers to a specific heat treatment designed to increase the toughness of steel after it has been hardened by rapid quenching.

Mechanical Properties of Aluminum

To generalize about the strength and ductility of aluminum is impossible without specific reference to the "temper" suffixes briefly covered above. Commercially pure aluminum, fully annealed (1100-0) has a yield strength of about 34 MPa (5000 psi) and a higher ductility than any steel (up to 40% elongation in two inches). When cold-worked for maximum strength (1100-H18), the metal's yield strength increases four-fold, to more than 140 MPa (22,000 psi) while per cent elongation drops to 15 per cent. In the case of alloy 2024 (which contains about 4% copper and 1.5% magnesium) the yield strength of the "-0" grade is about 75 MPa (with ductility less than that of mild steel) and of the "-T18" grade about 490 MPa.

We have already noted that aluminum loses strength rapidly at elevated temperatures. Conversely, as the temperature drops, the strength goes up. Every alloy of aluminum exhibits greater tensile and yield strengths at

-160°C (a temperature slightly below the boiling point of liquid oxygen) than at room temperature. Rather surprisingly, the ductility generally increases as the temperature drops, quite dramatically in some alloys (from 6% elongation to 20% in one case).

In aluminum, as in steel, hardness increases as tensile strength increases. However, no aluminum alloy approaches the high-carbon steels in sheer hardness; the property which usually accompanies maximum hardness in aluminum is high *shear strength*, which is very important in some applications.

Physical Properties of Aluminum

The melting point of commercially pure aluminum (1100) is about 660°C. Since it is so nearly pure, it melts completely at that temperature; it does not have the melting point *range* which you find in mild steel. No commercial aluminum alloy, regardless of alloy content, has a higher melting point than pure aluminum. For many alloys, the melting point range is quite broad (more than 100°C in some cases), and starts as low as 500°C. From the standpoint of the welder, the key fact about aluminum melting points and melting point ranges is the upper end of melting point range for alloy 4043, which is generally recommended for the welding of a wide variety of aluminum alloys. This is about 590°C, far below that of any aluminum alloy which does not fall into the "4000" (high-silicon) group. Welds made with 4043 filler metal remain plastic, and capable of absorbing contraction stresses during the period when surrounding metal, although solid, is extremely weak ("hot-short").

Aluminum is generally considered quite corrosion-resistant. To a considerable degree, that corrosion resistance is due to transparent layer of aluminum oxide that forms very rapidly on any surface exposed to air, and will restore itself if scratched or cut. For the oxy-acetylene welder, the key aspect is this: That the flux required when gas welding aluminum is formulated to react with aluminum oxide, and unless every trace of that flux is removed after welding, the corrosion resistance of the metal may be seriously reduced.

Aluminum and its alloys are generally good conductors of both heat and electricity. Some of the alloys, however, have less than half the conductivity rates of pure aluminum.

Preparation for Welding Aluminum

Joint Design. The joint designs suggested for oxy-acetylene welding of aluminum are much the same as those described earlier for steel. For sheet aluminum, up to 1.6 mm thick (16 gauge) the flanged joint is good. The square edge butt joint may also be used. For material 5mm to 11mm thick, the single-vee joint, with included angle of *at least* 90 degrees, is best. At the base of the vee, there should be a squared-off nose not less than 1.5 mm (1/16 in.) high. Whenever possible, material more than 11 mm thick should be welded from both sides. There are two ways to do this. One is to prepare the pieces with equal bevels on both sides and a squared-off nose in the center. The other is to make a single-bevel preparation, with a nose at the root of the joint which is deeper than normal. After making a weld on the top, chip out a fresh vee on the backside, making sure that the root of that vee extends into the weld metal deposited in the first pass, and then make a second weld through that new vee.

Cleaning. Surfaces to be welded must be free from dirt, grease, oil or paint. To remove oil or grease, use an alkaline cleaning solution (such as trisodium phosphate in hot water), not a flammable solvent. Scrubbing with a wire brush (stainless steel bristles are desirable) to remove as much surface oxide as possible is recommended.

Jigging. Whenever possible, prepare some kind of jig for welding sheet aluminum. Do not jig the aluminum so tightly as to prevent back-and-forth movement of the sheet as it expands or contracts; jigging is needed only to keep the surfaces of the sheet aligned at the joint. Do not use chill bars (as suggested for welding stainless steel). They will accomplish nothing, and may increase your gas consumption. Use asbestos paper, as shown in Fig.18-1.

Preheating. Some kind of preheating is essential in almost every situation. With sheet aluminum, to warm up both pieces along the line of the weld with your torch may be enough. More general preheating is desirable in the case of plate or castings. This can sometimes be done with an air-gas torch working ahead of the welder; for large parts or complex castings, furnace preheating is best. However, in all cases it is essential that the preheat temperature be held to a maximum of about 370° C. Temperature-indicating crayons make it quite easy to check temperature.

Tack-Welding. Welded joints in aluminum should always be tack-welded. The coefficient of thermal expansion for aluminum is double that of carbon steel; without adequate tack-welding, the whole job may be ruined. Tack-weld thin sheet every 4 cm or so (1½ in.). In plate, make a tack-weld at least every 15 to 20 cm (6 to 8 in.).

Welding Materials

Filler Metal. The two grades most widely used for oxy-acetylene welding are 1100 ("commercially pure") and 4043. The latter, a high-silicon alloy, has been found suitable for welding many of the "5000" and "6000" alloys when a precise match-up of properties or color is not required. It has relatively high strength. Perhaps more important, it has a melting point range well below that of most other alloys. This means that 4043 weld metal will remain plastic, and capable of absorbing contraction stress, after surrounding metal has solidified but is still extremely weak ("hot-short"). Because of this helpful property, it is sometimes used for welding 1100 and 3003 aluminum when color match is not essential and some reduction in corrosion resistance is acceptable. (3003 is a relatively "pure" aluminum containing no more than 3% other ingredients.)

In addition to 1100 and 4043, at least a half-dozen other alloys are marketed in straight-length welding rod form for use when more precise match-up of composition and properties is essential.

Flux. Oxy-acetylene welding without a suitable flux is impossible. No flux except one designed specifically for aluminum welding, such as OX-WELD Aluminum Flux, will do the job. The flux should be mixed with water (two or three parts flux to one part water) to form a thin pasty mixture which can be applied to the edges of the joint. Aluminum flux should never be mixed in a metal container; use porcelain or glass.

Welding Technique

Flame Adjustment. Aluminum welding should always be done with a flame which has a slight excess of acetylene (not more than 1¼X). Do not use a stiff, harsh flame, as you may in welding steel; adjust the flame so that it is rather soft. Use a welding tip at least as large as you would use of steel of the same thickness; an experienced welder will usually use a tip one size larger.

First Practice. Before trying to make your first weld, get a piece of sheet aluminum about 1.5 mm thick (¹/₁₆ in.) and find out how the metal behaves under the flame. For this trial, use a *small* tip. Apply flux to the surface of the sheet. Light the torch, and direct the flame almost vertically at the sheet, much as you might when starting a tack-weld in steel. You will probably find that before you have any warning that the metal is ready to melt, a

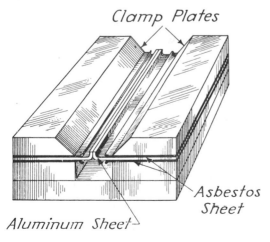

Clamp Plates

Asbestos Sheet

Aluminum Sheet

Fig. 18-1. Here's a way to jig aluminum sheet to minimize distortion. Use heavy clamping plates, but do not use C-clamps, since the sheet must be free to move laterally. Use asbestos paper on both sides of the aluminum.

hole will appear in the sheet. Start again, with the flame at an angle of about 30 degrees to the sheet. You should find that although there is no color change to warn you that the melting point is approaching, a puddle will form on the surface of the sheet and you'll have time to start moving the flame before burn-through occurs. Now try to move the puddle across the surface of the sheet. Note how quickly the puddle solidifies behind the flame, because of the high heat conductivity of the metal.

Once you have learned to move a puddle across sheet aluminum without burn-through, try a weld between two pieces of sheet aluminum, using a larger welding tip. Commercially pure aluminum (1100) fully anealed (temper 0) is recommended. Flange the edges, using a vise. The flange should be a height about equal to the thickness of the sheet; a bit extra won't create problems. Clean the edges, and all surfaces within 1 cm of each edge, by brushing with a wire brush and hot water. Mix flux with water in a glass or porcelain container. Apply the mixture with a brush to both sides of both pieces. If possible, jig the pieces with heavy plates and asbestos paper (see Fig. 18-1). Then make the weld without filler metal. When the weld has cooled, clean the flux off with hot water and examine the back side of the joint carefully to see if you have obtained uniform fusion.

Welding with Filler Metal. After making a successful weld in flanged sheet aluminum, either try making a butt weld in the same kind of sheet, or proceed directly to trying a butt weld in plate 5-6 mm thick. If possible, try this weld with 4043 filler metal, regardless of the grade of the plate. Bevel the edges as previously directed; be sure to provide a square nose at the lower edges. Use a welding tip designed to burn 12 to 15 cfh of acetylene.

If the two pieces of plate to be welded are about 15 cm long, tack-weld at each end of the joint to give a gap of about 3 mm at the starting end and about 9 mm at the finishing end. Then put a third tack-weld in the middle. Be sure to apply flux generously before tack-welding. Then start your weld well ahead of the first tack-weld, after playing your torch flame back and forth along the line of the weld to preheat the aluminum. Moving from right to left (forehand technique) carry the weld to the finishing end in one pass. Then turn the metal around and complete the weld from the starting point back through the first tack-weld.

Practical Hints

When you weld essentially "pure" aluminum plate (1100 or 3003) with 1100 filler metal, it is permissible to use a "back-step" method of welding; that is, you can put in a root pass for a short distance (4-6 cm) and then go back to fill in the vee before continuing down the line of the weld. However, when using 4043 filler metal (especially on heat-treated alloys) try to make any weld in one continuous pass, working as rapidly as possible. This will minimize loss of strength in the base metal.

Fig. 18-2. Here's what can happen, in welding aluminum, if the flame becomes even slightly oxidizing. The metal balls up.

Fig. 18-3. In making this weld, the operator directed too much heat on the welding rod, not enough on the plate.

Fig. 18-4. This is the underside of a weld that looked rather good on top. The operator welded so fast that he did not get adequate penetration.

Do not attempt to weld aluminum alloys of the "2xxx" family. These contain copper. Welding will cause the copper to precipitate out of solution in the aluminum, and serious corrosion cracking of the metal in service will be almost inevitable.

While some aluminum castings can be successfully welded with the oxyacetylene torch, using 4043 filler metal, general preheating and slow cooling are usually essential if further cracking of the casting is to be avoided. Many aluminum castings have undergone heat treatment designed to give them maximum strength, and any welding process is likely to reduce this strength. Don't tackle the welding of an aluminum casting with the torch unless you feel sure that you know what you are doing.

There are several grades of "clad" aluminum, which have cores of high-strength alloy with surfaces of relatively pure aluminum having maximum corrosion resistance. The choice of filler metal to be used in welding such clad aluminum must be made on the basis of service conditions. For maximum strength, generally use 4043 filler metal, or one which matches the composition of the core metal. For maximum corrosion resistance, use 1100 filler metal.

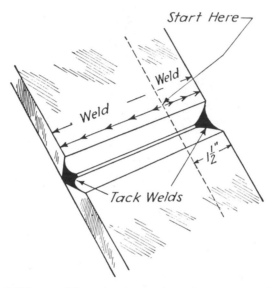

Fig. 18-5. When welding aluminum plate, do not start at the tack-weld, but "down the line" an inch or more. Carry the weld to the other end, then turn the plate around and complete the weld.

QUESTIONS – CHAPTER 18

1. What three properties of aluminum that are different from those of steel have an important effect when aluminum is welded?
2. Why is it not as easy to tell when aluminum is going to melt as it is to recognize when steel has just about reached the melting temperature?
3. What is the effect of the high thermal conductivity of aluminum when this metal is welded?
4. How does the presence of aluminum oxide affect the welding technique for this metal?
5. What does the designation 1xxx mean when applied to an aluminum alloy?
6. What are the general properties of the aluminum designated as 1100?
7. What are the thickness limits of aluminum sheet for which the plain butt-type joint is suitable?
8. What thickness of aluminum sheet can be satisfactorily welded with a flange-type joint?
9. What are the recommended joint designs for welding aluminum plate of various thicknesses?
10. What special cleaning operation should be performed on aluminum preparatory to welding?
11. What are the general principles covering the preheating of aluminum before welding?
12. How can the proper temperature of preheat be recognized?
13. Why is jigging desirable when aluminum is welded?
14. What is the flame adjustment for aluminum welding?
15. How should a weld in aluminum plate be made?

WELDING OTHER NON-FERROUS METALS

As we said early in this book, almost any metal which can be welded at all can be welded with the oxy-acetylene flame. Titanium is a conspicuous exception to that general rule. For copper, for magnesium and its alloys, and for nickel and its alloys, one of the inert-gas-shielded arc welding processes should always be selected in preference to oxy-acetylene welding if the necessary equipment is available. We shall discuss those metals only briefly in this chapter. However, the copper alloys — brasses and bronzes — are widely used, and can almost always be successfully gas welded, so we shall cover them in greater detail. While only a few people have occasion to weld lead, gas welding is the only logical way to weld that soft metal; a special technique is required, which will be described at the end of this chapter.

Copper Alloys — Brasses and Bronzes

The major copper alloys fall into three general categories: the *copper-zinc* alloys, commonly thought of as "brass", but frequently labelled "bronze"; the *copper-tin* alloys, which are the true "bronzes"; and the *copper-silicon* alloys (of which one is brand-named "Everdur"). In addition, there are *aluminum* bronzes, and several copper alloys containing up to 30% *nickel* ("cupro-nickel" and "nickel silver", for example).

The *copper-zinc* alloys have from 5% to 40% zinc content. The "free-cutting" brasses also contain 1-3% lead. Add a little iron and manganese to a high-zinc brass and you get "manganese bronze". The copper-zinc alloys can usually be fusion welded only by the oxy-acetylene process.

Copper-tin alloys in sheet or plate form are often called *phosphor bronze*. The term "phosphor" is derived from the fact that the copper used to make the alloy has been deoxidized by the use of phosphorus. The amount of phosphorus left in the metal after that deoxidation is extremely small. Phosphor bronze may contain as much as 10% tin, or as little as 1.25%. A "tin-bronze" casting will contain 4.5% to 11% tin. All copper-tin alloys can be oxy-acetylene welded.

Silicon-bronze plate and sheet contain only 1.75 to 3.0% silicon, though the silicon may go as high as 14% in a casting alloy. The silicon bronzes can be welded by almost any process, including oxy-acetylene. Silicon bronze has high strength and good corrosion resistance, but lower heat conductivity than pure copper.

The *aluminum bronzes* (7-11% aluminum) have high tensile strength. Oxy-acetylene welding is not recommended.

Welding of Copper-Zinc Alloys (Brasses). To oxy-acetylene weld brass is not difficult if you know what to do about the problems created by the zinc content. These are the things to remember:

(1) You must use a flux; either a braze-welding flux (such as OXWELD BRAZO flux) or a flux formulated for oxy-acetylene welding of stainless steel may be used. The flux should be mixed with water to form a paste, which should then be painted on the rod and on the surfaces to be welded.

(2) You must use an oxidizing flame. In fact, it must be quite strongly oxidizing. If you apply a neutral flame to brass, before actual melting has been observed zinc fumes will start coming off; and the surface of the metal will get quite bright. If you then start to make the flame oxidizing (by cutting back on the acetylene flow) you will find that at a certain point a distinct coating forms on the surface of the brass, and the fuming is virtually eliminated. An oxidizing flame that is just sufficient to create a visible coating on the surface of the base metal is what you want. Too much oxygen will increase the thickness of the coating and make welding more difficult.

(3) You can use a high-quality braze welding filler metal (such as OXWELD 25M rod) on almost any copper-zinc alloy, if precise color match is not essential. In the case of a low-zinc alloy (5% zinc) the melting point of the base metal will be so much higher than that of the rod (OXWELD 25M or equivalent) that you can actually braze weld rather than fusion weld. With most brasses, however, the difference in melting points will be far less.

(4) Use a welding tip at least one size larger than you would normally use on steel of the same thickness, because of the high heat conductivity of the metal. Otherwise, generally follow the forehand welding technique used for steel welding.

Flame-Shaping Brass. When brass piping systems are to be welded, the torch has often been used to shape openings in the pipe. To do this, lay out the outline of the desired opening with a templet, then paint a band of quick-drying iron cement (of the type used for caulking bell-and-spigot pipe joints) around the outline. (Mix the cement with water to the consistency of heavy paint, and apply with a brush.) Then melt through the brass in the center of the opening, using a flame angle of about 30 degrees until the edge of the opening has been reached, then changing to a 90-degree angle in order to get reasonably square edges. Melting sequence suggested for a hole about 5 cm (2 in.) in diameter is shown in Fig. 19-1. Be sure to use an oxidizing flame.

Welding of Copper-Tin Alloys. In general, what has been said about the welding of copper-zinc alloys applies to the welding of the true bronzes, or copper-tin alloys. For repair work, where a precise color match is not es-

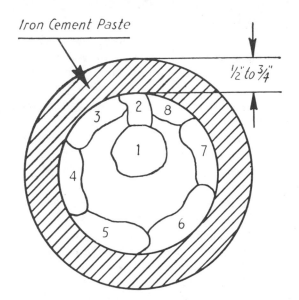

Fig. 19-1. Suggested sequence for melting a hole in brass. Start near the center, but then work around the edge, so that actual melting of all the brass is not required.

sential, standard braze welding rod (such as OXWELD 25M) and brazing flux can be used. For good color match, use filler metal with the same composition as the base metal. The flame should be oxidizing, often strongly oxidizing. The exact degree of excess oxygen needed for good work varies from alloy to alloy. Strong excess will always produce a noticeable film on the surface of the weld puddle. Try to reduce the oxygen just enough to eliminate that film and maintain a bright surface on the puddle.

Welding of Copper-Silicon Alloys. The copper-silicon alloys ("silicon bronzes") should usually be welded using a filler metal of similar composition and a special flux designed specifically for such welding. Even though there is often no zinc in a silicon bronze, use an oxidizing flame, and keep the weld puddle small. The silicon in the metal, combining with the flux, will form a transparent glass-like film on the puddle and prevent undue oxidation. Work as fast as possible. The metal is relatively weak at high temperatures ("hot short") so tight jigging is inadvisable.

Welding of Pure Copper

Fusion welding of copper with the oxy-acetylene torch is made difficult by two properties of copper: its exceptionally high heat conductivity and its high coefficient of expansion. To weld copper thicker than 3 mm you really need two men, and two torches, one working ahead of the other, with the leading torch preheating the metal strongly, or even putting in the root pass. Arc welding is used for fusion welding copper in must situations, since the arc is much hotter than the flame.

Many joints in copper are made by brazing or by braze welding. Brazing of copper tubing will be covered in a later chapter. Braze welding with the oxy-acetylene torch is faster than fusion welding when the chemical and color differences between the base metal and weld metal can be tolerated. For braze welding, use the same rod you would use on steel or cast iron (such as OXWELD 25M), use a slightly oxidizing flame, and use your normal braze welding flux.

Should you find it necessary to fusion weld copper with the oxy-acetylene torch, here are some things you should bear in mind:

1. "Pure" copper comes in two grades: electrolytic "tough pitch" copper, and deoxidized (sometimes termed "phosphorized") copper. Both contain at least 99.60% copper; the difference between the two grades lies almost entirely in the slight amount of oxygen retained in the "tough pitch" grade. When the metal is raised to a high temperature, this oxygen collects at the grain boundaries of the metal and causes substantial weakening of the metal. Therefore, if you must weld copper with the torch, be sure that the base metal is deoxidized copper, and use deoxidized copper filler metal.

2. Since the metal is pure, it will melt completely at one temperature (about 1100°C). There is no "mushy" range, and the liquid metal runs quite freely. However, it is essential that you keep the end of the filler rod in the puddle throughout the welding operation. Control puddle size by moving the flame, not by lifting the rod out of the puddle.

3. After the weld has been completed, it should be peened with a hammer to reduce the grain size of the solidified metal and release locked-up stresses. You can use a ball-end hammer first, and follow up with a flat-end hammer to remove the marks left by the ball-end hammer. Peening can be done while the metal is hot, or after it has cooled (if the metal is less than 6 mm thick). Peening will always improve the quality of the joint. If maximum ductility is required, the weld zone should be reheated to a red heat after peening.

Nickel and Nickel Alloys

While a major part of the world's production of nickel is used in the making of stainless steel, nickel is also used as a pure metal for some applications, and in the form of high-nickel alloys (such as Inconel and Monel) which have high strength and great corrosion resistance. Pure nickel, and virtually all of its alloys, can be successfully welded. We do not, however, suggest that you try to weld nickel or its alloys without first securing the necessary filler metals and fluxes, and instructions for their use, from a supplier of materials such as The International Nickel Co., Inc.

Magnesium

When magnesium and its alloys first became commercially available, they were sometimes welded with oxy-acetylene torch, using techniques similar to those used in welding aluminum. Today, virtually all welding of magnesium is done by one of the inert-gas-shielded arc welding processes. In fact, the tig welding process (GTAW) was initially developed and patented for the welding of magnesium. Unless you can secure the specialized fluxes and filler metals needed for the work, do not attempt to weld magnesium or its alloys with the oxy-acetylene torch. If you ever have occasion to weld magnesium, remember this fact: That magnesium burns rapidly when overheated and in contact with air. Don't get careless. A magnesium fire is no laughing matter.

Lead

Lead is a heavy, soft metal, dull gray in appearance except when freshly cut. It has little mechanical strength; large pieces of lead will collapse under their own weight unless properly supported. However, lead has a number of industrial uses — such as the lining of tanks — which require that it be welded. It is always welded with a gas flame, either the oxy-acetylene flame or another oxy-fuel gas flame. The operation is usually termed "lead burning" by the trade.

To weld lead is not extremely difficult if you use the proper technique. Whenever possible, lead sheets should be connected by *lap joints*. That is, the sheets should be overlapped 6 to 12 mm, and welds made along each overlapped edge. The metal *must* be supported during welding. A *small* welding tip (orifice size less than 1 mm) must be used. The weld cannot be made on a continuous basis; it must be made as a series of overlapping spot welds. Use a flame with a slight excess of acetylene. Hold the torch so that the flame is almost perpendicular to the work surface, with the inner cone almost touching the metal surface. The instant a small puddle has formed, lift the torch away. Then make a new puddle, overlapping the first one.

For a lap weld in lead, filler metal usually is not needed. For a butt weld, which may be required occasionally, filler metal can be provided by cutting sheet lead into strips, or by melting lead and pouring it into a channel mold of some kind.

Perhaps the most important thing to remember about the welding of lead is that you must scrape all oxides from the surface of the metal before you try to weld it.

QUESTIONS – CHAPTER 19

1. What are some familiar copper alloys?
2. What type of flame should be used for welding brass and other copper alloys? Why?
3. What size welding tip should be used for welding brass as opposed to welding steel of the same thickness? Why?
4. Why is it difficult to fusion weld pure copper?

BRONZE-SURFACING, HARD-FACING, AND REBUILDING

In many shops, the oxy-acetylene welding torch is used more frequently to rebuild or resurface metal parts than it is to join metal components. As indicated by the chapter title, we shall cover these applications under three general headings: *bronze-surfacing, hard-facing,* and other *rebuilding* operations. Actually, bronze-surfacing and some hard-facing applications could also be termed "rebuilding"; however, hard-facing is often applied to new parts which have not yet seen service.

Bronze Surfacing

When braze welding techniques and materials are used to rebuild or resurface worn parts, the operation is usually termed *bronze-surfacing.* When bronze is applied to steel or cast iron parts subject to sliding friction, such as pistons, bull rings, rotary valves, or large gears, the reconditioned parts will often give longer service than brand-new parts.

The advantages of bronze-surfacing are perhaps most clearly illustrated in the case of pistons. When pistons become worn, the efficiency of the engine or pump in which they operate is reduced. Eventually the pistons must be scrapped and replaced, or rebuilt to original dimensions, or smaller-diameter cylinder liners installed in the engine or pump. In many cases, bronze-surfacing is the only feasible method available for rebuilding. When the piston is large, the cost of bronze-surfacing and remachining can be substantially less than the cost of a new piston, and the rebuilt piston will often outlast a new piston.

Although the occasion for such work is perhaps less frequent in these days than it was decades ago, the use of braze welding techniques to replace broken teeth in large cast iron gears is another striking example of the versatility of the oxy-acetylene torch. While the replacement of such a gear tooth by a fusion welding process, oxy-acetylene or electric arc, is often feasible, use of bronze will almost always simplify the work and reduce the cost of replacement. Need for preheating is minimized; the time required for the rebuilding itself should be no greater; and the time needed to refinish the rebuilt tooth to proper dimensions should be less. The finished tooth will have ample strength and will resist the sliding-friction wear to which large gear teeth are subjected at least as well as the original cast iron.

Fig. 20-1. Here is a large piston which has been rough-turned in preparation for bronze surfacing.

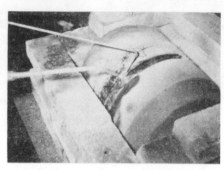

Fig. 20-2. As piston is rotated in a preheating furnance, bronze is deposited in the grooves.

Fig. 20-3. This 26-in. piston, with all grooves filled and then overlayed, is ready for machining.

Fig. 20-4. This photograph shows a resurfaced 18-in. piston during the final machining operation.

Restrictions on Bronze-Surfacing. While bronze is often the ideal metal to use in rebuilding surfaces which are subject to sliding friction (working against other smooth surfaces) there are some limitations which must be kept in mind. Temperature is a factor. The types of filler metal normally used for braze welding (such as OXWELD 25M bronze) lose strength rapidly at temperatures above 260°C. The surfaces of pistons in internal combustion engines (including diesel engines) seldom exceed this temperature. However, some steam engines operate on superheated steam (supplied at temperatures as high as 350°C); for pistons used in such engines, a bronze specifically designed for higher-temperature service, such as OXWELD 31T bronze, should be applied. Another limitation involves the repeated application of bronze surfaces to steel parts subject to alternating tensile and compressive stresses. (This applies to piston rods, but not to pistons). Such parts can be successfully bronze-surfaced once, but repeated application may result in weakening of the steel, due to diffusion of the bronze into the grain structure of the steel.

Fig. 20-5. Remains of this broken tooth in a large cast iron gear have been ground away.

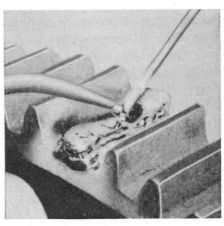

Fig. 20-6. Bronze is deposited in a series of layers, each a bit narrower than the one before.

Fig. 20-7. Build-up has been completed, and the deposit wire-brushed.

Fig. 20-8. Here is the new bronze tooth after machining, ready to go back into service.

Preparation for Bronze-Surfacing. When bronze is to be applied to a new surface, or one only slightly worn, the surface should be machined or ground before bronze is applied. However, since the thickness of the bronze layer required after final machining is very slight, some worn parts require no more than a thorough cleaning before application of bronze. A skilled operator can deposit a layer of bronze no more than 3 mm thick; to remove more than half that thickness in advance by grinding or machining is a waste of energy. If the material to be surfaced is cast iron, remove excess metal by grinding or sand-blasting. Machining smears graphite across the surface, and can make it difficult to get proper *tinning* when depositing the bronze.

Welding Technique. Since bronze-surfacing is essentially a braze welding application, the need for preheating the part to be surfaced should be based on the same factors which determine need for preheat before making a braze weld. You must be concerned about the possibility of cracking a cast iron part, or causing permanent distortion of a steel part.

Always use a slightly oxidizing flame, and a good brazing flux. Make certain that the base metal tins properly at all points. Remember that lack of proper tinning action is caused most frequently by overheating of the base metal. Try to plan the operation so that you can start at one point and complete the surfacing without interrupting the work for more than a few seconds at a time. Keep the layer of bronze just thick enough so that the lowest spots will still require a bit of finish machining. Don't put down a 5 mm layer of bronze if the final thickness, after finish machining, need be only 2 mm or less.

After the surfacing operation has been completed, always allow the part to cool *slowly* to room temperature before machining to final size.

Hard-Facing

Hard-facing is the term applied to the use of a welding process to deposit specialized alloys which are formulated to resist abrasion, corrosion, high temperature, or impact. Such an alloy may be deposited on the surface, an edge, or merely the point of a part subject to wear. A hard-faced part should be thought of as a *composite,* with the base material selected for strength and economy, and the hard-facing material (which might be unsuitable as well as too costly for use in fabricating the complete part) selected for the specific wearing conditions to which the critical sections of the part will be subjected in service.

Hard-facing can often increase the service life of a part ten times or more. In some applications, cost of hard-facing may seem exorbitant until the costs involved in periodic shutdowns to replace worn parts are taken into account. For example, during World War II, mobile oxygen plants were powered by gasoline engines which were expected to operate 24 hours a day. Used with leaded gasoline, unfaced exhaust valves burned out in 7 days; hard-faced valves ran 14 days. (Running time would have been longer had the most suitable hard-facing alloys been available). The hard-faced valves undoubtedly cost several times as much as unfaced valves. But every shutdown to replace the valves involved four hours of labor for replacement of the valves, and resulted in up to eight hours loss of oxygen production. Hard-faced valves would probably have been truly economical at 20 times the cost of plain steel valves, especially since the seating surfaces of the valves could be refaced five or six times before valve stem wear became excessive.

Hard-Facing Materials. Dozens of different hard-facing alloys are available. They fall into four general categories:

(1) *Low-alloy iron-base* alloys, materials, containing up to 12% alloy components, usually chromium, molybdenum, and manganese.

(2) *High-alloy iron-base* alloys, materials with 12-50% alloy content; in addition to the chromium found in all iron-base hard-facing alloys, some of these alloys may also contain nickel or cobalt.

(3) The *cobalt-base* and *nickel-base* alloys, which contain relatively small amounts of iron (1.3 to 12.5%). Of these, the most costly, but also the most versatile, are the cobalt-chromium-tungsten alloys. All the cobalt-base and nickel-base alloys have high resistance to corrosion and oxidation; they possess low coefficients of friction, making them especially suitable for applications involving metal-to-metal wear; and they are almost always selected for applications involving temperatures of 550°C or higher. The cobalt-base alloys retain much of their original hardness at red heat (800°C).

(4) *Tungsten carbide* materials. Tungsten carbide is one of the hardest materials available for industrial use. It cannot be melted by any flame. It is also rather brittle. For hard-facing purposes, it is crushed and applied in conjunction with a "binding" metal. The tungsten carbide particles are usually enclosed in a steel tube rod. Recently, a tube rod enclosing tungsten and vanadium carbides has been introduced. It is said to give more uniform surface coverage than the straight tungsten carbide rod.

Advantages of Hard-Facing with the Oxy-Acetylene Torch. The oxy-acetylene welding torch can be used to deposit all four types of materials listed above. So can several arc welding processes. Generally, the arc processes are much faster; that is, more pounds of alloy can be deposited in one hour of work, or more square inches of surface covered in one hour. However, oxy-acetylene hard-facing is often preferred for one of the following reasons:

(1) The dilution of the hard-facing alloy by base metal melted during the welding process can be held to a minimum. When iron-base alloys are used on steel, this factor may not be of much importance; the alloy can be selected with the dilution factor in mind. However, when the cobalt-base and nickel-base alloys are used, minimum dilution of the deposit by the base metal is of great importance. A skilled oxy-acetylene operator, using the techniques to be described shortly, can hold the dilution of the alloy by the base metal below 6%. With the electric arc processes, dilution rates from 15-25% must be expected.

(2) The thickness of deposit can be minimized. Especially in the case of the costly cobalt-base alloys, this can be quite important. With the oxy-acetylene torch, a skilled operator can deposit a layer of cobalt-base alloy

which is only about 1 mm thick. Only one arc process, using fully-mechanized equipment costing thousands of dollars, can do as well. While it is hard to think of an application where a 1 mm deposit, before finish machining, would be employed, for many applications it is desirable to hold the thickness of the deposit, after finishing, to 2 mm or less. Since the only practicable way to obtain absolute minimum dilution of the finished surface metal is to deposit at least two layers of hard-facing alloy, one over the other, the oxy-acetylene process has a real advantage in applications where minimum thickness of finished deposit is desirable or essential.

(3) The welding equipment can always be brought to the work, rather than vice-versa. No other type of welding equipment is as portable as an oxy-acetylene outfit.

Preparation for Hard-Facing. Surfaces on which hard-facing alloy is to be deposited must be thoroughly cleaned, and free from all scale, dirt, or other foreign material. Grinding or machining should be employed to clean and form the surface in almost every case. *Round off all sharp corners.* Hard-facing alloys generally have relatively low ductility, and often low resistance to shock or sudden impact. If a hard-faced edge or corner is to be subjected to shock, as on a punch, a shear blade, or a die, the steel should be machined in the pattern illustrated in Fig. 20-9(A). The support given the hard-facing alloy will then be adequate to withstand a shock applied vertically, or parallel to the thicker dimension of the alloy deposit. If no severe impact is expected, angles or corners to be hard-faced should be machined as shown in Fig. 20-9(B). If the alloy is to be applied to a longitudinal area, as on a rolling mill guide, machine a groove with radii equal to the depth of the groove, as in Fig. 20-9(C).

Machined Recess For Hard-Facing Alloy

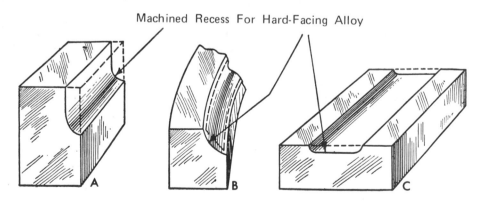

Dotted Lines Indicate Finish-Ground Dimensions

Fig. 20-9. These sketches illustrate how steel edges and corners should be machined before deposit of hard-facing alloys.

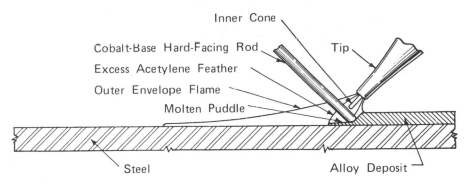

Fig. 20-10. This view shows the relationship of tip, flame and rod to work surface when hard-facing steel, using forehand technique and excess acetylene flame.

Preheating. Some degree of preheating is essential in almost every case, if cracking of the deposit as it cools is to be avoided. Very small parts can be preheated by the torch while applying the alloy. Larger parts must be fully preheated before welding starts, either with the welding torch (using a neutral flame) or in a preheating furnace. The desired level of preheat for steel is a dull red heat (as visible without goggles in a darkened room) of about 430°C. Do not overheat, however, as scale may form on the steel surface. Heating should be uniform, to avoid the chance that uneven contraction of the part will crack the deposit during cooling. Most important — and we shall stress this point again later — provision for *slow* cooling of the part after hard-facing must be made whenever possible.

Oxy-Acetylene Hard-Facing Technique. When working on steel, an excess-acetylene flame must always be used. Generally, a 2X or 3X flame is advisable (length of excess acetylene feather, measured from the tip, to be two or three times the length of the inner cone).* Such a flame causes the surface of the steel to pick up carbon, and lowers its melting point. When that extremely thin surface layer just melts, it glistens visibly, and the alloy will spread readily across the surface with minimum dilution.

After suitable preheating (if done with the torch, use a neutral flame to avoid the chance of leaving a sooty carbon deposit on the surface of the metal) direct the torch flame onto the surface of the steel at an angle of 30 to 60 degrees, with the tip of the inner cone about 3 mm (1/8 in.) from the surface. Hold the torch in this position, without movement, until the surface "sweats" — acquires a glazed appearance. When a medium-sized tip is used (15-20 cfh acetylene rating) the "sweating" should extend about 6 mm

---

*Always use the 3X flame with the cobalt-base alloys. With nickel-base alloys, a 2X flame is generally preferable, to minimize carbon pick-up by the molten hard-facing alloy. With some of the iron-base alloys, a 1 1/2 X flame may give the best over-all result.

beyond the area in direct contact with the excess acetylene feather. Then withdraw the flame enough so that the end of the hard-facing rod can be brought between the inner cone of the flame and the hot base metal. The tip of the inner cone should just about touch the rod, and the rod should touch the "sweating" area. The end of the rod will melt and form a puddle on the surface. If the first drop or two does not spread out uniformly, the base metal is probably too cold; in that case, withdraw the rod and bring the metal up to full "sweating" temperature with the flame.

If the first drops of alloy spread out, withdraw the rod from the flame and spread the alloy further with the flame. Direct the flame so that part of it plays on the puddle, part of it on the surrounding base metal. As the puddle spreads, bring the rod into the flame again, with its end touching the puddle, and melt more alloy into the puddle. Continue these steps until the desired area coverage has been obtained. Then, if necessary to obtain a thicker deposit, make a second pass. In making that pass, you won't have the "sweating" phenomenon to indicate surface temperature, so extra care must be taken not to melt the first layer of alloy any more than is absolutely necessary, lest you melt base metal at the same time and get serious dilution of the deposit.

The puddle should always be moved in the desired direction by flame pressure, not by stirring with the rod. Usually work should progress toward the hand holding the rod (forehand technique) but on some steels which scale readily, the backhand method may prove superior.

If any particles of dirt or scale appear in the puddle, or on the surface of the steel under the puddle, try to float them to the surface of the puddle by using the flame. Only when truly necessary, use the rod to dislodge a particle that resists flame action. It is essential that all visible particles be brought to the surface of the deposit.

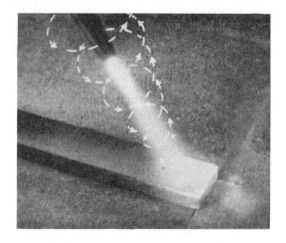

Fig. 20-11. When a deposit of hard-facing rod has been completed, always withdraw the flame slowly to prevent too-rapid cooling.

When cobalt-base or nickel-base alloys are properly applied with the oxy-acetylene flame, there will be very little dilution of the deposit by the base metal, yet the bond between the alloy and the base metal will actually be stronger than the alloy deposit.

Cooling. After completion of the welding operation, the part should be allowed to cool as slowly as possible. If possible, bury it in dry lime, shredded asbestos, dry sand, or wood ashes, or place it in a furnace capable of controlling the cooling rate.

Finishing the Deposit. After the hard-faced part has cooled, finish grinding will usually be necessary to remove high spots, or to grind the surface to the exact size desired. For most alloys, a soft grade vitrified wheel (not coarser than 46 or finer than 60 in Grades I or J of the Norton system) should be used. Wheel speeds should be not less than 2800 nor more than 4200 surface feet per minute. Too high a speed may damage the alloy surface.

Hard-Facing Cast Iron. Cast iron will not "sweat" like steel, so a strongly excess acetylene flame is not necessary. A 1½ X flame should be satisfactory. You will find that the cobalt-base and nickel-base alloys do not spread out so readily on cast iron, and that it may be necessary to tap the rod along the edges of the puddle to get it to spread evenly. Use a good cast iron fusion-welding flux if necessary. Often, it will make sense to deposit a layer of iron-base alloy, or plain carbon steel, before depositing the final hard-facing layer or layers of the more costly hard-facing alloys. Since the melting temperature of cast iron is lower than that of steel, and quite close to that of most hard-facing alloys, it will usually be quite difficult to avoid substantial dilution of the first layer deposited. On a thin section of cast iron, backing up the section with wet asbestos or carbon paste will help you to minimize the amount of melting on the working surface.

Hard-Facing Other Materials. Many grades of steel — even some stainless steels — can be successfully hard-faced. However, the high-manganese steels, high-silicon steels, and the "400" series of stainless steels will always present problems, and require special care in preheating and cooling. Because the nickel-chromium stainless steels (such as "18-8") have relatively high coefficients of expansion, they must always be preheated very evenly, and allowed to cool very slowly after hard-facing has been completed. Hard-facing of steels containing more than 0.50% carbon is seldom successful. Hard-facing any metal which has a relatively low melting point (brass, bronze, aluminum) is impossible.

Hard-Facing with Tungsten Carbide. To apply the composite hard-facing materials which are made up of crushed tungsten carbide and a binding alloy is relatively easy. Use an excess acetylene flame. Try to avoid melting the base metal any more than necessary, but do not hesitate to move the rod about a little to secure even distribution of the tungsten carbide particles. Surfaces hard-faced with tungsten carbide materials are almost always used "as is", with no attempt at finishing.

Rebuilding

As noted at the start of this chapter, many bronze-surfacing operations and some hard-facing operations can be considered "rebuilding". There are also other occasions when it may be necessary to rebuild a part using a metal substantially equivalent to that from which the part was made originally. If it takes several years for a steel part to wear to the point where something must be done to restore it to its original dimensions, it may not make sense to go to the extra trouble and expense of hard-facing the worn section. The same may also be true of a cast iron part. Opportunities for that kind of rebuilding are many. The skill required is usually no more than that needed to lay down a uniform bead on a flat surface. In the case of steel, it may be possible to obtain an increase in future service life by flame-hardening the rebuilt surface after it has been ground or machined to the proper contours and dimensions. We shall discuss flame-hardening in some detail in Chapter 22. Right here we would like to make the point that a small area can sometimes be flame-hardened with the same torch used for rebuilding, and an elementary water quench. Sometimes hardness and wear resistance can be doubled by a few minutes of work.

In closing, let us make this point again: That the use of the oxy-acetylene welding torch to increase the life of wearing parts is a *major* use of the torch. While many hard-facing applications call for the application of engineering skills, there are hundreds of bronze-surfacing and other rebuilding jobs that call for no more than a bit of ingenuity and imagination on the part of the man with the torch.

QUESTIONS – CHAPTER 20

1. What is bronze-surfacing?
2. What are the advantages of bronze-surfacing for parts subject to sliding friction?
3. What should be the maximum operating temperatures for parts that have been bronzed-surfaced?
4. Why should not steel parts subjected to severe alternating stresses be bronze-surfaced more than once?
5. What should be done in preparing steel and cast iron parts for bronze-surfacing?
6. What type of filler metal is recommended for bronze-surfacing operations?
7. Should flux be used in bronze-surfacing?
8. What is meant by the term "hard-facing"?
9. Why is it so often better to hard-face a part than to make the entire part out of a wear-resistant material?
10. What are some of the familiar hard-facing materials?
11. How is tungsten carbide applied to a part?
12. What are some of the advantages of using oxy-acetylene equipment for hard-facing various materials?
13. What are the important things to remember in preparing parts for hard-facing?
14. What flame adjustment is used for applying hard-facing materials?
15. How does the technique for applying hard-facing materials vary from steel welding?
16. What are some of the other materials besides ordinary steel and cast iron that can be hard-faced?
17. What flame adjustment should be used for hard-facing with tungsten carbide?

BRAZING AND SOLDERING

Brazing is a process which differs from *braze welding* in one very important way: In brazing, the filler metal is drawn into the joint by *capillary attraction,* rather than deposited in the joint in somewhat the same fashion as in oxy-acetylene fusion welding. While the majority of industrial brazing operations do not involve the oxy-acetylene fusion welding, in one field — the fabrication and installation of copper-tube piping systems — the oxy-acetylene torch is frequently employed. We shall cover this application shortly. First, let's take a general look at brazing, an extremely important process in metal fabrication.

By American Welding Society definition, *brazing* is a *welding* process in which the filler metal has a melting point higher than 800°F (425°C) but lower than that of the metal of metals being joined, and in which the filler metal is drawn into the joint by capillary attraction.

What do we mean by "capillary attraction"? To put it in very simple terms, it is the ability of a liquid to rise into a narrow gap or passage against the force of gravity. You can demonstrate capillary attraction with two thin pieces of clean glass, as shown in Fig. 21-1. Or you can use two short pieces of glass tubing, one with a very small diameter bore (1 mm or less) one with an inside diameter of 5-6 mm. The water will rise appreciably in the smaller tube, little in the larger tube. (Not all liquids behave in this fashion; many different factors are involved. With mercury, for example, the level in a small diameter tube inserted into a pool of the liquid will actually fall below the level of the pool surface.)

The process known as soldering is generally similar to brazing except that the filler metals used melt at temperatures below 427°C (800°F). In actual practice, most brazing alloys melt at temperatures well above 427°C, most solders at temperatures well below 427°C. Many of the brazing alloys based on silver (all of which melt above 600°C) were formerly termed "silver solders". Avoid that term, and its relative, "silver soldering". Even the term "silver brazing" is sometimes misleading, since some brazing applications for which silver alloys are generally used can also be handled with alloys which contain no silver.

What metals can be brazed? Almost every metal, and some combinations of metals that cannot be successfully fusion-welded together. While the silver-based brazing alloys are the most widely used, there are also families

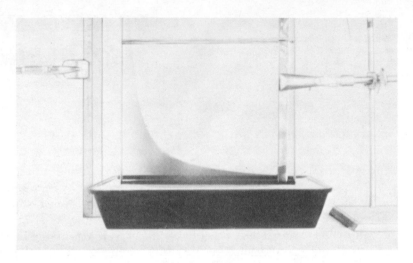

Fig. 21-1. To illustrate capillary attraction, two glass plates are clamped together, with a thin spacer between the plates at the right-hand side, and then inserted in a dish of colored water.

of brazing alloys based on aluminum and magnesium (for use with those metals), on copper and phosphorus, on copper alone or copper and zinc, on nickel, and even on gold. Brazing alloys are designated by the American Welding Society with the letter "B" followed by the chemical symbol or symbols of the major element or elements. "BAg-1, BAg-2", etc. are alloys based on silver (usually about 50%). The copper-phosphorus alloys are designated "BCuP-1, BCuP-2", etc., nickel-base alloys "BNi-1", etc. In the "BAg" group there are no less than 19 different compositions, all of which contain copper as well as silver; some also contain zinc, some cadmium, and a few contain tin or nickel.

In virtually all brazing applications, heat is applied directly to the parts which are to be brazed, not directly to the brazing alloy. Many different heat sources can be used; flames, furnaces, electricity (through resistance or induction heating), radiant (infrared) sources, even molten salt baths. When gas flames are used, the process is termed torch brazing. Do not think of that word "torch" as necessarily implying a hand-held single-flame device like your welding torch. Most production torch brazing is done with fixed multiple-flame burners.

The key to successful brazing is joint design. Because the process depends on capillary attraction, the spacing between the parts to be joined must be small and accurately controlled. While it is possible to make a square-butt joint (similar to that we talked about for fusion welding steel sheet) the two edges must be very carefully prepared, and spaced precisely, if the joint is to be successful. Such butt joints are occasionally employed, but are exceptions. Almost all brazed joints can be classified as lap joints. Several examples are illustrated in Fig. 21-2. The joint between a piece of copper tube and a socket-type fitting is a kind of lap joint. In such a joint, the separation between the two parts should usually be between 0.050 mm (.002 in.) and 0.150 mm (0.006 in.) While clearances greater than 0.150 mm can usually be filled with brazing alloy, the joint will lose some of its strength when subject to tensile forces.

In brazing operations, as in braze welding, a flux is required. The purpose of the flux is to remove from the surfaces of the parts any oxides which may remain after thorough mechanical cleaning, or which form as the parts are being heated to brazing temperature. The fluxes used with silver- or copper-based brazing alloys are all based on boric acid and other boron or flourine compounds. They are somewhat similar to the fluxes used in braze welding, but should not be considered interchangeable with such fluxes. The active ingredients are dry powders which are then mixed with a vehicle to form a paste or thick liquid which can be readily applied to the joint surfaces. When the joint is heated, the vehicle evaporates, and the flux then liquefies to do its work of dissolving oxides.

Brazing Copper Tube To Fittings

For many years, the water piping systems installed in new residences and other buildings have usually been fabricated from copper tubing and socket-type fittings. The materials for such a system may be more costly than steel

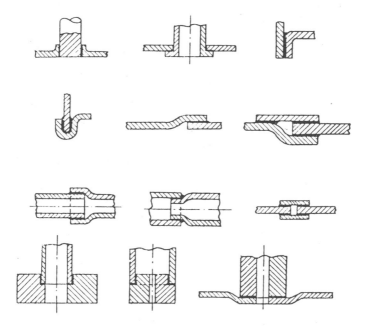

Fig. 21-2. A variety of joint designs suitable for brazing. Virtually all of them can be loosely classified as "lap" joints.

pipe with threaded fittings, but cost of installation is less, thanks to the flexibility of the tubing and the speed and ease with which joints can be made up. In addition, the system has no rust problems, and is likely to prove trouble-free for the life of the buildings. For similar reasons, most radiant-heating systems also use copper tubing. Hospital oxygen piping systems are invariably made up with copper tubing. Copper tubing systems are also used in industrial plants for water and other fluids, even for steam in some cases. While most copper piping systems use relatively small-diameter tubing, in the 1 cm to 5 cm range ($3/8$ in. or 2 in.), some industrial systems use tube as large as 20 cm (8 in.) or larger.

The fittings manufactured for use with copper tubing may be either wrought copper or cast brass. In either case, the depth of the fitting socket into which the tube is inserted is normally sufficient so that full-strength joints — by which we mean joints as strong as the tubing itself when subjected to short-duration tensile forces — can be made up with either soldering alloys ("soft solders") or brazing alloys.

Because soldering is both quicker and easier than brazing, and because the cost of soft solder is less than the cost of a brazing alloy in most cases, more copper tubing systems are soldered than brazed. The temperature levels required for soldering are so low that the oxy-acetylene welding torch is seldom used to make up soldered joints. For brazed joints, however, the oxy-acetylene flame has definite advantages over lower-temperature gas flames, such as those produced by air-acetylene and air-propane torches.

Since the steps involved in making up a brazed joint in copper tubing are essentially the same as those involved in making up a soldered joint, and since they are typical of the steps required to make up any kind of brazed joint with the oxy-acetylene torch, we'll cover them in detail first, then go back to discuss the minor differences between brazing and soldering.

Step 1. Make sure you have good fit-up. Both fittings and copper tubing are manufactured to close tolerances. In sizes up through 1 in., the minimum clearance between the outside diameter of the tube and the inside diameter of the cup in the fitting should be not less than 0.002 in. or more than 0.007 in. The only problem for the man making up the joint is to see that the end of the tube is cut cleanly, without distorting its shape, and that all burrs are removed from the cut end with a file or reamer.

Step 2. Clean the joint surfaces. This is essential if the brazing alloy is to fill the joint completely, without voids. Do not rely on the flux to do the cleaning for you. Clean the outside of the tube with emery paper; clean the inside of the fitting, right down to the bottom of the cup, with emery paper or a rotary wire brush.

Step. 3. Apply flux to the joint surfaces. The brazing flux should be matched to the brazing alloy. Follow the recommendations of the supplier of the brazing alloy. The flux will usually be supplied as a thin paste or viscous liquid. Apply the flux to both tube and fitting with a small brush

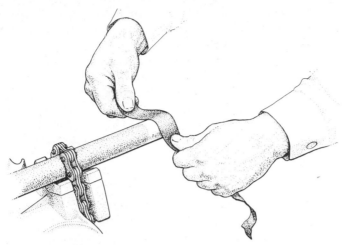

Fig. 21-3. Before brazing, always clean the copper tubing THOROUGHLY, preferably with emery paper.

Fig. 21-4. The fitting must also be cleaned thoroughly with emery paper or with a power-driven rotary wire brush.

Fig. 21-5. Apply flux evenly, using a brush of suitable size, to the inside surface of the fitting. Also apply flux to the copper tube.

that is used only for flux. (Don't ever attempt to use a soldering flux, or to use the same brush with both soldering and brazing fluxes.) Apply the flux in a thin, even layer. Use only enough to cover the surfaces of the joint. Do not apply flux until you are ready to proceed with the next two steps.

Step 4. Assemble tube to fitting. Run the tube into the fitting until it bottoms, if possible. However, bottoming is not absolutely essential. The depth of the cup in the fitting allows considerable leeway. A brazed joint that extends only halfway into the fitting cup will, properly executed, be as strong as the tube. Good alignment of the parts is important. If the tube is horizontal, it must be supported — either with temporary or permanent supports — to insure good alignment and to prevent loading of the fitting with the weight of the tube.

Step 5. Heat both tube and fitting to brazing temperature. This is the key step in the entire operation. At the start, it is best to use a welding head or tip one size smaller than an experienced operator might select. For tube sizes up through 1 in., a tip which consumes about 9 cfh of acetylene is suggested. Adjust the flame to neutral. Never allow the inner cone of the flame to actually touch the parts being heated. Start by heating the tube; you cannot transfer a great deal of heat from the fitting to the tube because of the air gap between the parts which, though small, acts as an insulator. Move the flame steadily around the tube until the flux appears dry and chalky, and starts to melt. Then start to heat the fitting. Keep the torch moving so that you will heat the fitting as uniformly as possible; move the torch back and forth so that you continue to apply some additional heat to the tube as you heat the fitting. Hold the brazing alloy wire in the hand which does not have the torch, and from time to time touch the end of the wire to the joint line between fitting and tube. When brazing temperature has been reached, the alloy will start to melt and draw into the joint. Be

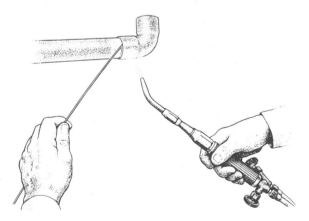

Fig. 21-6. While feeding in brazing alloy, keep the flame directed on the fitting, but away from the alloy itself.

very careful not to let the flame actually touch the brazing wire. Once the alloy has started to melt, apply gentle pressure to the wire and start moving it around the joint. Concentrate the flame on the fitting well back from the tube, and keep the flame moving ahead of the brazing wire. After you have moved the wire completely around the joint, there should be an even fillet of alloy visible between the tube and fitting, all the way around. If there is a gap in this fillet, it probably indicates that you tried to work a bit too fast. Withdraw the wire for a moment while you reheat both tube and fitting at the point where the gap appears. Then touch the brazing alloy to the joint again.

Probably the most important thing to remember is that overheating can be more harmful than underheating. If you overheat, you may not only damage the fitting but you may actually wind up with an incompletely filled joint. It is easy to tell when the parts are not hot enough; the brazing alloy will refuse to melt. It is not so easy to tell when you have overheated; when using silver-base brazing alloys, the brazing temperature range is below that which would cause a visible color change in the parts. (With the copper-phosphorous brazing alloys, however, the brazing temperature is high enough so that a very dull red color may be evident when the proper temperature has been reached.)

Step 6. After the parts have cooled, remove all excess flux. This can usually be accomplished by washing with warm water. Any considerable excess can usually be chipped off; it is hard, but brittle. After chipping, always complete the cleaning with warm water.

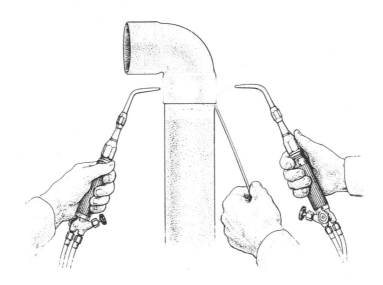

Fig. 21-7. When brazing tubing of 2-in. or larger size, use of a second torch to preheat the fitting will speed up the operation.

Some Additional Pointers

When the tube size is 2 in. or greater, it is almost impossible to bring the entire joint up to brazing temperature at one time, even with a larger welding head. The trick here is to try to bring about two inches of the circumference of the joint (in the case of 2-in. tube, that's about one-third of the joint) up to brazing temperature, then start to apply the brazing alloy, and finally work your way around the fitting, applying heat to both tube and fitting ahead of the brazing alloy. On very large joints (4-in. or more) it speeds up the job to use two torches. A helper uses one to preheat the joint, while the principal operator brings the joint to brazing temperature and applies the filler metal.

Soldering Copper Tube Fittings

As pointed out earlier in this chapter, the only essential difference between brazing and soldering lies in the melting points of the alloys used. Because soldering alloys all melt at temperatures much below 427°C, to use an oxy-acetylene flame for a soldering operation is not only pointless, but difficult, since that flame is so hot that overheating of the metal is hard to avoid. A variety of heat sources are available for the soldering of copper tubing systems. Most widely used are air-acetylene and air-propane torches. (Some of these can also be used for brazing of joints, although the work will go more slowly than it will with an oxy-acetylene flame). The relatively new "swirl" tips for air-acetylene and air-propane torches are strongly recommended, since they produce short flames which are little disturbed by breezes, and allow the operator to put the heat right where he wants it.

In making up soldered joints in copper tubing, follow the six steps previously given for brazing operations. Do not fail to bottom the tube all the way in the fitting, since the mechanical strength of a soldered joint is substantially less than that of a brazed joint. If you are allowed to choose your own solder (in many cases, the type of solder to be used in making up a system is covered by specification, and you have no choice) the so-called "50-50" tin-lead solder (about half lead, half tin) will prove the easiest to work with, since it has a melting range of more than 30°C. Some of the other widely-used solders melt completely at a specific temperature, and require more precise heating if the solder is to be completely and evenly dispersed in the joint.

Other Soldering Applications

It is beyond the scope of this book to describe all the different uses of the air-acetylene and air-propane flames for soldering. In air-conditioning and refrigeration service work, the soldering torch (which may also be used for brazing small-diameter tubing connections) is invaluable. Further, special stems are available, which attach directly to soldering torch handles, for detecting leaks of the "halide" refrigerant gases (marketed under the brand names "Freon", "Ucon", etc.). These leak detectors all take advantage of the fact that the halide gases (chlorine, fluorine, bromine) give distinctive colors to a flame when brought in contact with hot copper. Further, the color changes as the concentration of the halide changes, so that it is easy to pinpoint the source of the leak.

Open-flame soldering is also widely used for finishing off joints in copper wiring systems to make certain that they will remain fully conductive. The thing to remember about this type of joint is this: that copper wire is normally hard-drawn for maximum tensile strength, and that the heat required to make up a soldered connection will anneal the copper and greatly reduce that strength. However, there are several ways to make up twisted joints so that loss of strength can be avoided.

QUESTIONS – CHAPTER 21

1. What is brazing? How does it differ from braze-welding?
2. What is the difference between brazing and soldering?
3. What joint design is commonly used in brazing?
4. How does the amount of spacing provided in the joint design affect the strength of the completed joint?
5. What are the essential points for obtaining a good brazed joint?
6. What may happen if the joint was overheated?
7. What is the problem when you try to braze joints greater than 2-in. diameter?
8. Why is oxy-acetylene torch seldom used for soldering applications?

22

HEATING AND HEAT-TREATING

Considered solely from the standpoint of cost per unit of energy supplied, the oxy-acetylene flame is an expensive source of heat. To use oxy-acetylene flames to boil water or heat a room would be grossly extravagant except in an extreme emergency. Virtually every economically-justified use of the oxy-acetylene flame is based on its extremely high temperature, and on the rapid rate of heat transfer which that temperature, and the concentration of the flame, makes possible. In the case of several processes which will be covered in this chapter, high temperature and high heat transfer rate are absolutely essential. In other applications of the oxy-acetylene flame a third advantage—the ability to do the job faster—also becomes significant.

Here's a simple example: You wish to put a sharp bend in a steel bar that's about 25 mm (1 in.) thick. The high temperature of the oxy-acetylene flame is not required to get the bar hot enough to bend. You could even rig up a miniature blacksmith's forge—if you had some firebrick, charcoal, and a bellows—and do the job. But the fastest way to do the job, and in most respects, the best way, is to put the biggest head you have on your welding torch and use the oxy-acetylene flame to heat the bar. The time saving will more than make up for any extra fuel expense. The larger the head, the faster you can do the job, and the less acetylene you will use. For a job like this, a head which burns 100 cubic feet of acetylene per hour is more economical than a head which burns 40 cubic feet of acetylene per hour. It pays to have such a head as part of a welding outfit, even though it may never be used for welding.*

Flame Hardening

To industry, the most significant *heating* application is *flame-hardening*. The properties of steel—especially the properties of medium- and high-car-

---

*You may recall that in Chapter 3 we said that acetylene should not be withdrawn from a cylinder at an hourly rate greater than one-seventh of full cylinder capacity. You may therefore ask: is it not wrong to operate a 100 cfh head from a single cylinder? The answer to this: Yes, you can withdraw acetylene at seemingly excessive rates for 5-10 minutes at a time (and the job we cited shouldn't take longer) if you restrict such high withdrawal to rather short periods (not more than 10 minutes) and don't repeat such demands more than once every 30 minutes. For continuous operation of a 100-cfh head, at least two large cylinders of acetylene should be manifolded.

bon steels—are greatly affected by the rate at which it is cooled from a point above its critical temperature. All flame-hardening applications involve rapid heating, followed by quenching, in order to harden the surface of steel without making the entire mass of metal unnecessarily hard and excessively brittle.

Let's assume that we have a medium sized gear cast or machined from steel containing about 0.40% carbon. If we place this gear in a forge fire, heat it until it was bright red, then bury it completely in the fire and allowed it to cool slowly as the fire goes out and the ashes cool, we'll find the steel, after it has cooled fully, to have about the same hardness it had before we heated it. However, if we take an identical gear, heat it bright red, and then plunge it in a tub of water, we'll get a different result. The steel will be much harder; it may have been distorted by the sudden quench; it may even have small cracks as the result of the quench.

The simple heat-and-quench method of hardening steel has been known and applied for centuries. The blacksmith took advantage of this method when he heated a part bright red in his forge fire and then plunged it in a tub of water, or sprinkled water over it. Large quantities of small parts are

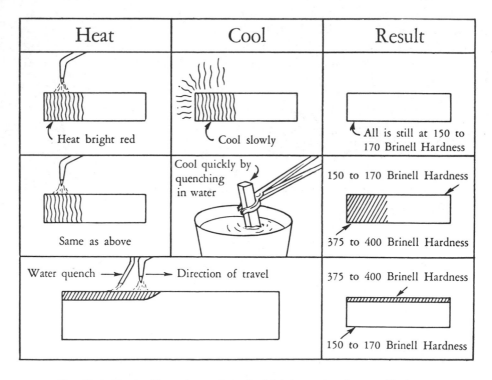

Fig. 22-1. Start with a piece of steel which has a hardness of between 150 and 170 Brinnell, heat it bright red, then cool it three different ways and get three different results.

often heated in a furnace in one batch, and then quenched in water or oil. Larger parts are sometimes individually heated and then quenched with an air blast.

In the heat-and-quench methods just described, there may be some variation in hardness between the surfaces of the finished parts and the interior sections. Generally speaking, however, the entire part has been hardened. For many types of parts, that is not detrimental. But for some parts that need maximum *surface* hardness, to make them resistant to wear, but also maximum toughness, to resist impact or suddenly-applied load, complete hardening is undesirable. That's where flame-hardening comes in. You use oxy-acetylene flames to heat the part so rapidly that the surface reaches a temperature above the critical before the bulk of the part does; then you withdraw the flames and apply a water quench to the surface. The surface layer is cooled rapidly, both by the water quench and by conduction of heat into the body of the part. Depth of the hardened layer can be controlled by varying the intensity of the flames used and the heating time. It is possible to harden a layer as thin as 2 mm or as thick as 12 mm. The increase in hardness value at the surface can be very substantial. The specific amount will depend greatly on the carbon content of the steel; a 0.40% carbon steel can be hardened to a greater degree than can a 0.30% carbon steel.

Because parts to be hardened may be round, flat, or irregularly shaped, the arrangements for flame application and water quench, and for relative movement between the flames and the part, are subject to many variations. The methods used for flame-hardening can be broadly sub-divided in this fashion:

Spot Method. When it is desired to harden just a spot on a part, such as the tip of a valve stem (to reduce the rate of wear when mechanical valve lifters are employed) the area is often heated with a single neutral flame. The flame is then withdrawn and the quench applied.

Progressive Method. For parts on which flat surfaces are to be hardened, the usual arrangement involves use of a mechanical device that will move the flames progressively across the part surface at controlled speed. The quench is arranged so that it follows the flames closely, but with sufficient separation so that it does not interfere with the flames. Large gear teeth are often flame-hardened in this manner.

Spinning Method. The outside surface of many round parts can be hardened by spinning the part rapidly in front of the flames, then shutting off the flames and immediately applying a quench spray, or dropping the part into a quenching medium. This method has been used for bearing surfaces on crankshafts, and for small gears.

Progressive-Spinning Method. When a long round part, such as a shaft, is to be hardened over a considerable length, a combination of the progressive and spinning methods may be used. Round shafts ranging in diameter from 25 mm (1 in.) to 600 mm (24 in.) have been hardened in this manner.

Fig. 22-2. For flame-hardening large gear teeth, special multi-flame heads have flame ports positioned and sized to give precise hardening contours. Quenching water is applied through orifices which trail the flame ports.

Forming and Bending

The oxy-acetylene flame has been used for bending and forming operations ranging all the way from the most delicate details of ornamental ironwork to the straightening of the stern post on an ocean liner.

In the making of ornamental ironwork, as well as many types of modern metal sculpture, the oxy-acetylene torch is the indispensable tool of the artisan or artist. He can use it to cut, to shape, to weld. Precise bending can be done because the flame can bring just the right spot to bending temperature rapidly.

In many cases, structural shapes, such as angle iron, channels, and tees can be modified for special purposes by using both the cutting torch and the heating torch. To make a square or rectangular angle iron frame, for example, by far the easiest method of arriving at the desired result is to use a single length of angle iron, notch it with a cutting torch at the corner positions, then use a heating head to secure sharp, properly-positioned corner bends. The corners are then welded.

Straightening

In a surprising number of situations, the oxy-acetylene flame can be used to accomplish straightening without application of mechanical force. Take

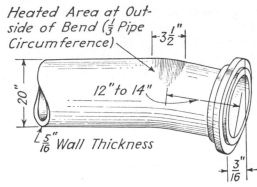

Heated Area at Outside of Bend ($\frac{1}{3}$ Pipe Circumference)

$3\frac{1}{2}"$

20"

12" to 14"

$\frac{5}{16}"$ Wall Thickness

$\frac{3}{16}"$

Fig. 22-3. The flange at one end of this 20-in. pipe was slightly out-of-line (sketch exaggerated). It was brought back into line by heating the outside of the bend.

the case of a section of large pipe, which must be straightened so that the face of a union joint can be brought into alignment with the next section. If we heat an area of the pipe on what we might call the "back" side of the bend (heating not more than one-third of the circumference) the force of expansion generated by the heating will not be sufficient to bend the unheated metal on the opposite side of the pipe. Instead, the heated metal will tend to *upset* slightly. On cooling, the heated section will regain its strength rapidly, and the force of contraction will become sufficient to bend the unheated side and pull the pipe into line. In general the same principle is applied in all straightening operations which do not involve use of external mechanical force. Sometimes it is necessary to quench the heated section with water to achieve the result desired.

Wrinkle-Bending

A technique described as wrinkled-bending was developed many years ago for bending of moderately large pipe. While no longer used extensively, it can prove extremely useful when an elbow fitting of the correct size and

Fig. 22-4. Wrinkle-bending a section of large pipe with a rather simple shop setup. In this case, about 10 wrinkles will be used for a 90-degree bend.

angle is not readily available. To wrinkle-bend, you heat a band of metal extending at least halfway around the pipe circumference and then pull the pipe to upset the metal in the heated section. To do this successfully, you *must* use a high-capacity head, and on large pipe (8 in. and up) it is best to use two torches at once. The bend achieved by one wrinkle should not exceed 12 degrees, so for a right-angle turn you need at least eight wrinkles, spaced a few inches apart. The virtue of wrinkle-bending is that there is very little reduction in the inside diameter of the pipe, since all the metal upset by the operation is displaced to the outside.

Flame-Priming and Flame Descaling

Steel which is hot-rolled or cast, and then allowed to cool in air, is usually coated with a layer of scale. This is actually the black oxide of iron and sometimes it helps protect the steel surface from further oxidation. However, on castings which must be machined, or subject to critical inspection for cracks and other defects, this scale is a drawback. It can cause excessive wear on sharp cutting tools; it can hide defects. To remove it, many different methods are used. *Flame-descaling* is one. Scale is a rather poor conductor of heat. If the outside surface of the scale is heated rapidly by a row of high-velocity oxy-acetylene flames, the rapid expansion of the surface layer will cause the scale to pop loose at the junction between the scale and the steel.

A layer of scale which is tightly bonded to the surface of rolled steel need not be removed before the steel is painted. However, scale absorbs moisture readily. To remove scale which is not tightly bonded, to drive all moisture out of the tightly bonded scale, and to burn off any other contaminating materials on the surface, the *flame-priming* process was developed. As in flame-descaling, a head which produces a row of closely-spaced, high-velocity oxy-acetylene flames is used, although the size of each flame (that is, the gas consumption rate) is less in flame-priming than in descaling. If the steel is wire-brushed immediately, to remove loose particles, and then

Fig. 22-5. Rivets or other irregularities are not obstacles to the flame-priming head, whose flame ports are protected by wear-resistant pads.

painted while still warm, before the surface has cooled enough to pick up moisture from the air, the life of the paint job can often be doubled or tripled.

For both flame-descaling and flame-priming, heads are made in several widths, with skids at each end of the head which permit the head to be dragged over the surface of the steel.

Stone-Shaping

When subjected to the high heat of the flame, some types of rock, especially granite and quartizite, *spall* readily. The heat causes such rapid expansion of surface crystals that they break away from the rock mass without melting. Commercial use of the oxy-acetylene flame in stonework is rare, although sculptors successfully use the flame to supplement their chisels. However, *jet-piercing* blowpipes, which burn oxygen and kerosene, are used in several quarries for piercing blast holes and for cutting channels through large rock masses. A larger, more elaborate type of jet-piercing blowpipe is used in drilling blast holes in taconite, the torch iron ore found in huge quantities in northern Minnesota.

QUESTIONS – CHAPTER 22

1. What is flame-hardening?
2. How is flame-hardening performed?
3. What effect does heating to a bright red and cooling in still air have on an ordinary steel containing about 0.40 per cent carbon?
4. What would be the effect if the same specimen were quenched in water while red hot?
5. What is spot-hardening?
6. For what type of parts of the progressive method of flame-hardening used?
7. How can the teeth of small gears be hardened?
8. How would the outside of a roll, 8-in. in diam. and 10 ft. long be flame-hardened?
9. How is the depth of the hardened area varied in flame-hardening?
10. What advantage is there in providing a hard surface on an unhardened core?
11. How can the oxy-acetylene flame be used for straightening bent parts?
12. What is wrinkle-bending? How is it performed?
13. What is the difference between flame-descaling and flame priming?

FUNDAMENTALS OF
OXYGEN CUTTING

In Chapter 2, we stressed the importance of oxygen cutting and related processes to U. S. industry. In Chapter 5, the general nature of oxygen cutting torches was explained. In the two chapters which follow, we'll discuss the mechanics of cutting, both hand-guided and machine-guided. Here we shall cover certain fundamental facts about the process, and define some of the terms used in connection with it.

Oxygen cutting is really nothing more than the burning of iron or steel. We raise the temperature of the metal to the degree at which it will burn in an atmosphere of pure oxygen (not air) and then feed it pure oxygen. The iron burns, and the reaction produces a great deal of heat, which serves to raise more iron to its kindling temperature. For practical purposes, it is almost always necessary to supply some additional heat to keep the reaction going. This is furnished by burning a mixture of oxygen and fuel gas. The process is therefore sometimes described as *flame cutting,* a term that is somewhat misleading, since the flame does not do the cutting. In some shops, the process is called *burning*, and the men who operate cutting torches are called *burners.* (While these terms are not acceptable to engineers, they are perhaps a bit closer to the truth than "flame cutting".)

Oxygen cutting in its pure form is confined entirely to iron and carbon or low-alloy steels. Since several other metals widely used will *start* to burn, in an atmosphere of pure oxygen, at temperatures well below the kindling temperature for iron, why can't they too be cut? The answer is quite simple. The oxides formed when aluminum, chromium and nickel and most other metals "burn" have much higher melting points than the metals themselves. They "stay put" and prevent the oxygen atmosphere from reaching more pure metal. The oxides of iron, fortunately, melt at lower temperatures, or at about the same temperature, as iron itself. They flow away and expose more iron to the oxygen.

To start a cut in a piece of steel plate, we let the flames from a cutting torch nozzle play on the steel until it is nearly white hot in one spot, or along one edge. Then we turn on the cutting oxygen stream, and the cutting starts. Theoretically, the amount of heat produced by the reaction between iron and steel is more than enough to keep the reaction going. Practically, we find that if the flames are shut off after the cut has been started, the reaction stops, and we "lose the cut". Why? Because the reaction between iron and steel isn't exactly instantaneous. It seems to proceed in two stages, the second of which releases far more energy than the first. At the top edge of the cut, there simply isn't enough heat liberated to maintain the iron at kindling temperature. We must keep the flames lit. However, the heat they put in is normally only useful at the very top of the cut. To put in more heat than is needed is not only wasteful, but can reduce the quality of the cut.

Theoretically, it takes about 4.6 cubic feet (0.13 m³) of oxygen to burn one pound (.45 kg) of iron. In practice, it usually takes a bit more than 4.6 cf to remove 1 lb. of metal. Some of the oxygen — often a substantial part of it — leaves the cutting zone without reacting with iron. On the other hand, as much as 30% of the iron removed may leave the cut as molten iron, mixed with iron oxides. The two factors tend to balance out; under the most favorable conditions, less than 4.6 cf of oxygen will remove more than 1 lb. of iron.

Dross

The mixture of molten iron oxides and molten iron which leaves the cutting zone is usually termed *dross* or *slag*. Under ideal conditions, virtually none of it will adhere to the lower edges of the cut. When some does adhere, it can usually be knocked off with little effort. When it adheres strongly, and cannot be readily detached, there is usually too much unreacted iron in it. Such tightly-adhering dross usually signals that some change in cutting conditions is needed.

Kerf

The gap left by the cutting reaction is called the *kerf*. The width of the kerf is related directly to the volume and character of the cutting oxygen stream, which in turn is largely controlled by the size and type of cutting nozzle used. Cutting speed also has an effect on kerf width. Because the volume of cutting oxygen needed increases as the thickness of the steel being cut increases, kerf width increases too. When the cutting torch is moved by mechanical means at a constant speed, variation in kerf width, along the entire line of cut, will seldom exceed 0.4 mm (1/64 in.).

Lag

When the speed of cutting is such that the stream of cutting oxygen leaves the cutting zone in direct line with its angle of entry, a cut is said to have *zero lag*. However, in many cutting applications, the cutting oxygen stream is bent somewhat as it passes through the steel. The cutting stream, at the point most distant from the nozzle, *lags* behind the nozzle. The amount of this lag, measured along the line of cut, is usually expressed in percentage, based on the thickness of the material being cut. If steel 10 cm thick is being cut, with the nozzle positioned vertically, and the stream leaves the steel at a point 1 cm back of the point of entry, the lag is 10%.

The highest cut quality is usually associated with zero lag. However, a slight amount of lag increases the efficiency of the cutting operation,

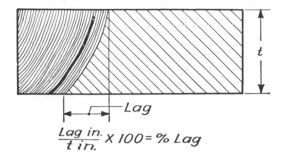

Fig. 23-1. Lag is usually expressed as per cent of plate thickness, as indicated.

$$\frac{Lag\ in.}{t\ in.} \times 100 = \% \ Lag$$

because a higher percentage of the oxygen in the stream gets a chance to react with the iron. To put it another way: If you can get a high-quality zero-lag cut with a certain nozzle and cutting oxygen pressure, you can usually cut at a speed at least 25% greater by allowing some lag. There will be more about lag in the chapters which follow.

Oxygen Purity

It is just barely possible to cut steel with oxygen which is only 95% pure (the other 5% being nitrogen or argon). Cuts of reasonably good quality can be made with 99% oxygen, but for best quality, oxygen with a purity of at least 99.5% is needed. Almost all oxygen made by the liquefaction of air is marketed at a purity of 99.5% or better. Claims have been made that 95% oxygen, made by selective adsorption processes, is satisfactory for cutting purposes. With 95% oxygen, it may be possible to make good welds in some metals, but nothing better than extremely rough cuts can be expected. Fig. 23-2 shows the tremendous improvement in cut quality achieved as the purity of the oxygen stream is increased from 95 to 99.5%.

Fuel Gas Selection

So far in this chapter, we have not used the word "acetylene". The one reference to preheat flames mentioned "oxygen and fuel gas". The fact is that the extremely high temperature of the oxy-acetylene flame is not essential to the success of the oxygen cutting process. Excellent cuts can be made using several other fuel gases which are widely available. The cost of some of these gases (for example, natural gas) is much less than the cost of acetylene (whether compared on the basis of cost per cubic foot, per pound, or per unit of energy provided). If that is true, why do so many users — probably the majority — still use acetylene for oxygen cutting?

For the relatively small user, who buys his gases in cylinders and has an outfit that he wishes to use for both welding and cutting, *convenience* is an obvious answer. He needs acetylene to do steel welding. He does not wish to go to the trouble of switching to another fuel gas when he wishes to cut steel. With acetylene he can do everything, so he sticks with it.

For the large plant, where dozens of cutting torches may be in use, and little or no oxy-acetylene welding performed, "convenience" is no answer. In fact, some other gas may be more "convenient". In such cases, acetylene has

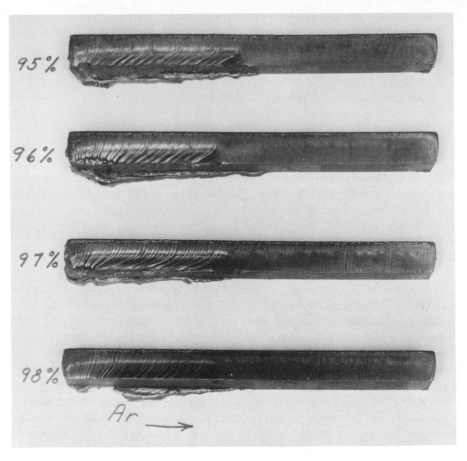

Fig. 23-2. Each of these four cuts was started with low-purity oxygen (obtained by adding argon to 99.5% pure oxygen) and finished with 99.5% oxygen. The change in quality is striking.

almost always had to prove itself on a *cost* basis. The *price* of acetylene is, and probably will remain, higher than the *price* of any competitive gas. How can its use then be justified on a *cost* basis?

The obvious answer to that question is this: That you need less acetylene to do the same amount of cutting. The flame is hotter, which increases the efficiency of heat transfer to the steel. Because the flame is hotter, the time required to raise the steel to kindling temperature, before cutting can start, is less. The amount of oxygen which much be mixed with the fuel gas is always less in the case of acetylene. Finally, advances in design of oxy-acetylene cutting nozzles during recent years have made it possible to reduce acetylene consumption — without loss of cutting speed or increase in oxygen consumption per unit of cut — by as much as 50%.

Not quite so obvious an answer is this: That acetylene increases productivity per hour, even if by no more than the amount of time saved in preheating. In this day and age, time is literally money. The hourly cost of operating, maintaining, and amortizing a large oxygen cutting machine can easily run to $25 or more. If use of acetylene can increase the productivity of that machine by even 3%, that saving should not be ignored.

The thought we wish to leave with the reader is this: The true cost of a particular fuel gas can never be determined merely by comparing the price of that gas (by unit of volume or unit of weight) with the price of another gas, nor even by comparing only total fuel gas costs. If *all* costs, and all potential savings, including time, are taken into consideration, acetylene will often prove to be the "cheapest" gas.

Related Processes

The use of the oxygen cutting reaction is not confined to the kind of operations suggested by the word "cutting". By controlling the angle at which the oxygen stream hits the steel, and the velocity of the oxygen stream, the cutting torch can be used for *gouging* or *grooving,* or for *washing* fins and pads from castings. With a special nozzle, a trained operator can wash the head off a rivet, and then pierce the rivet, without cutting any of the steel around the rivet. There will be more on *gouging, grooving* and *washing* in the next chapter.

Scarfing is a process used in every primary steel mill. Before steel slabs can be rolled into thin plate or sheet, all surface imperfections (which usually originated in the steel ingot) must be removed from the surfaces of the slab. Until about 1930, these imperfections (usually in the form of tracks or seams) were always removed by mechanical grinding or chipping. Then the hand scarfing torch — which is essentially a long, high-capacity cutting torch — was introduced for removal of these defects. During the 1930's, these torches were equipped with *starting rod feeders,* which allowed the operator to feed into the preheat flames an inch or two of ordinary steel rod which ignited and greatly speeded up the start of each scarfing pass. Then *scarfing machines* were developed. In these, a series of special nozzles produces what is almost a flat stream of oxygen which "skins" the entire surface of a slab or billett. The scarfing machine is inserted directly into the rolling mill line, and works on hot steel.

Lancing is a form of oxygen cutting which was devised early in this century, and is still widely used, especially in the steel industry. It is used primarily to pierce holes in thick steel sections, but can also be used to make true cuts. In its simplest form, the *oxygen lance* consists of a non-lubricated valve to which an oxygen hose can be connected, and a length of steel pipe attached to the downstream side of the valve. Cutting action is initiated by heating a spot on the surface of the steel and then feeding oxygen into that spot through the steel lance pipe. The pipe itself burns back as the hole gets deeper. It actually supplies the additional heat required to keep the reaction going.

Powder Cutting

As the alloy content of steel becomes greater, oxygen cutting in its basic form becomes more and more difficult. Some of the metals used in alloy steels do not oxidize readily at the kindling temperature of iron. When they do oxidize, the compounds formed have high melting points and effectively seal off the reaction zone.

During World War II, powder cutting was introduced. Earlier, it had been found that the cutting of cast iron, normally quite difficult because the graphite in the iron does not burn readily, could be made much easier by introducing a length of steel welding rod into the reaction zone. The extra heat provided by the burning of that rod, combined with the extra volume of molten slag produced, did the trick. It occurred to someone that if a way could be found to introduce powdered iron into the reaction zone, it might be possible to cut high-alloy steels. The idea was tried, and it worked. In fact, it not only worked on high-alloy steels, including the stainless steels, but on aluminum, and even on reinforced concrete. While plasma arc cutting, introduced years later, is today generally preferred for mechanized cutting of stainless steel and aluminum, powder cutting is still widely used for many applications. The powder cutting torch is an adaptation of the standard cutting torch, equipped with additional components to permit the introduction of a stream or streams of powder, conveyed through tubing by nitrogen gas, close to the preheat flames of the torch. Powder lances are also used; the lance pipe itself is non-consumable in this process. Powder scarfing torches are used to remove imperfections from stainless steel slabs or billets in steel mills. The process has even been adapted to scarfing machines which will "skin" stainless steel.

QUESTIONS – CHAPTER 23

1. What is oxygen cutting?
2. Why is oxygen cutting limited to just iron and carbon or low-alloy steels?
3. Where is the most useful heat applied during a cutting reaction?
4. What is dross? Kerf? Lag?
5. How pure should the oxygen be for best cutting?
6. What are some of the reasons that acetylene is still favored over cheaper fuel gases, such as natural gas, in oxy-fuel gas cutting?
7. What are some other applications for oxy-acetylene cutting related process?
8. What is the purpose of using iron powder in a cutting process?

MANUAL CUTTING

24

This chapter will cover the mechanics of cutting steel and cast iron with a hand cutting torch or cutting attachment. It will also cover gouging, grooving, and rivet removal. Before making your first cut, be sure to review throughly the precautions and safe practices given in Chapter 7. Note especially the precautions which relate to fire prevention.

Cutting Steel Plate

For your first practice, we suggest that you start with a piece of clean steel plate, about 12 mm (½ in.) thick and at least 250 mm (10 in.) wide. Rule a line with chalk or soapstone about 20 mm from one edge of the plate. Place the plate so that this line clears the far edge of your welding table by 25-50 mm. Make sure there is no combustible material nearby which could be ignited by sparks or hot slag. Place a shallow box of dry sand or a piece of sheet steel below the line of cut. If possible, position a piece of sheet metal to deflect sparks that might otherwise reach your pants or your shoes.

Be sure to use a cutting nozzle of the size recommended by the manufacturer of your equipment for the thickness of steel to be cut. Adjust oxygen and acetylene pressures to the specific levels recommended in the instructions supplied with your torch or cutting attachment. Then put on goggles, light the torch, and adjust the preheating flames to neutral *with the cutting oxygen valve open.*

Hold the torch in one hand so that you will have easy control of the cutting oxygen valve lever. Use your other hand to steady the torch, usually by resting the torch tubes on top of your closed fist. (If your torch has a 75 deg. head, rather than the right-angle or 90 deg. head, you may find it helpful to place a fire brick under your left fist. Your objective is to position the cutting nozzle so that it is perpendicular to the plate surface.) Before you start cutting, move the flames along the full line of cut, perhaps two or three times, to make sure that you can follow the line without difficulty.

To start cutting, hold the torch with the nozzle perpendicular to the surface of the plate and with the flame inner cones not quite touching the plate surface. Center the nozzle over the edge of the plate. As soon as a spot on the edge has been raised to bright red heat, *slowly* press the cutting oxygen valve lever. There should be a shower of sparks, and the cutting oxygen stream should rapidly pass all the way through the edge of the plate. Now squeeze the cutting lever to hold the valve wide open and start to move the nozzle down the line you marked on the plate. Your position should be such that you can actually watch the cutting action as the oxygen stream passes through the plate.

Try to move the torch steadily. Your tendency, during a first cut, will probably be to move it too slowly. It should take you little more than 30 seconds to make a cut 250 mm long, so don't be afraid to speed up a bit just as long as the oxygen stream seems to be passing straight through the steel. If you move the torch too slowly, the preheat flames will melt the top edges of the plate excessively. If you move it too fast, you will lose the cut; in other words, the reaction at the top surface of the plate will cease. If that happens, release the cutting oxygen valve lever, allow the preheating flames to bring the steel back to red heat at the point where the cut ceased, and restart the cut, remembering to open the cutting oxygen valve slowly.

When you have completed your first cut, you may find that the scrap section does not fall freely. What has happened is that the dross produced by the cutting reaction has bridged the gap created by the oxygen stream. This dross is quite brittle, and the scrap section, once the metal has cooled a bit, can be easily detached with a quick rap from a hammer. If you value your equipment, don't use your torch head instead of a hammer. One blow may do the torch no harm, but if you let yourself get into the habit of knocking off the scrap with the torch, you will probably wind up paying a substantial repair bill before many months have passed.

After you have made the first cut, we suggest that you compare the surface of the cut edge with the photographs given in Fig. 24-2. They should provide you with some clues as to what you did wrong (we are assuming

Fig. 24-1. (Left) The line of cut has been marked, and flames are preheating the top corner of the plate. (Center) The cutting oxygen has been turned on, and the cut is just starting. (Right) The cut is moving straight down the marked line.

that no one can make a perfect cut on the first try). Then make a second cut, a third, and a fourth, stopping after each to examine the cut surface closely and decide what to do differently on the next cut. You will probably be surprised and pleased to see how clean your fourth cut looks.

Bevel Cutting

Cutting right straight through plate is relatively easy. Making a good *bevel* cut in plate of the same thickness is considerably more difficult. Since one of the major uses of the cutting torch is to bevel plate edges in preparation for welding, you must master the art of bevel cutting before you can feel ready to use your equipment to best advantage.

Assuming that you started to practice on plate about 12 mm ($1/2$ in.) thick, and that you are going to try making a 45-deg. bevel cut in the same material, the first thing you should do (assuming that you had the correct size nozzle in the first place) is to change the nozzle in your torch. In a 45-deg. bevel cut, the actual depth of cut will be 1.4 times the thickness of the plate itself. So move up to a nozzle one size larger; if it is a four-flame nozzle, position the nozzle in the torch head rather carefully. In making square cuts with a four-flame nozzle, it helps a bit to have one flame directly leading the cut. In bevel-cutting, the four-flames should straddle the cut line evenly — two on each side.

Before you attempt your first bevel cut, experiment for several minutes with an unlit torch and try to learn the best way to move the torch along a straight line at a uniform angle. To hold *both* line and angle is of critical importance. You will probably find that the only way you can do this, for a straight bevel cut in plate, is to move both hands and torch as a unit, dragging your support hand along the surface of the plate. You can't keep your support hand in a fixed position, as you may have found it possible to do in making a vertical cut.

Once you feel confident about motion, light your torch. Adjust the preheat flames to maximum length (just short of the condition where a gap appears between the flames and the end of the nozzle.) Position the torch so that the preheat flames closest to the plate surface almost touch the plate. Don't try to make the bevel right up to the lower edge of the plate on your first try; allow yourself some leeway. Make the cut at as steady a speed as possible; remember that you probably can't cut quite as fast as in the previous exercise. If you find it difficult to observe the cutting reaction directly, keep your eye on the angle at which the stream of slag and sparks leave the lower surface of the plate. If you can complete your first bevel without losing it once along the way, feel that you've made a good start. Examine the surface of the bevel on the plate closely. If the top corner is badly melted over, perhaps your travel speed was a bit too low, or your flames a bit too strong. Make whatever adjustments you feel are necessary, and try another cut, moving

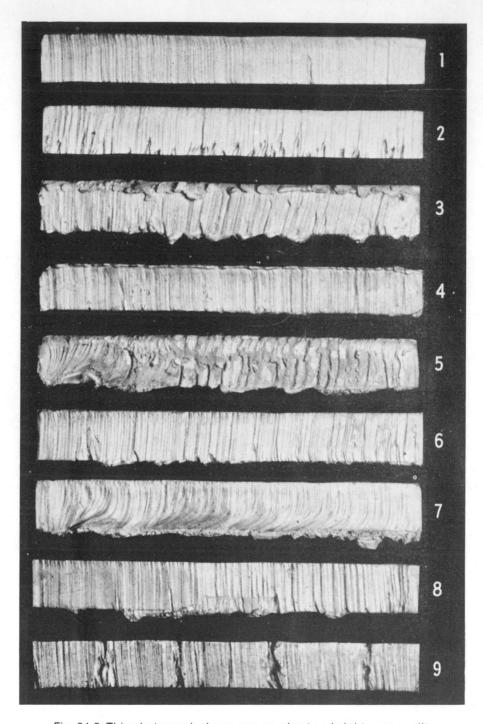

Fig. 24-2. This photograph shows one good cut and eight poor-quality cuts. Reasons for the poor quality are given on the facing page. All cuts were made in 1-in. steel plate.

back at least 1 cm from the original line of cut. Keep at it until you run out of plate or have made a cut that appears reasonably straight and uniform. Remember that it is the straightness of that lower edge, not the exact angle of bevel, or the smoothness of the cut surface, or the amount of melting at the top edge, which will be important when it comes to welding.

Once you have achieved some skill in bevelling of flat plate, try bevelling a piece of pipe, preferably at least as large as 4-in. Schedule 40 (which has a wall thickness of about 6 mm.). Only occasionally will an operator be called on to bevel flat plate with a hand torch in preparation for welding, since virtually every shop has a cutting machine, large or small, which can do the work more precisely. In the fabrication of steel piping systems, regardless of the welding method to be used, the ability to make good bevel cuts by hand is almost invaluable. Much of the bevelling involved in piping system work can be done by special machines, but there will always be some jobs that can only be done by hand. Near the close of Chapter 14 there is a sketch (made from life) which will give you some good ideas about how to hold the torch. Time spend in learning how to bevel pipe will be time well spent.

Cutting Holes

It is essential that you learn how to cut small holes in steel and be able to do it will a fair degree of accuracy. It's a job that the man with the hand cutting torch will often be called on to perform. Starting the cut is the key step

Legend for Fig. 24-2

1. This well-made cut has square edges; the drag lines are essentially vertical, and not too pronounced.
2. Because preheat flames were too small, this cut was made too slowly, causing bad gouging at the bottom of the cut.
3. Because preheat flames were too strong, the top edge is melted, the cut is irregular, and there is adhering slag.
4. Oxygen pressure was too low, and cutting speed too slow. The result was excessive melting of the top edge.
5. Here the nozzle used was too small, while the oxygen pressure was too great for the nozzle. Control of the cut was lost.
6. This would have been a good cut if the cutting speed has been somewhat greater. Drag lines are too pronounced.
7. In this case, the cutting speed was too high. The drag lines break sharply, and there is excessive slag adherence.
8. Failure to maintain a steady cutting speed was the major problem in this case. Part of the cut is excellent, part is poor.
9. The deep gouges in this cut are the result of careless restarting after interruption of cutting.

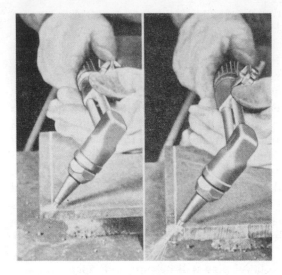

Fig. 24-3. When bevel cutting, be sure to preheat adequately before opening the cutting oxygen valve.

in the operation. First, position the flames over the center of the projected hole, with the inner cones almost touching the surface of the steel, until a spot on the surface actually starts to melt. Then raise the torch head some what (10-20 mm) and start to open the cutting oxygen valve slowly. As you open the valve, move the nozzle slightly off center in the start of what will become a spiral motion. As the cutting reaction starts, the slag and molten metal will be blown to one side, rather than scattered in all directions. Continue to move the nozzle gradually until the cutting oxygen jet has passed all the way through the steel. Then lower the torch head until the flames almost contact the surface again, and eat away the edge of the hole, keeping the nozzle in motion, until the hole has reached the size desired.

When you wish to cut a large hole (50 mm or more in diameter), use a different procedure. Outline the hole with chalk or soapstone, pierce a hole in the center of the circle, then move the cut outward to the marked line and follow the line. (To cut a circular piece of plate for use, start the cut outside the circle). For those who have occasion to cut circles frequently, circle-cutting attachments are available for all types of torches. Each attachment includes a ball-bearing central section which replaces the standard nozzle nut, a radius bar, an adjustable center point, and a follower wheel which enables you to maintain a constant nozzle-to-work distance. When using such an attachment, the starting hole must be pierced directly on the line of cut.

Cutting Rivets

Using special techniques, it is possible to completely remove a rivet head without damage to the structural member itself. There is always a layer of scale between the rivet head and the member, which will act as a temporary barrier against the cutting oxygen stream. To slice the head off a but-

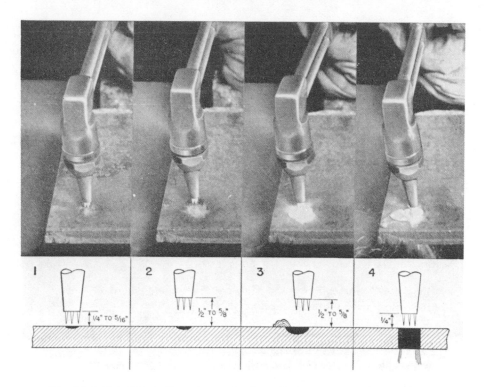

Fig. 24-4. This illustration shows the four distinct steps which must be followed if a hole is to be pierced cleanly without fouling the nozzle with spatter. First, a spot should be heated until the steel starts to melt. Then the nozzle should be lifted straight up until it is at least 1/2 in. above the surface. As the cutting oxygen valve is opened slowly, the nozzle should be moved off the center of the heated spot, and then moved slowly around that center until the cutting oxygen jet has passed through the steel. Then the nozzle can be dropped back to normal height, and the circular motion continued until the hose has reached the desired size.

Fig. 24-5. This is the actual result of the hole piercing operation shown in Fig. 24-4.

tonhead rivet, you can use either a standard cutting nozzle or a special bent type. With a special low-velocity rivet cutting nozzle, you can not only remove the head from any type of rivet, buttonhead or countersunk (flush head), but you can wash out the center of the rivet itself. The techniques are illustrated and explained in Fig. 24-6 and 24-7.

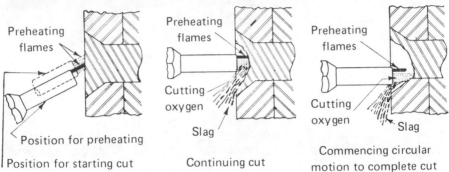

Fig. 24-6. To remove the head from a countersunk rivet, use a special low-velocity rivet-cutting nozzle. Preheat the center of the head with the nozzle angled as shown. Shift nozzle position slightly, open cutting oxygen valve, bring nozzle to the perpendicular, and sweep it around the center of the head.

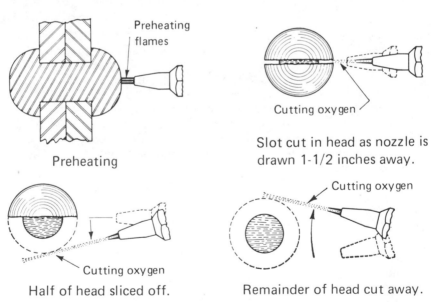

Fig. 24-7. To cut the head from a buttonhead rivet with a standard cutting nozzle, first preheat the center of the head. Then draw the nozzle away, angle it, and cut a slot across the head. The instant the slot is complete, swing the nozzle to slice off one side of the head, immediately reverse direction and slice off the other side.

Gouging and Grooving

With the oxy-acetylene cutting torch or cutting attachment, you can not only slice *through* steel; you can *gouge* or *groove* steel. You can remove defective sections from welds, or surface defects from steel castings. When heavy steel plate is arc welded, it is often standard practice to make a single-vee weld from one side, then turn the work over and make a second pass from the other side, after removing the root portion of the first pass. Oxy-acetylene grooving is often used to prepare the work for that second pass.

To perform gouging or grooving, all you need is a special bent nozzle designed to supply a relatively low-velocity cutting oxygen stream. The techniques used for spot gouging and for continuous grooving are slightly different, but the same nozzle can be used for either purpose. Two or three sizes of nozzles are generally available; the size most frequently used is designed to cut grooves which are about 6 mm in depth and 7-8 mm in width.

To make a continuous groove (as illustrated in Fig. 24-8) you should use neutral preheat flames and take especial care to adjust oxygen pressure to the value recommended by the manufacturer of your nozzle. To start a groove at the edge of a plate, hold the torch so that the end of the nozzle is at an angle of about 20 deg. to the plate surface, with the preheat flames (which are usually positioned above and below the cutting oxygen orifice) straddling the edge of the plate. When the spot where the groove is to start

Fig. 24-8. This action shot clearly shows the high quality and uniformity that a skilled operator can achieve with a well-designed gouging nozzle in a standard cutting torch.

has reached bright red heat, *slowly* open the cutting oxygen valve. Once the groove has started, gradually reduce the angle between the nozzle and the plate surface. Your aim is to keep all the slag flowing away from the nozzle, but not to reduce the angle so much that the groove becomes too shallow and you lose the cut.

If you wish to start a continuous groove from a point on the surface of the work, use a somewhat greater angle between nozzle and work at the start.

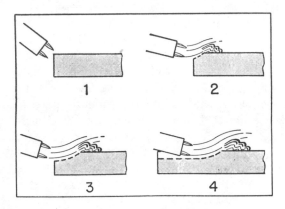

Fig. 24-9. The four steps in starting a groove at the edge of a plate.

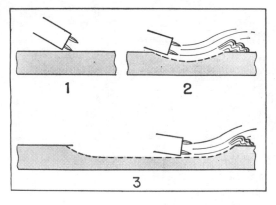

Fig. 24-10. When starting a groove on the surface, draw the nozzle back a bit as you open the cutting valve.

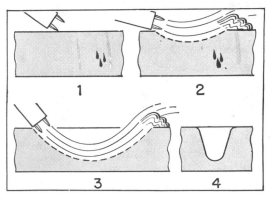

Fig. 24-11. Spot gouging to remove a defect. Trick is to increase angle without advancing nozzle. Profile of deep groove shown at 4.

Once the cutting action has been initiated, reduce the angle somewhat more rapidly than you would if starting at the edge of a plate. Regardless of where you start the groove, once you have it moving along you will find that the tips of the preheat flames will be at least 7-11 mm back of the point where the cutting reaction is taking place. Unless your nozzle is equipped with a skid of wear-resistant alloy, try to keep the nozzle just clear of the bottom of the groove as the work progresses. In practice, you will find that you can vary the width and depth of the groove by varying the angle between nozzle and work slightly. The greater the angle, the deeper and narrower the groove will be.

For spot gouging — such as the removal of a defective section of a weld — it is advisable to adjust the preheat flames so that they are slightly oxidizing (with cutting valve wide open). This will speed up the start, since an oxidizing flame is hotter than a neutral flame. Mark the area to be removed, start preheating just outside that area, with nozzle-to-work angle of about 40 degrees. Once cutting action has started, control the nozzle angle in terms of what you wish to accomplish. In some cases, you may wish to increase the angle in order to increase the depth of metal removal.

Cutting Cast Iron

Oxygen cutting of cast iron is difficult, but it can be done if you know how. It's the graphite in cast iron which causes the trouble; although a form of carbon, normally thought of as combustible, graphite simply won't burn; it must literally be washed away. To cut cast iron is slow work, and requires a special technique and plenty of patience.

To cut cast iron, use a nozzle of the size you would use for cutting steel of the same thickness. Select a nozzle with maximum preheat capacity; a nozzle designed for minimum acetylene consumption simply won't do the job. Adjust the preheat flames, with the cutting oxygen flame open, so that

Fig. 24-12. Gouging can be performed in any position. This operator is working overhead on a steel tank.

they have a decided excess of acetylene (the excess acetylene "feather" should have a length at least twice the length of the inner cone). Make the flames as strong as possible. Then preheat the edge to be cut, all the way from top to bottom. The more you preheat, the easier it will be to get the cut started. Once you have done this, concentrate the preheat flames at a spot on the top surface and heat a circle at least 8 mm in diameter until the metal is actually molten. Open the cutting oxygen valve for an instant, just to blow the slag off the surface of the puddle. Then turn your torch so the nozzle is pointed 45 deg. *away* from the direction of the cut line, open the cutting oxygen valve wide, and start to move the nozzle back and forth in a progressive series of short arcs which intersect the cut line.

Maintain the 45 deg. angle until the cut has progressed all the way to the bottom of the cast iron piece. Keep moving the nozzle from side to side across the line of cut. Now you can gradually increase the nozzle angle — to about 75 deg. or more. Do not attempt to make a cut with no lag; that is virtually impossible with cast iron of any thickness greater than 50 mm. When you reach the far edge of the surface, you must then move the torch down the far edge of the piece, trying to hold a constant degree of lag, until the part has been completely cut through.

If at any point you lose the cut, do not try to restart it the way you would a cut in steel. Instead, melt a new pool of molten metal that is somewhat to

Fig. 24-13. The first three steps in starting a cut in cast iron, as described more fully in the text. Cutting oxygen valve not open yet.

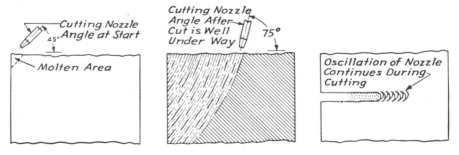

Fig. 24-14. Key points of cast iron cutting, starting with the opening of the cutting oxygen valve.

one side and a bit back of the point where the cut stopped. Make that pool big enough to include the leading edge of the cut if you can. In restarting, return to the original 45-deg. angle at the beginning, gradually increasing the angle once the cutting reaction has penetrated all the way through the piece.

When cutting cast iron less than 50 mm (2 in.) thick, it is often more difficult to maintain a continuous cutting reaction than when cutting heavier sections. The cut may frequently be lost due to inadequate preheating of the metal just ahead of the cutting oxygen stream. However, it is usually easier to retart the cut after you have lost it. Instead of heating a spot somewhere off the line of cut and a bit back of the spot where the cut was lost, move the nozzle directly forward along the line of cut about 6 mm and bring a new spot to full melting temperature. When you then open the cutting oxygen valve, bring the nozzle to a more nearly vertical position than you had it at the time the cut was lost, so that you briefly decrease the amount of drag.

Cutting Alloy Steels

Almost all low-alloy steels containing not more than 2% chromium can be cut without difficulty, in the same fashion as carbon steels. It is also possible to cut air-hardening steels containing 4-6% chromium, but these should be preheated to about 500°C if serious surface cracking of the cut

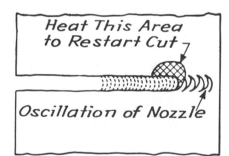

Fig. 24-15. When restarting a lost cut in cast iron, it is usually best to melt a spot slightly off the line of cut.

Fig. 24-16. Feeding steel welding rod into the reaction zone, as sketched here, will often make cast iron cutting easier.

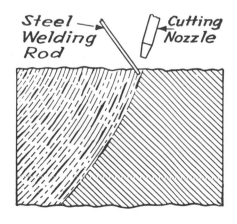

surfaces is to be avoided. In a pinch, if powder-cutting or plasma arc cutting equipment is not available, it is also possible to cut high-alloy steels such as 18-8 stainless steel. To do this, use preheat flames with a slight excess of acetylene. Be sure to thoroughly preheat the line of cut along the starting edge. Once the cut has been successfully started move the nozzle back and forth *along* the line of cut (not, as in the case of cast iron, *across* the line of cut) and keep the preheat flames a bit farther from the surface than you would in cutting carbon steel. Cutting will be noisy; the sound will resemble that produced by rapid sawing of hot wood. The slag formed will be incandescent, and will crackle and spark violently. Cutting will be slow, and if the cut is lost it will be extremely difficult to restart.

Cutting Heavy Sections

If you are called on to cut steel 150 mm (6 in.) or more thickness, keep these points in mind:

1. Oxygen cutting is a chemical reaction; the speed at which you can cut is not directly proportional to metal thickness. If you can cut steel 10-20 mm thick at a speed of 375 mm per minute, you can probably cut 50 mm steel at a rate of about 125 mm per minute.

2. The flow of oxygen required to cut 150 mm (6 in.) steel is *much* greater than the flow needed for 12 mm steel. One reason why cutting charts provided by apparatus makers usually call for higher oxygen pressures in cutting thick steel is because loss of pressure as the oxygen passes through the torch at those higher flow rates is greater than at lower flow rates. However, *never* fall into the trap of thinking that using oxygen pressures substantially higher than those recommended for your nozzle will make the work easier. It will make it harder. In cutting 20 mm steel, you can get away with using pressures well above those recommended; in doing so, you waste oxygen and reduce cut quality, but you don't lose the cut. In cutting heavy sections, excessive pressure can give you real trouble. The excessive pressure will create turbulence in the cutting oxygen stream as it leaves the nozzle, and you may wind up with a big cavity in the middle of the steel without getting the cut all the way through it.

3. Oxygen hose size must be adequate to carry the required high flow of oxygen without excessive pressure drop. The oxygen pressure recommended by the nozzle manufacturer for a large nozzle to be used in hand cutting will usually be that required at the oxygen regulator when 25 feet (8 m) of 3/8-in. (9 mm) hose is used between regulator and torch (unless otherwise stated). The pressure drop in that length of hose, if the nipples used in each end of the hose have the recommended 1/4-in. (6.3 mm) hole size, will be relatively small (3 psi or 0.2 bars) at an oxygen flow rate of 500 cfh (12 m3/h). The pressure drop in a similar length of 1/4-in. (6 mm) hose will be more than four times as great. Since the oxygen flow required for cutting 150 mm (6 in.) steel is nearly 500 cfh, hose size is extremely significant. Tables showing

pressure drops at various flow rates through several hose sizes are given in the Appendix. We urge you to consult these tables whenever you plan to do any heavy cutting, and that you try to avoid using any combination of hose length and size which will cause a pressure drop greater than 10 psi (0.7 bars). (Note: There is one way to be *sure* you have the correct pressure; that is to measure it at the torch inlet, with the correct size of nozzle in place and the cutting oxygen valve wide open. A simple test gauge adaptor, which can be temporarily inserted between the torch inlet connection and the oxygen hose, is relatively inexpensive.)

4. Don't expect too much from a small oxygen regulator with a 100 psi (7 bar) delivery-pressure gauge, even though it is rated to deliver pressures as high as 60-75 psi. The pressure drop through the regulator itself may be so great that it cannot deliver 400-500 cfh at 55 psi or more. Almost all standard-size one-stage and two-stage oxygen regulators equipped with 100-psi delivery-pressure gauges, however, will prove more than adequate for the hand cutting of steel 150 mm (6 in.) thick when used on full high-pressure cylinders of oxygen.

Cutting with Oxygen Lance and Torch

By using a cutting torch and oxygen lance in combination, steel thicker than that which could be cut by the torch alone can be cut. The torch is used to start the cut into the steel, and the lance to complete the cut all the way through. This must be a two-man operation. It is possible to fabricate a suitable lance from standard pipe fittings, and then connect it to a high-capacity regulator, mounted on a portable cylinder manifold, with ³/₈-in. or ¹/₂-in. oxygen hose. A lance valve factory-equipped with hose connection and a quick-acting chuck to hold the lance pipe can also be purchased ready to use.

Fig. 24-17. Oxygen lance used in conjunction with cutting torch to remove 7-ton riser from 9-ton steel casting.

1. What is the proper cutting procedure for steel?
2. What may happen if the torch is moved too slowly during cutting?
3. What is the effect of too rapid motion of the cutting torch?
4. What is the procedure to be followed in beveling?
5. What is meant by "drag"?
6. What effect does excessive drag have in shape-cutting?
7. In what way does the technique for cutting moderately heavy plate differ from that used for cutting light plate?
8. What is the procedure for piercing a small hole? A large hole?
9. What is the proper technique for removing countersunk rivets?
10. How does the technique differ for removing buttonhead rivets?
11. Can a standard nozzle be used for removing rivets?
12. How does the making of bevels for special pipe fittings differ from straight bevels?
13. What is flame-gouging?
14. Does flame-gouging differ from oxy-acetylene cutting?
15. What are the variable factors in gouging that make it possible to obtain shallow or deep grooves?
16. What preheating flame adjustment is used for cutting cast iron?
17. Why is the torch moved back and forth across the line of cut when severing cast iron?
18. How is a cut restarted in cast iron after it has been lost?
19. What is the temperature to which 4 to 6 per cent chromium steels should be preheated for cutting?
20. What is the technique to be used when cutting stainless steel?
21. What type of torch should be used when cutting these high-alloy steels?
22. What factors must be considered when cutting heavy sections?

25

OXYGEN CUTTING
BY MACHINE

The oxygen cutting torch had been in existence only about 10 years when the first machine on which a torch could be mounted for the cutting of irregular shapes was created. Today, oxygen cutting machines play such an essential role in the fabrication of steel structures and machinery that if all of them were to go out of service at one time, major sectors of industry would grind to a halt within days. Later in this chapter, we'll cover the features of big shape-cutting machines, one of which may represent a capital investment of nearly $100,000. First, however, we'll cover the simpler machines found in thousands of shops and factories.

The Small "Tractor" Machines

The simplest of all machines is the small "tractor" type, several thousand of which are sold every year in the U.S. Its essential components are a small motor-driven carriage which can run in a straight line along a track, a governor of some sort which can control carriage speed with accuracy, a torch holder which will permit the torch position to be adjusted in several ways, and the cutting torch itself. This type hasn't changed much over the years. The big improvements have come in the area of speed control. Early machines were usually fitted with centrifugal ("fly-ball") governors; such a governor always has a set of contact points which can give trouble and require occasional replacement. The latest machines have solid-state electronic governors which completely eliminate the need for make-and-break contact points, just as electronic ignition circuits in automobiles have eliminated the distributor points formerly required.

Most of these small "tractor" machines are designed to operate on simple steel tracks, sections of which can be linked together to provide any operational length desired, and are limited to essentially horizontal motion. However, one type "locks" onto a special aluminum track and can be operated in any direction—horizontal, vertical, or even overhead. This type is driven along the track by a pinion gear and rack combination, rather than by ordinary driving wheels.

All of these small tractor-type machines can be used for making either square or bevel cuts, and have provision (with accessories installed) for mounting two torches. Except for the type which locks onto its track, all can be used, with radius rods, for cutting circles of almost any desired size. They are not suitable for accurate cutting of irregular shapes.

Over the years, several types of small machines, of roughly the same size and weight as the small tractor types, have been designed for hand-guided cutting of irregular shapes. The most successful of these has been a three-wheel "tricycle" type, the OXWELD CM-16 machine, designed so that the cutting nozzle is centered directly opposite a large drive wheel, and as close to it as physically possible. With such a machine, a skilled operator can follow an outline marked directly on the plate very closely. The same machine can also be used for straight-line, bevel, or circle-cutting.

Fig. 25-1. A three-wheel machine of this type, here cutting a circle, is extremely versatile. The front end (torch, drive unit, drive wheel) can be revolved 360 degrees or locked in any position. The rear wheels can be left free to swivel, or locked for straight-line cutting. Because the drive wheel is close to the nozzle, the machine can easily be hand-guided to follow an irregular line on the work surface.

Shape-Cutting Machines

Early shape-cutting machines were driven by direct contact between a drive wheel and a line pattern, or a templet formed from aluminum strip, or a shaped steel templet (followed by a magnetized roller on the drive head). A typical machine had two free-moving carriages, one mounted on the other, or one carriage on which a swinging-arm mechanism, carrying both the tracing head and the torch, was mounted. They could turn out good work. However, the direct mechanical connection between drive head and torch created problems. Getting positive traction between the drive wheel or drive rollers and the drawing or templet was one. Making allowance for kerf width when preparing the drawing or templet was another. Inability to turn extremely sharp corners was a third.

Since the early 1940's there have been three major break-throughs in shape-cutting machine design. First came the photocell tracer, which used a beam of light to follow a line or the edge of a silhouette. (Today's photocell tracers will do either; early models were designed to do one or the other, but not both.) Then came the elimination of direct contact between the tracing table and the drive mechanism; instead of a single drive motor, machines were equipped with two servo drive motors, one for each carriage; the current fed to each motor was electronically controlled by the photocell tracer. Once this major step had been taken, several other innovations became possible. Huge ship plates could be cut from patterns one-quarter or one-tenth actual size, using an electronic multiplier. Patterns could be recorded on punched tape, and then fed back into the machine as required. Today, computer-controlled systems have become so versatile that the "tracing table", once the key section of a shape-cutting machine, has disappeared entirely from some of the latest machines.

A Small Shape-Cutting Machine

Although the magnetic tracer is no longer used to guide large shape-cutting machines, one type of small machine still employs it with great success. In this type of machine, a magnetized drive roller is mounted so that its center is directly above the center of the nozzle in the cutting torch. Both the torch and drive mechanism are mounted on a double-armed pantograph with two pivot points. Even a small unit of this type (the OXWELD CM-85 machine is an example) can be used to cut circles more than 750 mm (30 in.) in diameter, or shapes of comparable size, and the largest models have nearly three times that range. Templets for the machine can be made from almost any thickness of carbon steel from 2 mm up. In many cases, the machine can be used to cut its own templets. Since the machine can also be used for straight-line cuts and straight-line bevels, and requires a relatively small investment (less than $2000 as of 1976) it can prove extremely useful to the small shop which does not require high production rates, nor the ability to cut a new shape with only a few minutes notice.

Fig. 25-2. When this small shape-cutting machine is in operation, a steel templet is mounted between the two horizontal bars near the top of the unit. A magnetized drive roller, positioned directly over the centerline of the torch, follows the edge of this templet.

A More Versatile Machine

The type of shape-cutting machine which can be found in far more locations than any other general-purpose unit is exemplified in Fig. 25-3. In certain basic aspects, this resembles machines installed in U. S. railroad shops 50 years ago. It has two carriages; it has a tracing table positioned between the rails on which the lower carriage is mounted. Cutting is done outboard of the lower carriage rails. It will carry two or more torches, the positions of which on the upper carriage can be easily adjusted to permit cutting of multiple identical shapes. The torch hoses lead to a manifold block, so that the machine as a whole can be supplied its gases through a single set of three hoses.

About there, the resemblance ceases. In the pioneer machines, moving power was supplied by a drive motor and governor which were part of the tracing unit, and the carriages were free-rolling. In this modern machine, the photocell tracer follows the most intricate patterns without physical contact. In the tracer head, a synchronous motor spins at 3600 rpm. Mounted on the motor shaft are a permanent magnet and a mirror that picks up and reflects to a photo-transistor the light bouncing off the pattern from four lamps within the tracer housing. Three electrical signals — one from the photo-transistor, two from coils in which current is generated by the rotating magnet — are then transmitted to the control cabinet mounted on the upper carriage. From this unit, power is selectively fed to servo motors which drive the two carriages through pinions engaging steel racks. To accomplish all this, hundreds of electronic components are required; these are largely organized on easily-replaced circuit boards.

Complex though the electronic circuitry may be, operation of a machine like this is extremely simple. Everything is controlled from a single panel mounted on the lower carriage between the tracing table and the work stand. Once the pattern has been positioned on the tracing table, the steel to be cut placed on the work stand, and the gas pressure regulators adjusted, the entire cutting operation can be controlled from this one panel. If the

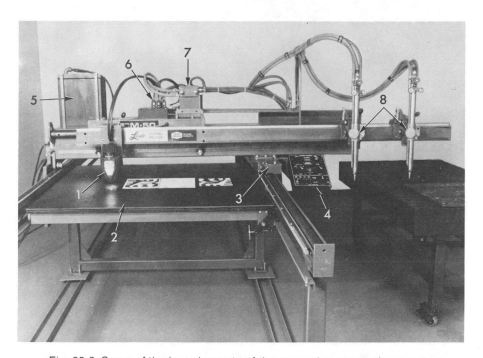

Fig. 25-3. Some of the key elements of the general-purpose shape-cutting machine described in the text are (1) photocell tracer head (2) movable tracing table (3) main carriage truck housing one of the two drive motors (4) control console (5) electrical manifold (6) gas manifold and (8) torch stations, which can be positioned as desired on the upper carriage beam.

machine is fitted with torch ignitors, the flames can even be lit from the panel. The tracer can be directed to move in any desired direction, speed can be adjusted, the cutting oxygen and preheat gases can be switched on and off, and straight-line cuts can be made, either parallel to the main rails or at right angles to them, without the use of any pattern whatsoever.

Fig. 25-4. Here is an action shot of the machine shown on the previous page. Two intricate, identical shapes are being cut simultaneously. For multiple cutting of smaller shapes, two more torches could be mounted on the machine.

Digital controls

While the modern photocell tracer permits the cutting of shapes with a high degree of precision, the computer-type controls, variously called *digital* or *numerical,* are much more versatile.

In a typical numerical control system, the "instructions" for the shape are punched into 1-in. tape which has sprocket holes on one side. The tape may contain complete information, including dimensions of the part, or may be a variable tape which will program the machine to cut a specific

Fig. 25-5. Here six identical shapes are being cut by a machine larger than that shown in the preceding figures, but having the same basic configuration. Tracing table is to the right of the operator. Torches are equipped with remote-control ignitors.

shape — such as a circle or rectangle — but does not include dimensional information. In the latter case, the operator enters the dimensional information into the control computer by pressing buttons on the control panel. (With each variable tape — dozens are available for general use — the operator receives instructions telling him exactly how to enter the variable information into the computer memory.) Once the tape has been loaded into the tape reader, and necessary variables entered through the control keyboard, operation can be checked by running the tape through the reader and allowing a scriber or punch to outline the shape on a piece of steel without cutting it. After that has been done, the tape can be quickly rewound without removing it from the reader. In full-automatic mode, when the tape is again started through the reader, it will set the travel speed, control the lighting of the preheat flames through an ignitor system, allow the proper time for the preheat flames to bring the steel to kindling temperature, then turn on the cutting oxygen and start machine travel, and finally shut off the cutting oxygen and preheat flames when the pattern has been completed.

One special variety of digital control doesn't use tapes at all. It will automatically control the cutting of any size circle or rectangle or circle (within the cutting limits of the machine itself) after the operator has set a few dials and switches to specify the diameter of the circle or the dimensions of the rectangle, the direction in which he wishes the cutting to lead into the shape (from outside or inside), and the width of the kerf. He can do this in less than a minute; then all he must do is push one button and the control will take over. Almost any shape that is formed from a combination of straight lines or arcs can be cut; following a fully-dimensional drawing, the operator can dial in the directions and dimensions as the cut progresses.

Super-Size Cutting Machines

Machines of the type just described, in which the torches are mounted directly on the uppper carriage, and cut outboard of the main carriage rails have inherent size limitations. The largest machines of this type presently offered have a useful tracing table width of about 4 meters (12 feet), can cut multiple shapes from plate as wide as 5 meters (15 feet), and can mount as many as eight torches on the upper carriage arm.

The "gantry-type" machine, which is shown in Fig. 25-6, can be made to virtually any size desired. Cutting is done between the main carriage rails. Like the smaller machines, it is driven by servo motors; two drive the main carriage (bridge) along the main rails, a third drives a small carriage along track mounted on the main bridge. Attached to this carriage is an endless stainless steel band which runs around rollers mounted at each end of the bridge. To this band, several additional "slave" carriages can be clamped in almost any desired relationship. These carriages ride on the same rails as the "master" carriage. They can be readily repositioned, or fully released from the driving band. A machine of this type, equipped with seven "slave" carriages, can be set up in minutes to cut simultaneously eight small shapes, or four larger shapes, or two large shapes, or a single shape with a width more than half the overall width of the bridge.

The standard cutting torch station for such a machine includes an electric motor drive for raising and lowering the torch, an ignitor system for lighting the torch, and a sensing device which will maintain constant nozzle-to-work distance while cutting is underway. It also provides for the mounting of an air-operated marking device which will either punch mark or scribe lines on the plate to be cut (for layout checking) and a water-spray attachment which generates a high-velocity air-water mist to minimize plate distortion and dust generation.

One of the major uses for such a machine, in many shops, is the preparation of plate edges for welding. For this purpose, a special torch station, incorporating three small torches, is available. This can be used to make bevel cuts (single-bevel, two-bevel, or two-bevel and nose) either parallel to the main rails or at right angles to them. When contour bevelling of either circles or irregular shapes is a requirement, there is a special type of station equipped with a motor which rotates the three-torch assembly, under electronic control, to maintain constant angle of bevel regardless of direction of carriage motion.

As noted earlier, large machines of this type are almost always tape-controlled, although they can be adapted for photocell tracing if necessary. At the heart of the control is a small computer. For years, it was necessary to position the main control, including the computer, at some distance from the machine. Recently, miniaturization has permitted the development of a control so small, and so completely protected from dust and fumes, that it can be mounted directly on the top of the machine bridge. In either case, the machine is operated from a console mounted at one side of the bridge. From his position at that console, the operator can do just about everything except change the relative positions of the carriages along the driving band.

Machine Cutting Precision

The inherent accuracy of tape controls is so great that if only the control were involved in cutting accuracy, shapes could be cut to a precision of 0.004 mm (0.01 in.) or less. However, there *are* other factors which must be taken into account. There is always some time lag between the signal taken off the tape and the physical response of the machine to that signal. This lag (sometimes called "machine gain") is a constant factor, so it will normally have little or no effect, except when the tape instructions tell the machine to turn a right-angle corner. This it cannot do perfectly because of that time lag. However, at a cutting speed of 760 mm per minute (25 in./min.) the radius of such a sharp corner will be less than 2 mm. There may be some inherent mechanical inaccuracy in the machine (gear backlash, etc.) which will have an effect on cutting accuracy, although in a first-class modern

Fig. 25-6. In a "super-size" shape cutting machine like this one, the tracing table has disappeared, and the torches are mounted between the main rails. Travel is controlled by punched tape and a small computer. This machine is fitted with six oxygen cutting torch stations and two plasma arc cutting torch stations (extreme left and right). Each station has an automatic height control unit to maintain constant nozzle-to-work clearance.

shape-cutting unit, properly installed, such inaccuracies have been substantially eliminated. Finally, the factor of kerf width enters the picture. Kerf width is determined by nozzle size and cutting speed. If actual kerf width for a given operation is accurately determined by actual test, a modern machine can be readily adjusted to compensate for exactly that width. If all factors are taken into account, the accuracy of machine cutting can be held within extremely close limits, on the order of plus or minus 0.4 mm (about $1/32$ in.) or less.

Cut Quality and Economy

The finest machine and the most precise control cannot, in themselves, guarantee high-quality precision cuts. Just as in hand cutting, poor cuts can result if the wrong nozzle is used, or if cutting speed is too low or too fast, or if the preheat flames are not properly adjusted. The factors affecting cut *quality* are essentially the same whether the cutting machine cost less than $1,000 or represents an investment of $75,000 or more.

Cutting Nozzle Selection and Case. Almost all nozzles designed specifically for hand cutting have cutting oxygen passages which, for at least the final inch, have straight *cylindrical* bores. The best nozzles designed for machine cutting have what are known as *conical divergent* bores at the exit end. What does "conical divergent" mean? Simply that the nozzle bore, for a short distance back from the exit port, has a slight flare, which allows the oxygen to start expanding just before it leaves the nozzle. This actually increases the straight-line velocity of the gas leaving the nozzle, permits cuts to be made at substantially higher speeds, and reduces oxygen consumption appreciably. If such nozzles will do so much in machine cutting, why are they not more widely used for hand cutting? Because they cost a little more; because it is difficult for the hand torch operator to take full advantage of their potential; and because they are harder to clean. You can clean a cylindrical-bore nozzle easily with special stainless steel tip cleaners which are available almost everywhere; you can even use a twist drill of the right size, if you remember to push it in and out, not twist it. Cleaning a tapered bore is more difficult; you must have a tool or drill with a taper which is exactly the same as that in the nozzle, and it must be used in a precise fashion if it is to do an effective cleaning job without altering the taper.

Which leads to the general subject of nozzle cleanliness. Bits of spatter from a cutting operation — especially the spatter created when cuts are started by piercing holes in the workpiece — often travel with such high velocity that they actually enter the nozzle and lodge in its cutting oxygen or preheat ports. A rather small particle, adhering to the bore, can have a drastic effect on cut quality. When you do machine cutting, the time spent checking nozzles to make sure they are clean *internally*, and the time spent cleaning them, is almost always time well spent.

In machine cutting, always try to use a nozzle of the size recommended for the thickness of steel to be cut. It is true that you can cut steel 12 mm thick with a nozzle which has the capacity to cut steel five or six times that thick. To use an over-size nozzle in hand cutting usually wastes oxygen, but may not affect cut quality noticeably. In machine cutting, using an over-size nozzle will often make it difficult to get a high-quality cut, as well as waste gases. Without fail, use a cutting oxygen pressure within the range recommended for the nozzle selected.

Preheat Flame Adjustment. To use the strongest possible preheat flames will speed up the starting of a cut, but will often result in excessive melting of the top edges of the cut. The more elaborate cutting machines are often equipped with preheat flow control devices which permit strong flames to be used for preheating, but automatically cut back the preheat gas pressures, and thus the flame strength, when the cutting oxygen is turned on. When you don't have the advantage of such a device, you must compromise somewhere; it is usually better to accept somewhat longer preheating time then to tolerate excessive melting of the top edges.

The inner cones of the preheat flames should never actually touch the surface of the steel. It is better to have them a bit too far from the surface than a bit too close. Machine cutting nozzles of the latest design will tolerate a rather substantial increase in nozzle-to-work distance except when the machine is being operated for maximum cutting speed.

Cutting Speed: Although a nozzle manufacturer's cutting chart will almost always recommend a specific nozzle size and a specific cutting oxygen pressure for a given thickness of steel, it will usually show a *range* of cutting speeds. When no other specification is shown, you can usually assume that the lowest speed indicated is that which should be used for a "no-lag" cut of the highest quality, and that the highest speed indicated is for a cut with an appreciable amount of lag, but not so much lag that the torch will fail to sever the bottom corner of the steel at the finish of the cut. (For the latter condition, the term "drop cut" is often used.) For cutting of irregular shapes, always use the lowest speed specified, since any lag will affect the squareness of the cut surfaces. For straight-line cutting, a speed in the upper part of the range will usually give satisfactory results. In almost every shop which does repetitive cutting, the cutting speed for any operation is established by actual trial, in order to establish the highest speed which can be used without undesirable loss of cut quality, or serious risk of losing the cut because of variations in the surface condition of the steel.

Machine Cutting Variations

Stack-Cutting. The shop with a large-scale cutting machine can cut up to eight identical shapes at once by using eight torches and a common pattern or tape. The shop with a small machine, which will mount only one or

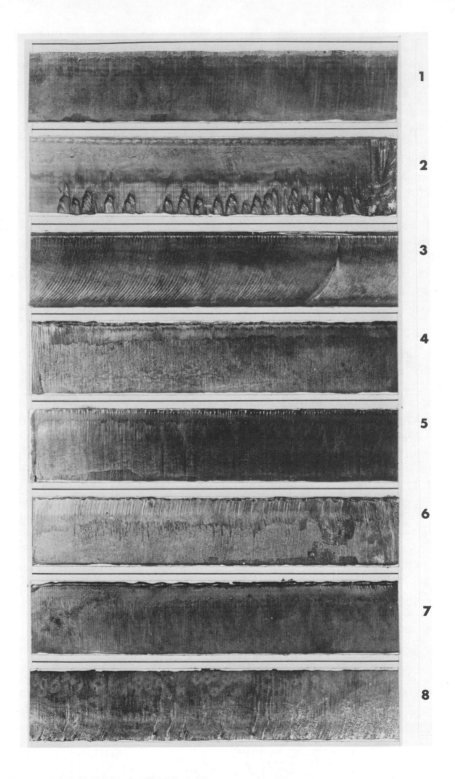

Common Faults in Machine Cuts
(Fig. 25-7, on facing page)

1. This is a first-class cut. The surface is regular; the draglines are essentially vertical; the top edge is sharp. For many purposes, cuts of this quality require no further finishing.
2. This cut was made at a speed too low for the nozzle in use. There is melting at the top edge, and serious undercutting along the bottom of the cut.
3. This cut was made at maximum speed. Despite the high per cent of lag, the surface is quite smooth. For many purposes, this cut would be satisfactory.
4. The excessive melting at the top edge of this cut was due to operating a standard all-purpose nozzle with excessive clearance between preheat flames and the work surface. (However, if high-efficiency nozzles of the latest design are used, extra "stand-off" will not cause such melting.)
5. When the nozzle is too close to the work, and the preheat flames are actually burning somewhat below the surface of the plate, cutting action near the top of the cut becomes unstable.
6. When cutting oxygen pressure is greater than that recommended for the nozzle in use, the cutting oxygen stream expands too rapidly as it leaves the nozzle. Serious irregularity develops, and oxygen is wasted.
7. Everything about this cut is good except for the melting of the top edge caused by using preheat flames which were too strong.
8. A dirty nozzle made this cut. Even very small particles of slag inside the cutting oxygen port can cause this sort of irregularity and loss of quality. It pays to clean nozzles regularly.

two cutting torches, can sometimes increase its capacity to turn out identical shapes in quantity by *stack-cutting*. For example, if the parts are to be cut from steel 12 mm ($\frac{1}{2}$ in.) thick, and the steel plate is clean and flat, eight pieces can be stacked, clamped securely, and then cut all at once.

Plate-Edge Preparation. The term *plate-edge preparation* refers almost always to *preparation for welding*. The simplest form of plate-edge preparation, when only a single bevel is required, can be done with a small tractor-type machine, using standard accessories. The plate edge is first cut square and straight. Then, using a plate-riding attachment and a bevel-cutting adaptor, the plate can be given a uniform bevel with little difficulty. Most plate-edge preparation, however, is done on larger machines capable of mounting a three-torch unit equipped with a height-sensing device which will maintain essentially constant nozzle-to-work clearance. Such a unit can be set up to simultaneously square the edge of the plate and cut either one or two bevels.

QUESTIONS – CHAPTER 25

1. Is there any difference in principle between manual and machine cutting?
2. How do the nozzles designed for machine cutting differ from those designed for manual cutting? Why?
3. What factors should be considered for a good cut?
4. What is a "drop cut"?
5. What is stack cutting?
6. What is meant by plate edge preparation?

TESTING AND INSPECTING

26

Whenever materials are manufactured some procedure has to be established to determine whether the manufactured material or part meets the requirements that have been established. In the steel mill, samples are taken periodically from the furnace and checked to make sure that the chemical analysis of the steel is correct. After the ingots have been cast and are being rolled, they are visually examined to determine whether there are cracks or other defects present, and any defects found are removed before the work progresses. In the foundry and forge shop, the manufactured articles are examined to make sure that there are no holes in them and that they are of the size required. In the machine shop parts are gauged or otherwise measured to make sure that they are of the right dimensions.

The completeness of any testing program and the carefulness of the inspection will depend naturally upon the requirements. It is obviously useless to use micrometer calipers on a part that is being rough-forged, and it is equally useless to check the measurements of an airplane motor cylinder with a foot rule. In the same way, it is a waste of effort to X-ray all the welds in a clothes locker; yet serious difficulty could occur if nothing were known about the corrosion resistance of the welds in a chemical piping system.

Factor of Safety

A part obviously need be no better than demanded by the requirements of service. It is important, however, that every service condition that is likely to be encountered be taken into consideration in the planning. A tent made out of ordinary cloth is sufficiently good to keep off the night dew, but if one expects to stay dry in a rainstorm, the cloth of the tent must be waterproof and a trench must be provided around the tent to make certain the water does not flow in underneath. If the rain is to be accompanied by a strong wind, the tent must be erected substantially enough not be blown over, an event that would make all the other precautions useless.

To protect one's self against all eventualities, however, is usually not economical. In an area in which earthquakes are frequent, considerable expense in building "earthquake-proof" buildings is justified, whereas such expense would be entirely unjustified in an area in which earthquakes are not known.

In designing or planning the construction of a part, therefore, all of the service conditions for which it is economically justifiable to provide are taken into consideration. It is not quite enough, however, for the part to be built just strong enough to meet those requirements. The rain may come down just a little bit faster or the wind may blow just a few miles an hour harder than had been experienced before and all of the work would have been lost just as if these factors had never been considered.

After the requirements of the part are determined, therefore, they are multiplied by what is known as a safety factor. Depending upon the circumstances, this factor may be anywhere from $1\frac{1}{2}$ to 12. The designer of a bridge, for instance, calculates the strength required to accomodate all of the people or automobiles that might be on it at one time, even in winter when the bridge might be loaded down with ice and snow and a strong wind blowing. Because some part might not be quite up to the strength expected or because just as the bridge was completely loaded under the worst conditions some accident like a tugboat bumping one of the pipes might occur, the strength required is multiplied by, say, 2. The bridge therefore is built twice as strong as it is expected will be required under the worst possible conditions. Whether the factor of safety is 2, 3, or even 6, is a matter that is determined by experience.

An understanding of the factor of safety is important to the welding operator because if the weld that he makes in a structure has defects in it or otherwise does not match up to the strength that the designer expected him to obtain, he is using up at least part of that factor of safety. Of course, one of the reasons for having a factor of safety is to allow for such circumstances, but it is easy to see how several poor welds in a structure could quickly use up the entire allowance for safety, even though the structure did not break down immediately. To make sure that materials and workmanship come up to requirements, inspectors are kept on the job and inspection and testing procedures are established and carried out.

Sampling. Every part that is constructed cannot be completely tested to determine just how strong it is, because such a test would destroy the part. Yet it is important to know just how strong each part is. Such assurance can be obtained by a combination of four factors:

1. A procedure that has been proved to give the desired results.
2. A control of operations such that the procedure will be followed exactly all along the line.
3. Constant inspection to make certain that operations are being performed correctly and that materials meet specifications.
4. Occasional testing to make sure that unforeseen factors are not creeping in.

Translated into welding these four factors are carried out in the following manner:

Procedure Qualification. In the first place it must be proved that the procedure will give the required results. A workman who has proved himself to be a good operator over a period of time is used in developing a method of making a weld. The welds made by that operator are then completely tested to determine whether the results desired are being obtained by the procedure used. As soon as the desired results are obtained, the procedure has been established.

That is what is known as a procedure qualification. Other operators are then tried out on the proved procedure and as soon as the welds they make will also withstand testing, those operators are qualified to follow the procedure.

Procedure Control. As the proved welding method then goes into use in production work, a procedure control is established so that continued satisfactory work can be assured.

Constant Inspection. As work progresses and as more parts are turned out by the production operation, they are examined to make certain that the factors that can be determined by inspection methods are what were expected.

Periodic Inspection. From time to time parts are taken from the production line and tested to destruction to make certain that the three factors already discussed are given the desired results. The frequency with which destructive tests have to be performed is determined from experience and from the severity of the requirements.

What Constitutes a Good Weld

All weld inspection and testing methods have but one purpose—to determine whether the work done constitutes a good weld.

Weld Defects Externally Apparent. The defects that can occur in welding can be classified into two groups depending upon whether they are externally apparent or not. A visual examination of the underside of a weld will determine whether complete penetration has been obtained or whether there are excessive globules of metal. If the underside of the weld cannot be examined, such as in pipe welds, this determination must be done by other means.

Oversize or undersize welds can be readily observed from visual examination. Weld gauges have been developed that make it easy to determine whether a weld has excessive or insufficient reinforcement. Likewise undercutting or overlap at the sides of welds can usually be observed visually.

Weld Defects Not Necessarily Externally Apparent. Such defects as lack of fusion, porosity, and cracking, may or may not be externally apparent. Excessive grain growth or the presence of hard spots also cannot be determined from visual examination of the external part of the weld. It cannot be assumed, however, that such defects are not present just because they cannot be observed externally, and other means must be taken to find out.

Methods of Testing

Methods for examining welds can be described as destructive or non-destructive tests. Methods of examination that cause a destruction of the welded part we shall call "methods of testing," while "methods of inspection" will cover procedures for examination that do not cause destruction of the part.

Tension Test. One of the most familiar and most widely used of the methods for determining the quality of welds is the tension test, by means of which the ultimate tensile strength of the part can be determined. Frequently this same test is also used to determine the yield strength and one measure of ductility.

Nick-Break Test. The specimen for a nick-break test is notched on two sides at the center of the weld and then the specimen is broken by a sharp blow. Examination of the exposed surfaces will indicate any inclusions, lack of fusion, or other similar defects that extend through that section of the weld through which the break progresses.

Free-Bend Test. The free-bend test as a means for measuring ductility is described in Chapter 9.

Guided-Bend Test. In the guided-bend test the specimen is placed across a U-shaped anvil and the matching punch forces the specimen to bend into a predetermined shape. This test is frequently used as a "go or no go" test in qualifying operators. In other words, any specimen that can be given the prescribed guided bend test without causing failure is satisfactory, and the man taking the test is considered to have passed. With the free-bend test as a qualification test there are frequently opportunities for argument.

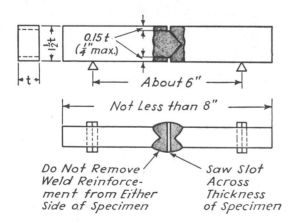

Fig. 26-1. For a nick-break test, the specimen is cut on two sides. After it is broken by a sharp blow, the fractured surfaces are examined for defects.

Grain Size - very fine

           fine

           normal

           coarse

Laps or Cold Shuts

Lack of penetration

Gas pockets

Slag inclusions

Net cross-section of base metal

Fig. 26-2. In Fig. 26-3 through 26-8, a series of fractured welds are shown. The sketches at the right in each figure represent the actual fracture by means of the symbols shown above.

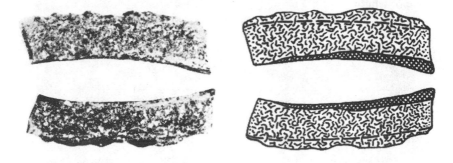

Fig. 26-3. This is a fairly good specimen cut from a pipe weld. The fine grain sections were created by the heat of cutting the specimen.

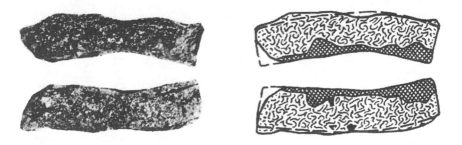

Fig. 26-4. This specimen reveals lack of penetration, and slag inclusions. There is also a low spot in the reinforcement.

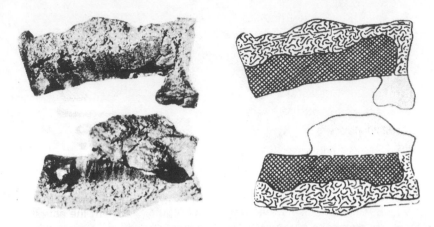

Fig. 26-5. This weld specimen shows incomplete penetration except at a spot where the weld metal ran through badly.

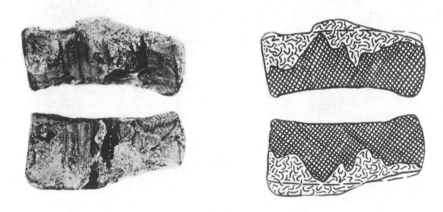

Fig. 26-6. Lack of fusion in this weld makes it worthless. Weld metal was probably deposited to the bottom of the vee, but the sides of the vee were not raised to the temperature necessary for fusion.

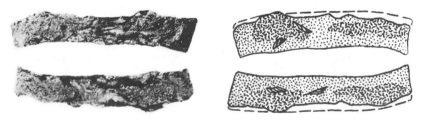

Fig. 26-7. This specimen from a horizontal weld shows excellent penetration, but the weld level did not reach the surface level of the base metal.

For instance, if the ductility determined by the test amounted to 19 per cent when the specification was that the test should show 20 per cent, it is difficult to say a man has not passed. With the guided-bend test the specimen either breaks or it does not, and on the strength of that test the man either passes or does not. The free-bend test is of considerable value nevertheless because of the speed with which it can be applied and because it is a severe test of quality.

Root, Face, and Side Bends. Either the free-bend test or the guided-bend test can be applied in any one of three ways. If the root of the weld is at the outside of the bend, it is called a root bend test. Similarly if the face or the side is at the outside of the bend it is called a face or side bend test.

Hardness Tests. Frequently after a weld has been completed hardness explorations are made. In other words, a regular pattern of points extending over the weld zone and the base metal outside the weld zone are tested so that any hard spots can be located. An estimate of the probable cause of hardness can frequently be made from the location of the hard areas.

Other Tests. There are a number of other tests that are used less frequently than those already described and that are rarely if ever used to determine operator qualifications.

In the *impact test* a standard-size specimen is broken off by a sharp blow and the amount of energy required to break the specimen is determined. The test thus reveals the amount of resistance to shock or impact that the part made of that material would have. Of course the conditions of the test and the relative sizes of the test specimen and completed part must be considered in making such calculations.

In the *fatigue test,* as the name implies, a part is subjected to repeated changes in applied stresses. This may be done in any one of several ways de-

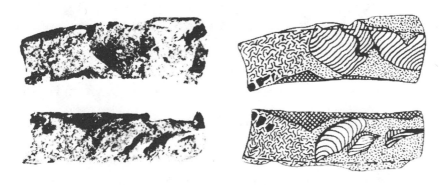

Fig. 26-8. This weld specimen displays some lack of full penetration, but its major detect is a serious lack of fusion within the weld itself. Specimen was taken from the closing section of a pipe weld.

pending upon the type of service the tested part must withstand. The results are usually expressed as the number of reversals, perhaps ten million, an identical, new specimen is frequently tested with a higher total stress upon it.

The *shear test* reveals the resistance a part has to a shearing action. This test is not of wide use in welding work.

In the *etch test*, a specimen is polished and etched with an acid to reveal its grain structure and any small inclusions of slag or other foreign matter. This test is occasionally applied in tests for the qualification of operators.

Methods of Inspection

The application of certain methods of inspection may include one or more of the tests already described, but not on the whole welded part. For instance, small test specimens may be cut out of a welded part and these subjected to any one of the methods of testing, but as far as the entire welded part is concerned such a method of sampling is considered a method of inspection. At times extra material is left at the end of a weld, and this is later removed and tested to destruction. This inspection method is variously known as *couponing, sectioning,* or *trepanning* depending somewhat upon the method of removing the specimen.

The most frequent method of inspection is *visual* examination. Here the purpose is to determine that the welds are of the correct size and that there are no overlaps or undercuts, porosity, lack of fusion, or lack of penetration that extend to the surfaces examined.

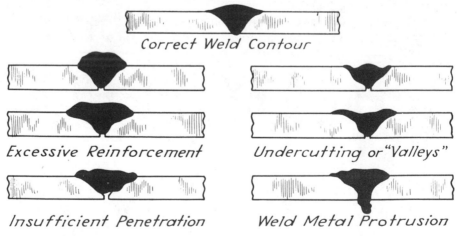

Fig. 26-9. These sketches show several types of defects readily spotted by visual inspection.

Piping systems and similar structures are frequently subjected to a *pressure test*. If it is used for a piping system, this would mean capping the open ends and then subjecting the pipe to a hydraulic pressure of the required amount. The part is examined while under the test for any pinhole leaks or evidences of porosity. Usually pressure tests are at least one and one-half times the expected working pressure of the part.

Parts under pressure test are frequently further subjected to a *stethoscope test*. In this method a stethoscope, such as a doctor uses, is employed to listen to the sound of hammer blows in the neighborhood of the weld. Experience in applying this test permits the inspector to locate such defects as lack of fusion or cracks, because of the effect that they have upon the conduction of the sound through the part. Parts that are not under pressure tests may also be inspected with some success by listening to the sound produced by hammer blows.

The *radiographic* or *X-ray* method provides a means by which it is possible to look through a metal part or weld. X-ray pictures of welds will reveal blowholes, cracks, lack of fusion, or inclusions, provided these are not located in certain restricted positions with respect to the direction of the X-rays.

The *magnaflux test* can be used only on magnetic substances. When an electric current is passed through a conductor surrounding a magnetic substance, magnetic forces are set up in the core material. Any defects at or near the surface, such as hairline cracks, porosity, or blowholes, will result in a disturbance of the lines of magnetic flux. In the practical application of the magnaflux method, small iron filings are dusted onto the part, or they may be suspended in a liquid, usually kerosene, and then the part submerged in the liquid. Discontinuities in the flow of magnetic flux will cause the iron particles to collect at that point on the surface at which a defect occurs and thus call attention to the defect. Frequently parts that are subjected to magnaflux testing are painted a light color so that the iron filings can be more readily spotted.

Codes, Standards, and Specifications

The industrial experience accumulated over the years that welding has been used, as to the type of test that must be applied for certain types of service, the frequency with which sampling must be done, and the methods of testing that are satisfactory to qualify operators for various classes of work, have been formulated into a series of codes and standards. In general, these codes are published by technical organizations and are available from the interested societies.

Listing of Appendices

Appendix A   Temperature Data

Color Scale A	Color Scale B	Degrees Celsius	Melting Points
		1600 —	
			— Pure Iron
		1500 —	— Low-Carbon Steel
	White	1400 —	— 18-8 Stainless Steel
White			
	Yellow White	1300 —	
	Orange Yellow	1200 —	Cast Iron
Light Yellow			
	Orange Red	1100 —	
Lemon			
	Bright Cherry Red	1000 —	Brasses and Bronzes
Orange			
	Cherry Red	900 —	
Bright Red			
	Dull Cherry Red	800 —	
Cherry Red			
	Dark Red	700 —	
Dark Cherry			
		600 —	Aluminum Alloys
Blood Red			
Faint Red		500 —	
		400 —	
		300 —	— Lead
			Lead Alloys
		200 —	

Color scale A is an approximation of what the naked eye will see in dim light. Color scale B is close to what a welder will see through his goggles. Neither should be considered precise.

Appendix B   Physical Properties of Metals

A. **Chemical symbol.** (Many of the symbols are derived from Latin names for the elements; for example, "Pb" from "plumbum", "Au" from "aurum", and "Sn" from "stannum".)

B. **Specific gravity;** the relative mass of the metal by comparison with water. Since one cubic meter of water has a mass of 1000 kilograms, the **density** of any of the metals, in terms of kg/m^3, is 1000 times the figure shown. To arrive at density in terms of pounds per cubic foot, multiply specific gravity by 62.5.

C. **Melting point, degrees Celsius.**

D. **Melting point, degrees Fahrenheit.**

E. **Coefficient of thermal expansion, per degree C, X one million.** To illustrate use of these figures: An unrestrained bar of aluminum, one meter long, will change its length 23.6 millionths of a meter (or 23.6 thousandths of a millimeter) for each 1°C change in temperature. Rate of expansion is not constant at all temperatures; data given represent coefficients at room temperature.

F. **Thermal conductivity.** Specifically, the figures shown represent calories per square centimeter cross-section, per centimeter length, per degree C. (Cal/ $cm^2/cm/°C$). Data provided primarily to emphasize the wide variation in thermal conductivity, and fact that there is no general relationship between rate of expansion and rate of heat conductivity.

		A	B	C	D	E	F
Aluminum	Al	2.70	658	1216	23.6	.57
Chromium	Cr	7.14	1615	2939	6.2	.16
Copper	Cu	8.94	1083	1981	19.6	.94
Gold	Au	19.3	1063	1945	14.2	.71
Iron	Fe	7.86	1535	2795	11.7	.18
Lead	Pb	11.35	328	622	29.3	.08
Magnesium	Mg	1.74	651	1204	25.2	.37
Nickel	Ni	8.90	1452	2646	13.3	.22
Platinum	Pt	21.5	1755	3191	8.9	.16
Silver	Ag	10.5	960	1760	19.7	1.0
Tin	Sn	5.75	232	450	23	.15
Titanium	Ti	4.5	1800	3272	8.4	.04
Tungsten	W	19.3	3370	6098	4.6	.40
Zinc	Zi	7.14	419	787	39.7	.27

Appendix C

Tests for Identifying Metals

Spark Test. Occasionally, it may be necessary to attempt to weld a metal that cannot be readily identified by surface appearance alone. It is not hard to distinguish aluminum from stainless steel, and easy to distinguish copper from brass, or lead from almost any other metal. It is not easy to distinguish ordinary low-carbon mild steel from some of the low-alloy steels, or to distinguish malleable cast iron from ordinary gray cast iron. However, there are some simple tests you can perform which will help you identify at least the major class of ferrous metal, and by so doing help you decide whether welding is possible, and what type of welding rod or flux may be best suited to the job.

The best and simplest of all tests, at least so far as the ferrous metals are involved, is the *spark test.* A power-driven high-speed grinding wheel will produce spark patterns which are quite distinctive. Try to do the grinding so that the spark stream is thrown horizontally against a reasonably dark background. The spark patterns typical of six major types of ferrous metals are shown on the facing page. Study them carefully before you run a test; you can't look at the page and at the spark stream simultaneously.

Here are a few notes to supplement the patterns and descriptions given on the facing page:

Gray cast iron vs. malleable cast iron: Difference between actual spark patterns may be less than indicated by our sketches. Under identical test conditions, malleable iron spark stream should always be longer than gray iron stream, with less breakdown into sprigs and small sparks near the wheel. If spark test is inconclusive, apply chip test.

White cast iron vs. gray cast iron: The white iron pattern is not shown, since white iron can usually be distinguished by its color. Under the same test conditions, length and volume of spark stream from white iron will be less than for gray iron.

Low-carbon steel vs. wrought iron: Chief difference lies in color of spark stream near wheel. It will always be white for the steel, straw yellow for the iron, although both will appear white farther out.

(continued on p. 270)

SPARK PATTERNS

Gray Cast Iron

Length, about 25 in.; spark color red near wheel, straw yellow farther out; volume, small.

Malleable Iron

Length, about 30 in.; spark color same as gray iron; volume, greater than gray iron.

Alloy Steel

Length, variable (depending on alloy) but always shorter than carbon steel stream; color, straw yellow to wnite.

High-Carbon Steel

Length, about 55 in.; large volume; spark color, white.

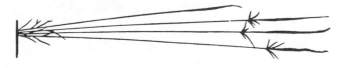

Wrought Iron

Length, about 60 in.; spark color, straw yellow near wheel, white elsewhere. Volume, large, with long straight shafts.

Low-Carbon Steel

Longest of all spark streams, up to 70 in.; spark color, white throughout; moderately large volume (less than medium- to high-carbon steels.) Pattern shown is also typical of most cast steels.

Appendix C

Tests for Identifying Metals
(continued)

Chip Test. If a high-speed grinder is not available, or the results of a spark test seem inconclusive, a chip test with a small cold chisel and hammer will often reveal striking differences between metals of similar surface appearance. The table below summarizes the chipping characteristics of five types of ferrous metals.

	Appearance of Chip	Size of Chip	Facility of Chipping
Gray Cast Iron	Small partially broken chips	1/8 in.	Not easy
Malleable Iron	Noticeably longer than those from gray cast iron	1/4 to 3/8 in.	Very tough; harder to chip than gray iron
Low Carbon Steel and Cast Steel	Can be made continuous; chisel leaves smooth groove	Almost any length	Very easy
High Carbon Steel	Fine grain fracture noticeable, although chip may be continuous	Almost any length	Difficult, due to hardness of metal
Nickel or Monel Metal	Chipping characteristics are so similar to those of low-carbon steel that chip test cannot distinguish one from the other.		

Appendix D

How to Install Hose Connections

As illustrated in Chapter 5, and below, four different combinations of parts are in general use for making up hose connections:

A — "Screw-type" nipple with heavy brass ferrule

B — "Push-type" nipple with crimped ferrule

C — "Push-type" nipple with "Sherman-type" hose clamp

D — "Push-type" nipple with "Circle-type" hose clamp

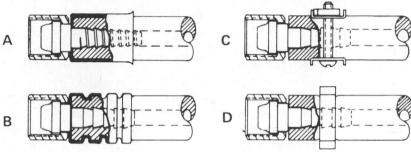

Virtually all packaged hose assemblies are fitted with push-type nipples and crimped ferrules (B). To make up connections of this type in the field without special equipment is impossible. The combination of screw-type nipple and brass ferrule (A) makes a strong, very neat connection, but it is essential that the ferrule be sized to fit snugly over the hose before the nipple is installed. For most field purposes, the combination of push-type nipple and circle-type clamp (D) is recommended. Circle-type clamps cost less than Sherman-type clamps and aren't subject to possible loosening in service.

Blowing Out Hose. Before installing fittings on new hose, the hose should be blown out to remove traces of the talc used in the manufacture of the hose. To do this, attach a push-type nipple of appropriate size to the outlet of an oxygen regulator connected to an oxygen cylinder. Be sure that the regular connection nut has been tightened with a wrench and the regulator pressure-adjusting screw fully released. Open the cylinder valve SLOWLY. Then push one end of the cut hose over the end of the hose nipple, hold it firmly in place, and turn in the regulator pressure-adjusting screw until the regulator delivery-pressure gauge registers about 5 psi (0.3 bars). Close the cylinder valve and release the regulator pressure-adjusting screw. After acetylene hose has been blown out with oxygen, blow through the hose by mouth to reduce the oxygen concentration in the hose. Do not blow out acetylene hose with acetylene. NEVER use compressed air to blow out oxygen or acetylene hose, since it may contain traces of oil used to lubricate the air compressor.

Appendix D (continued)

Installing Connections with Circle-Type Clamps. Make sure that the end of the hose has been cut squarely and cleanly (use a sharp knife). Slip hose connection nut onto push-type nipple, slip circle-type clamp over end of hose. Push nipple into hose until end of hose is within about 1/16 in. of the hose connection nut. Slide circle clamp toward end of hose until it is within 1/4 in. or less of the connection nut. Tighten each "ear" on the clamp with pincers.

Installing Connections with Sherman-Type Clamps. Follow the instructions given above for installing circle-type clamps, except: (1) It is permissible to use a screw-type nipple in place of a push-type nipple, although the push-type is preferable; (2) The clamp is tightened with a screwdriver.

Installing Connections with Screw-Type Nipples and Brass Ferrules. As noted earlier, the ferrule MUST be properly sized for the hose. It should fit snugly, with no play, over the cut end of the hose. (A ferrule designed for use on 2-braid 1/4-in. hose should not, for example, be used on 1-braid 1/4-in. hose.) Push the ferrule *all the way* onto the end of the hose. Attach the screw-type nipple and nut (tighten the nut very firmly) to the outlet of a regulator mounted on a securely-chained cylinder. Moisten the nipple with water, or a soap-and-water solution (use Ivory soap only) and then screw the hose onto the nipple until the end of the ferrule is within about 1/16 in. of the hose connection nut. An alternative method is to attach nipple and nut to the inlet connection on a torch handle, tighten the nut very firmly, and then turn the torch handle to screw the nipple into the hose, with the hose held stationary.

Installing Connections on Twin Hose. When installing connections on twin hose, slide a hose brace over the hose (before you separate the sections), position it 6-8 in. from the end of the hose, and then tighten it by squeezing it with a pair of pincers in the center. Then use a sharp knife to start the separation of the two hose segments at the end of the hose, and complete the separation, up to the brace, by pulling the two sections apart. If you are using screw-type nipples and brass ferrules, it may be necessary to use a sharp knife to trim away the remains of the interconnecting web before you can slide the ferrules over the hose ends.

To Install Hose Splices: Hose should NEVER be repaired with tape. If a section of hose suffers mechanical damage (cut in cover, etc.) cut out the damaged section and install a hose splice. Both screw-type and push-type splices are available. The screw-type, for use with properly-sized brass ferrules, is a bit unusual in that the "threads" on the nipples are right-hand at one side, left-hand at the other. All you need to do is to push ferrules all the way over the ends of the two sections, lubricate the nipples with water or soap solution (use Ivory soap only)

Appendix D (continued)

and then screw the splice into both sections of the hose simultaneously by using a wrench on the central hex section of the splice. Be sure that you push the nipple ends of the splice into each hose section an equal distance before you start to work with the wrench. You will need a helper to hold the hose while you turn the wrench.

It is even easier to use a push-type splice. Place circle-type clamps over the two hose ends, push the ends of the hose over the nipples of the splice until they butt up against the central hex section of the splice, then slide the clamps up to within about $1/4$ in. of the hex and tighten them with pincers.

Appendix E

Pressure Drop in Fitted Hose Assemblies

The table on the facing page shows the *approximate* pressure drop for which allowance should be made when using various lengths and sizes of *fitted* hose assemblies.

For hose lengths of 12-1/2 and 25 feet, pressure drop through the nipples at each end of the hose assembly accounts for the major part of the drop shown. All figures assume that hose nipples have hole diameters as follows:

3/16-in. nipple.................... 0.125 in. (3.2 mm)
1/4-in. nipple .... 0.1405 in. (3.5 mm)
5/16-in. nipple.................. 0.1935 in. (4.9 mm)
3/8-in. nipple .... 0.250 in. (6.3 mm)

Not all commercially-available nipples have hole diameters equal to those given above, although industry-wide standardization is expected within a few years. In some cases, actual pressure drop through a fitted hose assembly may be substantially greater than that indicated in the table.

Because pressure drop through the fittings is such a significant part of the total pressure drop, when two lengths of hose are coupled together, calculate the drop for each piece separately, and make some additional allowance for pressure drop through the hose connection coupling. For example: If you need a 50-ft. run of hose for a cutting job which calls for an oxygen flow of 250 cfh at 50 psi delivery pressure, and to get that run you must couple two 25-ft. lengths of 1/4-in. fitted hose, the pressure drop will not be 8 psi (as shown in table for 50 ft. of 1/4-in. hose at 250 cfh and 50 psi delivery) but more than 10 psi (5 plus 5 plus an allowance for drop through coupling).

Figures shown for delivery pressures of 5 psi and 10 psi are based on acetylene data; for equivalent oxygen flows assume pressure drops about 20% greater. Figures shown for delivery pressures of 25, 50, and 100 psi are based on oxygen flow data.

Pressure drops greater than 5 psi are not shown for delivery pressures of 5 and 10 psi, since maximum acetylene pressure at the regulator outlet must be limited to 15 psi. If you wish to estimate pressure drops for oxygen at flow rates of 100-250 cfh through 3/16-in. and 1/4-in. hose, with 10 psi delivery pressure, use drops about one-third higher than those shown for corresponding flow rates at delivery pressure of 25 psi.

PRESSURE DROP THROUGH FITTED HOSE
(see text on facing page)

Del. Press. (psi)	Gas Flow (cfh)	3/16-in. Hose Length in Feet				1/4-in. Hose Length in Feet				5/16-in. Hose Length in Feet				3/8-in. Hose Length in Feet			
		12-1/2	25	50	100	12-1/2	25	50	100	12-1/2	25	50	100	12-1/2	25	50	100
5	25	*	*	1	2	*	*	*	1	*	*	*	*	*	*	*	*
	50	1	2	4	●	*	1	2	3	*	*	*	1	*	*	*	*
	75	3	4	●	●	1	2	3	5	*	*	1	2	*	*	*	1
	100	5	●	●	●	2	3	5	●	*	1	2	3	*	*	1	2
10	25	*	*	1	2	*	*	*	1	*	*	*	*	*	*	*	*
	50	1	2	3	5	*	1	1	2	*	*	*	*	*	*	*	*
	75	2	3	5	●	1	1	2	4	*	*	*	*	*	*	*	*
	100	3	5	●	●	2	2	4	●	*	*	1	1	*	*	*	1
	150	●	●	●	●	3	5	●	●	1	1	2	4	*	1	1	2
	250	●	●	●	●	●	●	●	●	2	4	●	●	1	2	3	4
25	100	4	6	8	13	**	**	3	4	**	**	**	**	**	**	**	**
	250	13	18	28	●	6	8	12	17	**	2	3	7	**	**	**	4
	500	●	●	●	●	22	26	●	●	6	9	12	20	3	5	7	12
50	100	2	3	6	9	**	**	2	3	**	**	**	**	**	**	**	**
	250	8	13	19	30	3	5	8	11	**	**	2	4	**	**	**	3
	500	26	31	●	●	14	18	26	●	3	6	8	13	**	3	5	8
	750	●	●	●	●	29	37	●	●	9	12	18	27	4	6	10	11
100	100	**	**	3	5	**	**	**	**	**	**	**	**	**	**	**	**
	250	5	7	10	17	2	3	4	6	**	**	**	2	**	**	**	**
	500	14	21	32	●	8	11	15	21	2	3	5	7	**	**	2	5
	750	29	●	●	●	18	23	32	●	5	7	10	15	**	3	5	9
	1000	●	●	●	●	31	37	●	●	9	12	17	25	3	5	9	14

* Drop is less than 1 psi

** Drop is less than 2 psi

● Drop is greater than 5 psi (for 5 and 10 psi delivery) or greater than 37 psi (for 25, 50, or 100 psi delivery).

All data given in "English" measure, rather than metric, because currently (1976) all U.S. regulator gauges are calibrated in "psi" and virtually all flow data are presented in "cfh". To convert to metric measurement, multiply figures by 6.9 to arrive at kPa; multiply cfh figures by 0.028 to arrive at m³/h or by 0.472 for L/min.

Appendix F

Steel Pipe Specifications

This table is extracted from ASTM Standard A-53-73, "Standard Specifications for Welded and Seamless Steel Pipe." It covers most sizes from 1/2-in. through 6-in., Schedules 40 (Standard) and 80 (Extra Strong).

Size (in.)	Schedule	Outside Diameter (in.)	Wall Thickness (in.)	Weight per foot (lb.)
1/2	40	0.840	0.109	0.86
	80	0.840	0.147	1.09
3/4	40	1.050	0.113	1.14
	80	1.050	0.154	1.48
1	40	1.315	0.133	1.68
	80	1.315	0.179	2.18
1 1/2	40	1.9	0.145	2.72
	80	1.9	0.200	3.64
2	40	2.375	0.154	3.66
	80	2.375	0.218	5.03
3	40	3.5	0.216	7.58
	80	3.5	0.300	10.3
4	40	4.5	0.237	10.8
	80	4.5	0.337	15.0
5	40	5.563	0.258	14.7
	80	5.563	0.375	20.8
6	40	6.625	0.280	19.0
	80	6.625	0.432	28.6

Appendix G   Twist Drill Sizes

Drill No.	Diam., In.	Diam., mm	Drill No.	Diam., In.	Diam., mm	Drill No.	Diam., In.	Diam., mm
80	0.0135	0.343	44	0.0860	2.184	9	0.1960	4.978
79	0.0145	0.368	43	0.0890	2.261	8	0.1990	5.055
78	0.0160	0.406	42	0.0935	2.375	7	0.2010	5.105
77	0.0180	0.457	41	0.0960	2.438	6	0.2040	5.182
76	0.0200	0.508	40	0.0980	2.489	5	0.2055	5.220
75	0.0210	0.533	39	0.0995	2.527	4	0.2090	5.309
74	0.0225	0.572	38	0.1015	2.578	3	0.2130	5.410
73	0.0240	0.610	37	0.1040	2.642	2	0.2210	5.613
72	0.0250	0.635	36	0.1065	2.705	1	0.2280	5.791
71	0.0260	0.660	35	0.1100	2.794	A	0.234	5.94
70	0.0280	0.711	34	0.1110	2.819	B	0.238	6.04
69	0.0293	0.743	33	0.1130	2.870	C	0.240	6.16
68	0.0310	0.787	32	0.1160	2.946	D	0.246	6.25
67	0.0320	0.813	31	0.1200	3.048	E	0.250	6.35
66	0.0330	0.838	30	0.1285	3.264	F	0.257	6.53
65	0.0350	0.889	29	0.1360	3.454	G	0.261	6.63
64	0.0360	0.914	28	0.1405	3.569	H	0.266	6.76
63	0.0370	0.940	27	0.1440	3.658	I	0.272	6.91
62	0.0380	0.965	26	0.1470	3.734	J	0.277	7.04
61	0.0390	0.991	25	0.1495	3.797	K	0.281	7.14
60	0.0400	1.016	24	0.1520	3.861	L	0.290	7.37
59	0.0410	1.041	23	0.1540	3.912	M	0.295	7.49
58	0.0420	1.067	22	0.1570	3.988	N	0.302	7.67
57	0.0430	1.092	21	0.1590	4.039	O	0.316	8.03
56	0.0465	1.181	20	0.1610	4.089	P	0.323	8.20
55	0.0520	1.321	19	0.1660	4.216	Q	0.332	8.43
54	0.0550	1.397	18	0.1695	4.305	R	0.339	8.61
53	0.0595	1.511	17	0.1730	4.394	S	0.348	8.84
52	0.0635	1.613	16	0.1770	4.496	T	0.358	9.09
51	0.0670	1.702	15	0.1800	4.572	U	0.368	9.35
50	0.0700	1.778	14	0.1820	4.623	V	0.377	9.57
49	0.0730	1.854	13	0.1850	4.699	W	0.386	9.80
48	0.0760	1.930	12	0.1890	4.801	X	0.397	10.1
47	0.0785	1.994	11	0.1910	4.851	Y	0.404	10.3
46	0.0810	2.057	10	0.1935	4.915	Z	0.413	10.5
45	0.0820	2.083	--	---	---	--	---	---

Appendix H

Decimal Equivalents of Common Fractions

8ths	16ths	32nds	64ths	Decimal Equivalent In.	Decimal Equivalent mm
			1	.016	0.397
		1	2	.031	0.794
			3	.047	1.191
	1	2	4	.063	1.587
			5	.078	1.984
		3	6	.094	2.381
			7	.109	2.778
1	2	4	8	.125	3.175
			9	.141	3.572
		5	10	.156	3.969
			11	.172	4.366
	3	6	12	.188	4.762
			13	.203	5.159
		7	14	.219	5.556
			15	.234	5.953
2	4	8	16	.25	6.350
			17	.266	6.747
		9	18	.281	7.144
			19	.297	7.541
	5	10	20	.313	7.937
			21	.328	8.334
		11	22	.344	8.731
			23	.359	9.128
3	6	12	24	.375	9.525
			25	.391	9.922
		13	26	.406	10.319
			27	.422	10.715
	7	14	28	.438	11.112
			29	.453	11.509
		15	30	.469	11.906
			31	.484	12.303
4	8	16	32	.50	12.700
			33	.516	13.097
		17	34	.531	13.494
			35	.547	13.890
	9	18	36	.563	14.287
			37	.578	14.684
		19	38	.594	15.081
			39	.609	15.478

Appendix H

8ths	16ths	32nds	64ths	Decimal Equivalent In.	Decimal Equivalent mm
5	10	20	40	.625	15.875
			42	.641	16.272
		21	43	.656	16.669
			43	.672	17.065
	11	22	44	.688	17.462
			45	.703	17.859
		23	46	.719	18.256
			47	.734	18.653
6	12	24	48	.75	19.050
			49	.766	19.447
		25	50	.781	19.844
			51	.797	20.240
	13	26	52	.813	20.637
			53	.828	21.034
		27	54	.844	21.431
			55	.859	21.828
7	14	28	56	.875	22.225
			57	.891	22.622
		29	58	.906	23.019
			59	.922	23.415
	15	30	60	.938	23.812
			61	.953	24.209
		31	62	.969	24.606
			63	.984	25.003

Appendix J

Reference Publications

Published by the American Welding Society
2501 N.W. 7th Street, Miami, Florida, 33125

Safety in Welding and Cutting ....ANSI Z49.1

Recommended Safe Practices for the Preparation for Welding and
Cutting of Containers and Piping That Have Held
Hazardous Substances .... AWS F4-1

Standard Methods for Mechanical Testing of Welds ...... AWS B4.0

Terms and Definitions ....AWS 3.0

Welding Symbols ....AWS 2.0

Operator's Manual for Oxyfuel Gas Cutting .... AWS C4.2

Welding Handbook (The 7th edition of the Welding Handbook is
being published in five volumes; the first volume, "Fun-
damentals of Welding" was issued in 1976).

Published by National Fire Protection Association
470 Atlantic Avenue, Boston, Mass. 02210

Standard for the Installation and Operation of
Oxygen-Fuel Gas Systems for Welding
and Cutting.. NFPA No. 51

Standard for Fire Prevention in Use of Welding and
Cutting Processes...................................... NFPA No. 51B

Published by American National Standards Institute
1430 Broadway, New York, N. Y. 10018

Acceptable Concentrations of
Toxic Gases and Fumes... ANSI Z37

This standard is published in several parts, each covering a specific
gas, compound, or group of compounds. Only a few parts have any application to welding and cutting problems. For more information, consult the complete list of standards published annually by the Institute.

INDEX

G

H

I

J

K

L

M

N

O

P/N 781F00   F-4430-A
5/81   35M 81-0853